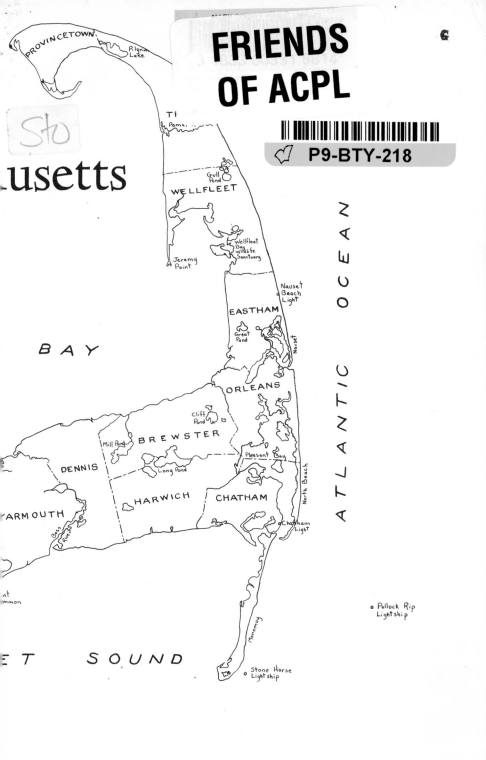

PROVINCETOWN

Pilgrim
Lake

usetts

Tr
Pamet

Gull
Pond

WELLFLEET

Jeremy
Point

Wellfleet
Bay
Wildlife
Sanctuary

BAY

Nauset
Beach
Light

EASTHAM

Great
Pond

Nauset

ORLEANS

Cliff
Pond

BREWSTER

Mill Pond

Pleasant Bay

DENNIS

Long Pond

North Beach

HARWICH

CHATHAM

ARMOUTH

Bass River

Chatham
Light

nt
mmon

o Pollock Rip
Lightship

ET SOUND

Monomoy

o Stone Horse
Lightship

ATLANTIC OCEAN

The Birds of Cape Cod, Massachusetts

The Birds of Cape Cod,

Introduction by Roger Tory Peterson

Massachusetts

by Norman P. Hill, M.D.

William Morrow & Co.   New York 1965

Drawings by
Marcia G. Norman

Photographs by
Allen H. Morgan, Norman P. Hill,
Edwin W. Teale

Endpaper maps by
Bernice A. Hill

1293717

Dedicated to those who would follow in the footsteps of Henry D. Thoreau, William Brewster and Ludlow Griscom in the sands of Cape Cod.

Introduction

by Roger Tory Peterson

TWENTY OR THIRTY years ago the New England bird watcher, dreaming of his retirement, often picked the coast of California as the promised land where he might spend his twilight years in happy birding. Some who did pull up stakes soon found their homesteads on the Pacific quickly surrounded by mushrooming subdivisions. The speed with which the bulldozer is removing the last vestiges of native greenery from large stretches of the southern California coast is appalling. Highway construction, shopping centers, housing developments, stream-channel "management," bulldozing and burning are making the once attractive coastal lowlands almost as synthetic and unbearable to the outdoorsman as Las Vegas, Nevada.

Today many Californians dream instead of Cape Cod, a "New England backwash," if you will, but a place where nature still refreshes the spirit—and where birds can be seen against the appropriate background. The Cape Cod National Seashore Park on the outer arm of the Cape, the U.S. Fish and Wildlife Service refuge on Monomoy and the Wellfleet Bay Wildlife Sanctuary (formerly the Austin Ornithological Research Station and now operated by the Massachusetts Audubon Society) all guarantee that Cape Cod will remain a mecca for bird watchers when Megalopolis takes over much of the seaboard from Boston to Philadelphia.

Audubon and Thoreau both visited the Cape, but their contributions to the local avifauna was slight. There was greater activity by the turn of the century but ornithology did not really come of age on the Cape until 1929 or 1930 when the Austin Research Station was founded. The massive assault by binocular and telescope gathered force in the mid-thirties when Ludlow Griscom acquired a house at Sears Point near Chatham which he and his numerous field companions used as a base of operations during summers and on weekends. A book on the birds of Cape Cod was his dream, and for twenty years he kept meticulous journals with this constantly in mind. Because of other commitments and failing health, he was unable to bring it beyond the notebook stage and the task fell to one of his most faithful associates, Dr. Norman Hill, who himself had built up a considerable file of unpublished data.

Those of us who knew Ludlow Griscom for more than thirty years miss him greatly for he symbolized an era, the rise of the competent field ornithologist. More than any other man he bridged the gap between the shotgun naturalist of the old school and the modern field biologist. Although he backed up his field work with a bit of judicious collecting, he demonstrated that most birds could be recognized instantly, even at a distance, by their *field marks* and that it was seldom necessary to resort to the collecting gun. A whole generation of students now owe their skill to his pioneering.

A high point in any Cape Cod field day with Griscom was a drive down Monomoy. He was phenomenal in spotting rare sea birds beyond the breakers and vagrant waders on the mudflats. His conversation was salty and original, punctuated with such stock comments as: "Let's stop here and flap our ears . . . Let's get out of here, it's getting dull . . . just dribs and drabs left . . . Check me on that one . . . Well, we bumped that one off . . . What's the tide schedule? . . . Now somebody find a bird with some zip in it . . . That's a weed bird . . . Please lower your voice to a howl . . . I don't like the look of that bird . . . Unprecedented! . . .

Put it down to sheer ignorance, incompetence and inexperience . . .
We got skunked on that one . . . That's a 10¢ bird . . . Well, we
didn't do so badly . . . Having a good time?" . . . etc.

For many of us, these phrases and a hundred other Griscomisms
bring to mind some of the richest hours of our lives, hours that
often started before dawn at the cafeteria on Harvard Square in
Cambridge or in the kitchen of the Sears Point House at Chatham
and ended after a late afternoon run down Monomoy or Nauset.

Ludlow Griscom would have been very pleased at the results of
Norman Hill's labors. The disciple had learned well and not
only synthesized the vast collection of data at his disposal but
also made his own distinguished contribution. I like particularly
his terminology, although "status" as he uses it might appropriately
have been called "evidence." One term is particularly inspired—
presumptive. This is the perfect answer to the dilemma of sorting
out the hypotheticals (those birds not supported by a specimen
or other tangible evidence) into "good" hypotheticals and the
more shaky hypotheticals. The Brown Pelican is listed as *presumptive* because, presumably no one could mistake a pelican. On
the other hand, a tricky bird such as the White-winged Black Tern,
far out of its range, is termed *hypothetical* even though it was
seen by a skilled observer. Dr. Hill has been a wise arbiter and in
very few instances (such as with the Louisiana Heron and Short-
billed Marsh Wren) might the student quibble about his interpre-
tation of *hypothetical*.

Regional bird books, when possible, should make comparisons
with the past. No recent publication has attempted to do so more
conscientiously than this book. Norman Hill's paragraph on
HISTORY under each species is a stroke of brilliance and might
serve as a model for other regional works. In general, we find
that on Cape Cod several major influences have affected the known
status of birds during the past half century: (1) *environment,* such
as the spread of the pine barrens over abandoned fields and farm-
lands; (2) *climate,* wherein a cycle of warmer winters has en-

couraged many species to winter farther north; (3) *protection,* wherein the slaughter of shore birds, terns, herons and other water birds was halted shortly after the turn of the century; and (4) *observation*—the greater efficiency of bird watchers due to better transportation, optical equipment and field guides—not to mention sheer numbers. The first three are actual influences, the fourth quite an artificial one.

It is axiomatic that a regional bird publication is literally out of date before the printer's ink is dry. This book will be no exception. The greater part of a year has elapsed since the manuscript was turned in; it takes that long to manufacture a book. In the interim, new birds have doubtlessly been recorded and changes in status noted. And, I might point out, the critical scholar may find the occasional "unsanitary" spot where his own special bit of information was not available to the author. This is true of all regional books. They should be used as springboards for extending our knowledge. Part of the fun is making new records, breaking old ones.

What new tack should field work take on Cape Cod—in anticipation of the inevitable successor to this book? It seems to me that the time is ripe to assess the summer resident birds through breeding bird censuses such as those published by the National Audubon Society in Audubon Field Notes. By using the singing male method on sample plots a few hard-driving observers could work out the average density and territory size of most common species. The basic environments on Cape Cod are few and could easily be broken down by acreages—pine barrens, fields, cranberry bogs, dunes, etc. Then it would be a matter of simple mathematics to estimate, for example, the Pine Warbler on the Cape—20,000 or 30,000 or whatever. Finland, 290 times as large as Cape Cod, has such estimates for nearly all species. These were worked out by a single man, Einari Merikallio, over a fifteen year period, using the line-survey method.

There is some evidence that the widespread use of chemical

pesticides is taking a serious toll of certain birds on the Cape. The birds at the ends of long food chains are being poisoned by stable hydrocarbons that have built up in their prey and their prey's prey. What under normal conditions would have been natural selection is now unnatural selection. My own conviction is that the recent sharp declines of such breeding birds as the Black-crowned Night Heron, Cooper's Hawk, Sharp-shinned Hawk, Osprey, and Screech Owl are due to these poisons. We know that migrant Bald Eagles are affected, and DDT-killed terns give us a disturbing clue to the recent reduction in the famous Cape Cod terneries.

The serious bird watcher on Cape Cod will monitor the trends and this book, as of the year 1965, will be his bench-mark.

ROGER TORY PETERSON

November 27, 1964
Old Lyme, Connecticut

Contents

List of Illustrations

Foreword

THIS REPORT ON *The Birds of Cape Cod* is one of a series of such reports on local regions within the state of Massachusetts which have been published from time to time, beginning with *The Birds of Essex County, Massachusetts,* by Charles W. Townsend in 1905, and *The Birds of the Cambridge Region of Massachusetts,* by William Brewster in 1906. Since then, many areas within the state have been discussed by a number of authors and the state itself reviewed in 1955 in *The Birds of Massachusetts, by* Griscom and Snyder. That all of this material can be written concerning this single state, and one of the smaller states at that, is ample evidence of the degree of interest in field biology in general and in ornithology in particular which is here present and of the long duration of this interest.

This report was conceived nearly twenty years ago by Ludlow Griscom but was repeatedly displaced, first by more urgent and pressing work and later because of failing health; nonetheless, it always remained in his mind as a most important project. After Mr. Griscom's death in 1959, many local ornithologists felt that this project should be revived in order that the vast amount of field work and other data would not be lost. Hence, I have undertaken the work with the wholehearted assistance of many other interested persons, to each of whom I here express my thanks.

There are some, however, to whom special words of appreciation are due: to Mrs. Ludlow Griscom for the loan of Mr. Griscom's field notes and for unfailing interest in the progress of the work; to Allen H. Morgan for permission to use the records of the Austin Research Station and for providing some of the photographs; to Henry M. Parker for review of many museum specimens; to Mrs. Ruth Emery and Wallace Bailey for providing details on many field observations; and to my wife, Bernice, for endless assistance in cross-checking data, in proofreading, and in providing the accompanying map of Cape Cod.

It is my purpose to present as complete a picture as possible of the avifauna of Cape Cod. Though this is largely built on the data of the thirty years prior to 1961, I have attempted to outline the known history of each species and thus to reconstruct the pattern of ornithological changes from the virgin forest, unfortunately nearly unknown, through deforestation and regrowth and more recently the more complex human interference with the ecology. It is my hope that this report may serve as a yardstick with which to measure the profound and apparently inevitable changes anticipated in the future.

NORMAN P. HILL, M.D.
2308 Highland Avenue
Fall River, Massachusetts.

The Birds of Cape Cod, Massachusetts

Beach grass (Ammophila breviligulata) *and shells*

Description of The Area

THE AREA COVERED by this report on Cape Cod is Barnstable County, Massachusetts. It is thus possible to be very precise regarding the land boundaries as they correspond exactly to the political division, including the narrow strip of land north of the Cape Cod Canal. However, we must note that, as usual, the political and biological boundaries are not identical. Biologically, the natural boundary for this report should be the transition from the largely deciduous woods of the mainland of Massachusetts to the pitch pine barrens of the southeastern coast; this takes place approximately on a line from the town of Plymouth south to the town of Wareham. The southeastern part of Plymouth Township should thus be included with Cape Cod. However, the data from this area are limited in amount, and little or nothing can be added to the Systematic List by their inclusion. Actually the opposite situation prevails and the birds of this section of Plymouth can be predicted by extrapolation of the Cape Cod list, providing the limitations of habitat are kept in mind, i.e., largely pitch pine barrens with some oak now infiltrating, a considerable number of freshwater ponds with sandy bottoms but very few surviving freshwater swamps, a coast line of bluffs with rocks offshore and practically no salt-water marsh or extensive mud or sand flats.

The offshore boundaries of the study area are less exact. However, it includes all of Cape Cod Bay from Manomet Point as the western headland north to about the middle of Stellwagon Bank off Provincetown, east around the outer Cape to about thirty miles offshore, south to the middle of Nantucket Sound, Vineyard Sound, and the channel between Woods Hole and the Elizabeth Islands, and then west to the middle of Buzzards Bay.

Cape Cod is a peninsula which extends into the North Atlantic Ocean from the southeastern mainland of Massachusetts and which is contained in the quadrangle between 41° 21' and 42° 10' North Latitude and between 69° 45' and 70° 40' West Longitude. It is thus on approximately the same latitude as Chicago, Illinois, Great Salt Lake, Utah, and the California-Oregon boundary. Elsewhere in the world this is comparable to Barcelona in Spain, Rome in Italy, the Dardanelles, the Caspian Sea, the Gobi Desert, Mukden in Manchuria, and southern Hokkaido in Japan. It lies due south of Portland, Maine, the city of Quebec, P.Q., Labrador, and Baffinland. Southward, the first landfall is Hispaniola in the West Indies and then the northern point of South America in Venezuela. This peninsula includes about 434 square miles and extends thirty miles east from the mainland and then at a right angle thirty miles north. It was poetically described by Thoreau (1951 ed.) as "the bared and bended arm of Massachusetts: the shoulder is at Buzzards Bay; the elbow, or crazy-bone, at Cape Mallebarre [Monomoy]; the wrist at Truro; and the sandy fist at Provincetown." A glance at the accompanying map will show how apt is his description.

The western part of the peninsula from Bourne south to Falmouth and east to the elbow is relatively broad, containing rolling uplands northward and a smoothly sloping plain toward the sounds. The hills along the western shore of Buzzards Bay and the southern shore of Cape Cod Bay rise to 240 feet westward, diminishing to 150 feet eastward. There are a number of ponds on the southern plain, all with sandy bottoms. Along the Sound shore there are inlets and estuaries which are tidal, and some fresh-water ponds separated from the ocean by a barrier beach. Most of the fresh-water swamps have been destroyed by the cranberry industry. Rivers, as such, are lacking, though there are some brooks and creeks dignified by the title of "river," these being tidal in their lower reaches. There is a small area of sand dunes on the Buzzards Bay shore of Falmouth and a large area of high dunes on the barrier beach at Sandy Neck at Barnstable which encloses very extensive salt marshes.

The eastern part of the peninsula, the so-called "outer Cape," from Chatham and Brewster north to Provincetown, is narrower, lower, and generally flatter with plains in Chatham, Eastham, and Truro and a dissected plain in Wellfleet. In general, the highest land is the steep bluff along the outer beach, so the drainage is toward the Bay. Again there are many sand-bottomed ponds but few swamps. There are many areas of salt marsh, but only that at Nauset is really extensive. Barrier beaches are quite prominent and appear at Monomoy, Harding's Beach, North Beach, Nauset, Billingsgate, and Jeremy Point and the whole of the Provincetown area. There are harbors on the bay side at Provincetown and Wellfleet and two estuaries on the eastern side, a small treacherous one at Nauset, and a large one at Pleasant Bay.

Prior to the last Pleistocene glaciation, Cape Cod either did not exist at all or was present in an unrecognizable form. The present land forms consist of terminal, recessional, and lateral moraines plowed up by three lobes of this glacier. The first was located where Buzzards Bay now exists; the second filled the depression now occupied by Cape Cod Bay; and the third lay east of the present outer shore line. The higher lands along the eastern shore of Buzzards Bay and the southern shore of Cape Cod Bay are known as the Falmouth-Sandwich moraine and were formed by the first and second lobes. The outer Cape is a lateral moraine which formed between the second and third lobes. These moraines are of jumbled gravel and boulders, some very large, whereas the southern section, sloping to the sounds, is a sandy outwash plain and contains almost no stone. The multiple ponds are believed due to isolated ice pockets which melted out to leave potholes. The soil on the Cape is thus gravelly and thin, not suited to agriculture, with much sand in inland areas as well as along the shores. It is very loose and porous, so rains drain rapidly and minerals are leached out. Along the shores there has been very extensive erosion with rapid destruction of much land and the building of barrier beaches from the shifting material. These shore-line patterns are very unstable and are subject to marked change with each storm and even with mere tidal action. For example: the lighthouses at Truro and Chatham have been moved back several times; Billingsgate Island off Wellfleet has nearly disappeared; ancient features described by the early explorers such as a point off Eastham and Webb's Island off Chatham are totally gone; Monomoy and North Beach are extending steadily southward and the former westward; Nauset Inlet shifts north and south, lying sometimes in Eastham and sometimes in Orleans; Monomoy, North Beach, and Nauset are frequently cut in one or more places; channels, tide rips, and mud flats are constantly shifting, etc. The greatest changes are along the outer coast; within Cape Cod Bay there is more protection and the changes are less extensive and less rapid, and in Buzzards Bay the shores are largely so rocky in addition that little change has been recorded.

The waters surrounding Cape Cod are all shallow and lie over the continental shelf. The hundred-fathom line is beyond Georges Banks and thus a hundred miles east of the area under discussion. The sea bottom is mostly sand but occasionally with some boulders and ledge. The marine biological situation is rather unique, however, in the marked contrast between the north and south shores. Cape Cod marks the boundary between the warm waters southward, dominated by the Gulf Stream, and the cold waters northward, dominated by the Labrador Current which extends this far south on the landward side of the Gulf Stream. It is reported (Randall and Vinal, 1958) that there is more difference in marine organisms between the north and south shores of the Cape than between the south shore and Chesapeake Bay or between the north shore and Nova Scotia; this is reflected in the pelagic bird distribution. Tidal currents are quite marked in Buzzards Bay, the sounds, and off the eastern shore. Tidal rise and fall vary from about five feet in Buzzards Bay to eight or nine feet generally and occasionally ten feet in Cape Cod Bay. In Cape Cod Bay and the outer Cape the tide schedule nearly coincides with that of Boston; in Buzzards Bay and the western parts of the sounds it averages three hours earlier.

The vegetation on Cape Cod has been so disturbed over three centuries of civilization that it is difficult to describe briefly. The original forest was never adequately described; it seems most likely it was of mixed hardwoods on the better soils and perhaps pitch pine on the poorer soils. This forest was rapidly and completely destroyed and the regrowth repeatedly cut for fuel, shipbuilding, and naval stores. Furthermore, the very frequent forest fires progressively impoverished the soil and inhibited regrowth of most trees. Thus we are left with pitch pine (*Pinus rigida*), some oaks (*Quercus* sp.), and sassafras (*Sassafras albidum*). The interior of the Cape east to Orleans and south to Chatham is covered with this forest, mostly low and scrubby, but with fairly large trees in a very few areas. Around the villages many areas have been kept relatively clear and there are many old pastures with red cedar (*Juniperus virginiana*) and deciduous thickets, especially chokecherry (*Prunus virginiana*) in assorted stages of growth. In Eastham there are extensive grassy moors with brush along the hedgerows. Northward there is a mixture of moors, blueberry barrens, and some woods in the hollows of Wellfleet. In addition, there are many acres of plantings, both evergreen and deciduous, around habitations, some of these now of considerable size and maturity. In some areas fresh-water habitats have developed, some with cattails (*Typha* sp.), some with alder (*Alnus* sp.), and some with red maple (*Acer rubrum*). Dense white cedar (*Chamaecyparis thyoides*) swamps are not infrequent, particularly along the southern shore, and there are still a few scattered stands of fine beeches (*Fagus grandifolia*) in remote locations. However, much former fresh-water swamp has been turned into cranberry bogs which are quite extensive and widespread. Where the uplands drop down to the marshes, there is a progressive change from brush through various grasses to the areas subject to periodic salt-water flooding. The salt marshes are one of the characteristic features of the Cape Cod landscape; they consist of three zones, that of the black grass (*Juncus gerardi*) in the upper areas, that of the fine soft *Spartina patens* over most of the area, and that of the rough *Spartina alterniflora* along the wetter edges of the streams which themselves contain eelgrass (*Zostera maritima*).

The weather on Cape Cod is significantly different from that on the mainland, this difference increasing as one proceeds eastward. This difference is due to the surrounding ocean which is slow to warm in the spring and slow to cool in the fall; in addition, it provides abundant moisture and allows strong winds to sweep across the land. Thus, the springs and summers are cooler than on the mainland, the falls and winters milder, and the extremes of temperature largely eliminated. Ice and deep snow occur less often and always disappear earlier; sometimes the Cape escapes both. The dampness of the air is quite apparent and is often manifested as fog and mist, though the rainfall is not much greater than on the mainland. Paradoxically, the stronger winds, though damp, are rather drying, both mechanically and in the spray zone chemically. Salt spray may be carried many miles inland in the northeast and southeast gales which, because of the exposed position, are often intense and prolonged so that heavy surf pounds the beaches. In addition, in late summer and fall, tropical hurricanes often strike or graze the area with their drenching rains, destructive winds, and flood tides.

Certain areas within the Cape are so frequently mentioned in the Systematic List that special description is indicated. First and foremost is Monomoy, a long barrier beach mostly less than a mile wide running eleven miles south from Chatham and separating Nantucket Sound from the open ocean. In the earliest records it was called Cape Mallebarre and throughout its history has been sometimes an island, sometimes a series of islands, and sometimes a peninsula; it is constantly extending southward and westward. It is formed of loose, wave-borne sand, the eastern side a fairly steep beach backed by dunes in long rows. These slope gradually westward to extensive sand flats with some muddy areas ideal for shore birds. In the interior, there are moors covered with *Hudsonia* and a number of fresh or brackish ponds in the hollows, some with small mud flats when the water is low and some with fairly extensive cattail beds. In the areas more protected from salt spray there are dense thickets of bayberry (*Myrica pennsylvanica*), beach plum (*Prunus maritima*), and poison ivy (*Rhus toxicodendron*). A few stunted pines and other trees are found widely scattered, but exposure prevents development of anything approaching a forest. These thickets in the hollows of the sand dunes are the "shore line traps" and are often full of land-bird migrants in the fall. There are many shacks but very few occupied camps, an old lighthouse, and several abandoned Coast Guard stations. At the northern end interposed between Monomoy and the mainland of Chatham lies Morris Island, a glacial deposit, mostly well covered with a pitch pine forest but with a dense white cedar swamp and a small stand of beeches on the slopes of the swamp. East of Monomoy is Stone Horse Lightship about a mile offshore and Pollock Rip Lightship about nine miles out. These are located over the many square miles of shoals which are the great gathering places for the fall and winter waterfowl which feed on the plentiful mussels. Monomoy, south of Morris Island, is now a national wildlife refuge under the management of the U. S. Fish and Wildlife Service.

Nauset Beach and Marsh lie mostly within the town of Eastham. The narrow dune-covered barrier beach extends about three miles from the Nauset Coast Guard Station, now the headquarters of the Cape Cod National Seashore Park, south to Nauset Inlet and is subject to yearly change by storms and tides. It encloses a large tidal marsh with lagoons and salt creeks. This, like Monomoy, is a major shore-bird gathering area providing feeding in the meadows at low tide and roosting on the outer beach at high tide. South of Nauset Inlet and mostly in Orleans is another barrier beach, sometimes confusingly called Nauset also, but herein called North Beach. This extends nearly ten miles to below Chatham and is steadily extending southward and westward. It encloses the extensive estuary of Pleasant Bay with flats and tidal marshes which also provide a shore-bird gathering area. Also in Eastham lies the complex of ponds around Great Pond; these are important duck ponds in migration and in the winter. The bay shore in Eastham is most easily approached at First Encounter Beach where there is both a fair-sized marsh and very wide mud and sand flats which are exposed at low tide.

The Provincetown area north of High Head in Truro consists of multiple rows of barrier dunes with swampy depressions between. On the older and more stabilized slopes a forest has grown up, but much of the area is loose, wind-blown sand constantly threatening to engulf the forests, swamps, and even the town. Immediately off High Head lies Pilgrim Lake or Eel Pond, once part of Provincetown Harbor, but diked in 1869, following which extensive reed beds developed. This was once a fine breeding area for rails, ducks, etc., but has now deteriorated due to changes in the water level.

The Wellfleet Bay Wildlife Sanctuary, formerly the Austin Ornithological Research Station, now under the management of the Massachusetts Audubon Society, is on the line between Wellfleet and Eastham. It includes many acres of typical Cape Cod landscape with pitch pine forest, rolling moors, and salt marsh; it abuts on Wellfleet Bay and also includes several small freshwater ponds. Wellfleet Bay is a broad estuary and is separated from Cape Cod Bay by a chain of islands and bars.

On the bay shore of Brewster, Orleans, and Eastham, the beach is unusually level and nearly a mile of flats is uncovered at low tide; these are great gathering places of geese and particularly brant. Inland in Brewster, there are three complexes of ponds of great importance for waterfowl. The southernmost lies on the Harwich line and is grouped around Long Pond or Pleasant Lake. The westernmost is the Mill Pond group and includes the Mill Run, a swift stream between high banks and which never freezes, thus providing a refuge for wintering marsh birds. Finally, Nickerson State Park of 1700 acres includes the Cliff Pond group; here the surrounding woodland of pine and oak is the finest on Cape Cod and marks the most easterly point reached by many breeding land birds.

In Barnstable, Cory's old estate at Great Island is on the shore of Nantucket Sound just east of Hyannis Harbor; it is connected to the mainland by a causeway. On the Bay shore of Barnstable is Sandy Neck, the most extensive area of dunes on Cape Cod after the Provincelands. This is a barrier beach enclosing the very extensive Barnstable Marshes. When salt hay was cut each year, these marshes were important areas for Lesser Yellowlegs and Pectoral Sandpipers; the mud flats of the harbor are still important gathering places for shore birds on the inner coast migration route. The marsh supports the largest Sharp-tailed and Seaside Sparrow colonies on the Cape.

The Mashpee River which empties into Vineyard Sound near the village of Cotuit is the only remaining river-bottom woodland of any extent. Inland, there are the inevitable cranberry bogs, but below these the river runs nearly a mile through a maple-filled valley before widening out into cattail swamps and finally becoming a tidal estuary. South of the village of Falmouth there is a complex of ponds separated from Vineyard Sound by a narrow beach. These often remain open all winter and are important duck ponds; the waterfowl populations in these ponds appear more closely related to those in the ponds on the south shore of Martha's Vineyard than to those elsewhere on Cape Cod. In addition, the vegetation of the Woods Hole area and the Buzzards Bay shore of Falmouth is of a richer deciduous nature than elsewhere and thus in marked contrast with the rest of the Cape; this, therefore, attracts a high density of a number of species and also some from the mainland which do not occur elsewhere on the Cape.

Sagamore faces Cape Cod Bay at the eastern end of the Cape Cod Canal and thus is located on a "bottleneck" of the inner coastal flyway. The rolling upland is covered with pitch pine and oak and there are bluffs where these uplands meet the shore close to the boundary between Plymouth and Barnstable Counties; off-shore from these bluffs there are many submerged boulders, but south of this is another barrier beach. On the lower slopes of the upland to the southward there was formerly moorland, but this has now grown to dense thickets. Once there was a good-sized marsh here; this was bisected with the construction of the Canal in 1908 and further filled with the widening of the Canal about 1935, so that it is no longer subject to salt-water flooding and is now growing up to wet woodland. Until about 1930 the isolated beach near the mouth of the Canal supported a tern colony, now extinct, as this area is developed as Scusset State Beach. Much of the inner coastal migratory flights crosses the Cape along the line of the Canal.

Many other locations within Cape Cod have contributed records for the Systematic List, but their importance is not as great as the above-mentioned ones. They may be located on any standard map, particularly the U. S. Geological Survey maps for land locations and the U. S. Coast and Geodetic Survey charts for alongshore and offshore areas.

A winter sketch of an abandoned nest

Ornithological History

Early Period

THE EARLY PERIOD of the ornithological history of Cape Cod began with the discoverers and explorers and ended about 1865. This period is characterized by a paucity of real information; there are some specific items of great historical value and many traditions of somewhat less authenticity but still of much interest.

The earliest explorers left the first bird records as these men were intent on determining the capacity of the New World to support Old World communities and hence they were interested in potential food supplies. The Vikings undoubtedly reached the coast of North America, and their Vinland has often been identified with our Cape Cod, though without proof as yet. The sagas tell of multitudes of nesting sea birds in Vinland, and in one translation these are called Eiders. Eiders do not now nest on Cape Cod, so if this identification is correct, it indicates either that Vinland was not Cape Cod or that Eiders then nested further south than at present even though the climate of 1000 A.D. is generally believed to have been milder than at present. Be that as it may, we reach more solid ground with Gosnold, who is credited with the discovery of Cape Cod and who has left descriptions of Great Auks off Monomoy in 1602. Three years later, Champlain clearly described Black Skimmers at Nauset.

In 1620 the Pilgrims landed briefly at Provincetown before settling in Plymouth. In 1630 Cape Cod was annexed to the Plymouth Colony; Sandwich, Barnstable, Yarmouth, and Eastham were settled in the next decade, and from these four settlements other villages and towns gradually separated. Throughout this period most ornithological references were vague and referred chiefly to game birds and waterfowl, with some mention of the more spectacular though non-edible species such as eagles and "white cranes." The settlers were far too occupied in wresting a living from the land to notice and record much else. Settlement produced marked changes in the ecology, most strikingly the steady reduction in the forests and the appearance of the open moors, this process being accelerated after the Revolution. Until nearly 1850 Cape Cod was isolated from the rest of Massachusetts and much neglected, even though the Old Colony was merged with Massachusetts Bay in 1692.

About 1830 Audubon passed through Cape Cod waters but recorded little. The early publications, such as Nuttall's *Manual* (1834) and the formal state lists of Emmons (1833) and Peabody (1840), contain very few references to Cape Cod other than the mention of specimens therefrom which were shipped to the Boston Market. The most important personality of this period was Henry D. Thoreau (1817–1862), the remarkable genius of Concord, who made four visits to Cape Cod in October 1849, June 1850, July 1855, and June 1857. These were largely on foot, and he chronicled in detail innumerable facets of the landscape and the way of life on the Cape. All in all, he covered the Cape from Eastham to Provincetown quite thoroughly, also along the north shore from Manomet eastward and the south shore in the region of Yarmouth and Harwich. Relatively few birds were mentioned, but some of these have great historical value. Many common species are not mentioned, though his other "Journals" (see *Notes on New England Birds, H. D. Thoreau,* edited by F. H. Allen, 1910) are full of such records. This must not be taken as evidence that such species were lacking, however, as he specifically stated that the birds mentioned were not to be found around Concord. This material was published first in serial form (*Putnam's Magazine, The Atlantic Monthly*) and later in several book editions (Tickner and Fields, 1864; Riverside Press, 1896; Norton, 1951), only the last of which included the 1857 trip. This report was largely responsible for bringing the Cape to the attention of the remainder of the state, though the full effects of this new interest were delayed until after the Civil War.

The only other important person of this period was Dr. Thomas M. Brewer (1814–1880), who wrote the text of Baird, Brewer, and Ridgway's *Water Birds of North America* (Mem. Mus. Comp. Zoology *12*, vol. 1 & 2, 1884). This mentioned Cape Cod specimens seen in the Boston Market and in the Boston Society of Natural History, most of which are now lost. Brewer's reputation has suffered over the years as Brewster (1906, page 306) considered him "not a reliable field ornithologist," but it must be remembered that Brewer had the misfortune to span two periods of ornithology, the new one having very different standards of scientific accuracy. Actually Brewer's chief interests were the nests and eggs of North American birds in which he was an authority; the collection and preservation of specimens of the birds themselves and the careful documentation of the records of others was foreign to his training and to others of his generation.

Second Period

The second period of Cape Cod ornithology may be described as that of the rise of scientific ornithology and of the "sportsman-naturalist," the two designations overlapping. It extended from about 1865 at the end of the Civil War to 1912, when effective conservation laws were established.

The railroad had reached Sandwich in 1848 just before Thoreau's visits and progressed in stages to Hyannis, to Orleans, to Wellfleet, and finally in 1873 to Provincetown with a spur line to Chatham, replacing the stagecoaches on shore and the packets at sea. This produced a major revolution in the way of life on Cape Cod which at last established easy contact with the mainland. Vacationists and summer visitors discovered its charms and soon became an important part of the economy. Fine residences were built and much wealth imported and created. Commercial fishing slowly declined and the cranberry industry eliminated many fresh-water swamps. Previously unheard of comforts and luxuries were demanded. Food arrived in larger and more varied quantities, par-ticularly previously unavailable red meat, so filleted breasts of gull, loons, scoters, etc., were no longer eaten. Farms and pastures de-creased, and the replacement of wood by oil as a fuel allowed rapid regrowth of forests.

With railroad travel, the rising ornithologists of the 1870's had easy access to Cape Cod, quickly arousing the interest of local gunners who learned to identify rare specimens which they dis-posed of to museums and taxidermists. This was the period of unrestricted market shooting, of taxidermy, and of the plume trade, which rapidly decimated the tern and water-bird colonies and made massive inroads in the shore-bird populations. At sea, fishermen shot Alcids in winter and shearwaters in summer for bait. Surprisingly the ducks escaped until late in the period as local conditions prevented mass killing, but loons, grebes, gannets, hawks, owls, and herons were fair targets; even the Meadowlark, euphemistically called "Marsh Quail," was heavily hunted and eaten. This was also the period of the world-famous Monomoy Brant Club, of the many gunning stands on the ponds and marshes (see Phillips' *Shooting Stands of Eastern Massachusetts*, 1929), and of the Chatham Beach Hotel, located on the beach which then extended east of Morris Island. It was run by Captain Nathanial Gould who was formerly captain of the Chatham Coast Guard Station and who eventually left Cape Cod to live in North Carolina. It was frequented by an extraordinary number of well-known collectors and sportsmen. The shooting record of this establishment from 1897 to 1904 has been preserved by Forbush. With all this activity, it is small wonder that the many museums have great series of water birds from Cape Cod and that rarities could not be adequately recorded in the available publications. The seeming paradox of the relative lack of land birds in the museums is best explained by a socially ingrained tradition that such were simply not interesting, whereas sound knowledge of the game, water, and sea birds, hawks and owls, etc., was proper and brought respect. Toward the end of this period rivalry broke out between the collectors and much enmity was generated, so that finds were concealed and colleagues outbid and double-crossed.

The following review of the leading personalities of the period and of their work on Cape Cod has been adapted from notes left by Ludlow Griscom.

William Brewster (1851–1919) was the leader of this generation of ornithologists and made frequent trips to Cape Cod in his younger days; he accumulated a vast body of information and specimens but published practically nothing. The details of his career have been discussed by this biographer, Henshaw (*Auk*, 37, 1, 1920), and his records and journals described by Griscom (1949). Brewster's visits to Cape Cod were as follows, arranged in chronological order and with some digest of significant items in the notes:

1870. To Hyannis with C. J. Maynard en route to Nantucket.

1871, October 17–20. To Centerville, stayed with Sidney Baxter. Snipe abundant and said to winter commonly; Grouse commoner and tamer than near Boston; informed that Heath Hens from Naushon Island had been released but had disappeared; Dove and Horned Owl notably common.

1874, June 17–18. Back to Centerville with Baxter, chiefly blue-fishing out of Cotuit Harbor. Noted with interest the limited breeding bird fauna of the pine barrens.

1874, November 4–7. Quail shooting with Melvin Carter and a Mr. Buttrick. Crossbills, Red-breasted Nuthatch and Pine Siskin very abundant, "more so than ever near Cambridge"; Meadowlark abundant as usual; Sora and Henslow's Sparrow shot.

1875, May 5–8. To Chatham with C. B. Cory, reached Harwich by train at noon and Chatham by stage at 2:00 P.M., had dinner at the lighthouse and spent the night at the Brant Club. Saw many Caspian Terns in flocks; 5000+ Scoters; one Parasitic Jaeger; remarked that Meadowlarks were very abundant, more so than ever before in his experience. On May 7 tried Brant shooting with no luck. On May 8 he took a walk on the south side of Chatham and noted the abundance of the Field Sparrow; then back to Cambridge in the afternoon.

1875, May 15–18. Returned almost at once to Chatham with Frank C. Browne. Saw some Willets, was told they used to breed abundantly on Monomoy. On May 16 they sailed from Harding's Beach around Monomoy and spent the day "coot" shooting, saw many thousands. Returned May 17 to Monomoy and spent the day tramping the point, saw 100 pairs of Least Terns, 20 Bonaparte's Gulls and 5–6 Parasitic Jaegers. Returned home May 18.

1875, July 8–10. At Centerville, mostly fishing with John W. T. Nichols. Vesper Sparrows notably abundant; saw six Eagles which were said to nest around inland pools.

1876, December 5–9. Checked wintering Snipe and Rail reports and found them entirely correct; collected a Vesper Sparrow on December 6 and a Winter Wren on December 7; Mr. Baxter had shot Woodcock in December 1873 and January 1874.

1886, November 21–23. Visited C. B. Cory at Great Island, Hyannis.

1887, October 15–16. With W. H. Henshaw visited C. B. Cory at Great Island.

1888, December 15–16. Visited Great Island again.

1889, July 4–August 4. Resided in a rented house in Falmouth. Apparently did no birding but recorded the Black Rail calling at night.

1889, August 11–15. Visited the William Stones at South Yarmouth. No birding records.

1889, December 4–7. Quail shooting at Marstons Mills. No bird notes.

1890, June 24–25. At Falmouth. Had a long session with Black Rail at night. On June 24 to West Falmouth, was astonished at the absence of common and familiar summer residents such as vireos, grosbeaks, and tanagers and at the abundance of Quail, Meadowlarks, and Vesper Sparrows. Recorded four Chestnut-sided Warblers and listed a Bobolink singing which he crossed off in later years when he realized the species did not occur on the Cape. On June 25 to Falmouth Heights where he regarded the number of Towhees as remarkable. Surprised to find the Black-throated Green Warbler nesting in pitch pines; listed a Least Flycatcher calling on Main Street.

1890, July 1–6 and August 17–September 2. At Falmouth. Virtually no birding except when Walter Faxon came down on July 6, found a pair of White-eyed Vireos feeding young, Hermit Thrushes in numbers, and an early Lesser Yellowlegs.

1891, May 31–June 3. To North Truro with Outram Bangs to visit Gerritt Miller.

1894, May 18. Taken to Barnstable by Bangs to visit the Night Heron rookery, then containing 1500 pairs; recorded a Sora singing and nest found.

1894, June 3–5. Visited C. B. Cory at Great Island.

1895, May 17. Returned to the Night Heron rookery at Barnstable, found it diminished to 1000 pairs. Saw only one Meadowlark, none elsewhere on the Cape.

1895, May 18–20. Again to North Truro with Bangs with a drive to the Provincelands on which only thirteen species were recorded.

1895, June 16–17. Visited C. B. Cory at Great Island.

1895, July 11–28 and August 1–5. At Falmouth. Almost no birding except on July 20 when he recorded both Cuckoos, Virginia Rail, a Nighthawk, and found a large Robin and blackbird roost in a white cedar swamp; no Black Rail.

1899, August 11–15. Visited the William Stones at South Yarmouth. No birding notes.

1902, September 13–22. Visited the Stones at South Yarmouth, C. B. Cory at Great Island, and the Almys at Cotuit; no birding records.

1903, September 6. Visited the Stones at South Yarmouth. Noted a Turkey Vulture.

1905, June 26. Visited the Stones again. No birding; Brewster's last trip to Cape Cod.

Charles B. Cory (1856–1921) had a fabulous and tragic career (Osgood, *Auk, 39*, 151, 1922). Born to a wealthy family, he was early interested in bird collecting and various sporting activities. He joined the Nuttall Club in 1876 and became a founder of the American Ornithologists' Union in 1883. His great ornithological contributions were in his study of the birds of Florida and the West Indies and in his *Catalogue of Birds of the Americas*, which was completed after his death by Hellmayr and Conover. In 1883 he acquired a princely estate at Great Island, Hyannis, which he was forced to sell in 1906 after misfortune had wiped out his entire wealth. During these twenty-three years, however, he did much collecting throughout the Cape, though he published very little. Many other well-known ornithologists frequently visited him and the locality of Great Island is often met in collections.

John C. Cahoon (1863–1890), of an old and respected family from Harwich, became a professional collector of water and sea fowl in the early 1880's. He shot frequently on Monomoy and elsewhere and published a series of articles in *Ornithologist and Oologist* in 1888 entitled "The Shorebirds of Cape Cod." He also collected terns, gulls, jaegers, shearwaters, etc., in enormous numbers, but shot scarcely any land birds. He subsequently collected in Arizona and Mexico for Brewster and was killed on a sea cliff in Newfoundland while collecting for C. F. Batchelder.

Outram Bangs (1860–1932), a native of Wareham and one of the most eminent systematic ornithologists this country has ever produced, collected extensively all over Cape Cod from 1879 to 1895. He, however, kept no journals so that his records must be extracted from the collections or from the notes of Brewster, Miller, or others who accompanied him. Brewster's notes, in particular, are full of the notation, "Mr. Bangs tells me that . . ."

Gerritt S. Miller (1869–1956) was keenly interested in birds in his youth and joined the Nuttall Club in 1888. He lived at North Truro from 1888 to 1891 where he collected and observed birds with great diligence and skill. His score of rarities and the proof that the Cape was often flooded with fall migrants astounded New England ornithologists and induced Brewster to visit him in 1891. In looking over Pilgrim Lake, teeming with ducks, herons, and rails, Brewster was astounded at the absence of Swamp Sparrows and Marsh Wrens in what appeared to be an ideal habitat but was assured by Miller that these species occurred as fall migrants only. Miller's collection was acquired by the British Museum when he became curator of mammals at the United States

National Museum, but his brief stay at North Truro made a lasting impression on Cape Cod ornithology.

Charles R. Lamb (1866–1939) was another typical New England sportsman-naturalist and an ardent hunter and collector of sea and water-bird rarities. He had a cottage at East Orleans and shot actively on Cape Cod from 1883 to 1913. He knew all the regular sportsmen and local gunners and often picked up rare birds from them; occasionally he sold rarities to Brewster and others and he permitted Brewster to examine his records. His private collection is now in the Boston Museum of Science.

John C. Phillips (1876–1938), who became an authority on water birds and particularly ducks, visited and collected extensively over various parts of Cape Cod. His writings are full of Cape records.

Arthur C. Bent (1866–1954), famous for his "Life History" series, visited Cape Cod on numerous occasions. The records are scattered through his writings.

Herbert K. Job (1864–1933) was, in his early years, an energetic collector and often on Cape Cod. Most notably, he was the first ornithologist to undertake sea trips for pelagic birds out of Chatham and was also a pioneer in bird photography. He later became a Congregational minister and finally went into conservation work.

Many other sportsmen-naturalists of this era collected on Cape Cod. These include: Augustus Denton, Frank E. Tileston, M. Abbott Frazer, Charles W. Townsend, F. Seymour Hersey, S. Prescott Fay, Frederick H. Kennard, Reginald H. Howe, George C. Shattuck, William S. Slocum, John D. Smith, Dwight Blaney, John A. Farley, D. C. Atwood, Everett Eldredge, Nathanial Gould, Warren Hapgood, Lombard C. Jones, and many others.

The wholesale destruction of the bird populations which reached their lowest levels from 1900 to 1910 brought about the end of this period, both by disappearance of the *raison d'être* of many of the activities involved and by the rising popular outrage over the slaughter. Bitter were the battles and serious were the economic hardships suffered by many, but eventually protection was established, the millinery trade killed, market gunning stopped, and taxidermy as a big business exterminated.

Third Period

The third period of Cape Cod ornithology is characterized by the extension of protection, the recovery of decimated species, and the development of field ornithology on a basis of sight observation rather than collection. This period extends from about 1912 to the present.

The development of the automobile age bears the same relation to this period as the extension of the railroad to the last. Private vehicles increased and the sandy tracks through the pine barrens were gradually replaced by hard roads and more recently by superhighways. The railroads are now following their predecessors into oblivion. Life on Cape Cod is no longer any different from that on the mainland in its material comforts, and thus the Cape is regrettably losing some of its unique charm. No place on the Cape is now much more than three hours' drive from Boston, so that energetic persons can do a day's birding without an overnight stay, while increased accommodations make longer visits easier. Balloon-tired jeeps and trucks can take them down Nauset, Monomoy, etc., and many small-scale fishermen will take charter trips offshore for pelagic birds.

Actually this period opened with a marked hiatus in the ornithological record, partly due to illness and death of the older generation of ornithologists, partly due to low levels of bird life, and partly due to World War I. After 1920 interest slowly returned. Professor Earle began observations around Orleans about then, and in 1929 and 1930 Dr. Oliver L. Austin and Dr. Oliver L. Austin, Jr., founded the Austin Ornithological Research Station in South Wellfleet. The station included six hundred acres of typical Cape Cod terrain, rolling moorland, pitch pine forests, salt marsh, and a rambling old house (Austin, *Bird-Banding, 3*, 51, 1932). It was devoted to large-scale banding operations and remained in nearly continuous operation until 1957. Dr. Austin and his assistants banded many thousands of birds over the years. Special attention was paid to the tern colonies of Cape Cod, and the results of this work as published in many papers in *Bird-Banding* are milestones in ornithological research. In addition, traps for land birds were kept in operation throughout the year, boxes for nesting Tree Swallows and Bluebirds were put up, and a technique devised for trapping shore birds on the nearby marsh. More recently mist nets have been used with spectacular success. The station has made four outstanding contributions to the ornithology of Cape Cod: 1) the previously mentioned studies on the terns; 2) banding records of land birds which when made by competent ornithologists are an excellent substitute in well-marked species for the specimens lacking in collections; 3) data on the number of individual birds involved in migration, the number banded being regularly much greater than can ever be seen by the most active and competent field man; and 4) data to prove the existence of separate populations within a species, a fact that can at most only be suspected in field observations, e.g. the Mourning Dove. The Austin Station was acquired by the Massachusetts Audubon Society in 1958, after the death of Dr. Austin, Sr.

Ludlow Griscom (1890–1959) is widely and justly known for his great achievement in raising field ornithology to the dignity of a science. Though his career at the American Museum of Natural History in New York and at the Museum of Comparative Zoology at Harvard University was distinguished in both botany and ornithology, field work in ornithology was always his great interest. His virtuosity in field identification has become legendary, though he was always first to point out that he was not infallible. Nonetheless, those of us who have had the opportunity to accompany him in the field will recognize that his extensive training and background had equipped him for feats, seemingly impossible, which we have repeatedly seen him prove by selective collecting. Though he inspired affection and loyalty in most of those he met, I would be less than objective did I not report that his was such an unusual personality that he was inevitably a controversial figure and often embroiled in bitter disputes. After moving to Cambridge in 1927, he made his first visit to Cape Cod in 1929. He became deeply attached to the Cape and soon knew it intimately in history, geography, botany, and of course ornithology. In turn, he has left an indelible mark there. He began renting a cottage at Sears Point in Chatham in 1934 and purchased it in 1943. Except in the depth of winter, he used this as a base for his field trips and delighted in filling it with congenial companions, thanks to the loving tolerance of Mrs. Griscom. He made many, many hundreds of field trips to all sections of the Cape at all seasons with particular interest in the Brewster-Chatham-Eastham triangle and with special attention to Monomoy and Nauset Points; sea trips off Chatham and to a lesser extent elsewhere were a special project and delight. His journals, which are in reality composite notes of all who ever accompanied him, are so voluminous, comprehensive, and detailed that they form the backbone of the data from 1934 to about 1955. In addition to the use of these notes, I value highly my recollections of many field trips with him and of stimulating and instructive conversations—for he was always kind and patient in teaching and encouraging younger men. This report would never have been written without both the journals and these recollections.

Since about 1940 the Massachusetts Audubon Society has developed an increasing importance on Cape Cod. Due to the economic disruptions of the early 1900's caused by the protection laws, conservationists had long been treated with suspicion and contempt, but a well-planned and tactful program of education, first under C. Russell Mason and now Allen H. Morgan, has

markedly changed this feeling, so much so that chambers of com-
merce now list bird watching as a tourist attraction! Teaching in
schools has been carried out locally, and an annual Audubon
Camp-out at Chatham has provided guided tours to interesting
areas on the Cape each September. In 1958 the Society purchased
the Austin Ornithological Research Station and renamed it the
Wellfleet Bay Wildlife Sanctuary. The emphasis here now is on a
broad-based popular approach to nature study rather than on
strictly scientific ornithology, though some banding continues and
some research is underway. The sanctuary is now managed by
Wallace Bailey who is also in charge of nearly daily field trips to
the outer beaches and elsewhere, thus introducing the birds of
Cape Cod to a growing legion of visitors from all over this coun-
try and even the entire world. In addition to Wellfleet Bay, the
Massachusetts Audubon Society manages sanctuaries on Sampson's
Island off Cotuit, the famous Tern Island in Pleasant Bay off North
Chatham, Outermost House at Nauset and Ashumet at Falmouth.

The rising interest in the outdoors since World War II is reflected in the really large number of persons who now "go birding" on Cape Cod. The mere listing of these, even the more active
ones, will serve no useful purpose as their names will be met in
the Systematic List. Most of these are "amateurs" in the correct
usage of this word, and their interest covers the spectrum from the
most careful and studious workers to the most casual and careless
of observers. Though there are some fantastically improbable reports, the properly screened data of this army of observers is of
great value in determining the present status and the immediate
trends of the bird populations.

For many years the town and state governments have set aside
and maintained reservations and recreation areas. These include
Nickerson State Park in Brewster, Goodwill Park in Falmouth,
Sandy Neck in Barnstable, and others. More recently the federal
government has entered into the conservation picture on the Cape
and is assuming very great importance. Monomoy was taken in

1944 by the Fish and Wildlife Service as another in their chain of refuges throughout the country and is now managed chiefly for the waterfowl, particularly Canada Geese and Black Ducks, though many other species have benefited. Finally, the appallingly rapid destruction of the Cape Cod landscapes has at last resulted in the establishment of the Cape Cod National Seashore Park. Though its establishment was bitterly opposed by certain persons and interests, and though it is understood that some economic losses were imposed, it seems quite clear that the eventual result, as with the establishment of protection fifty years ago, will be for the over-all good by preserving the aesthetic appearance and the biological communities of the Cape. As of this writing, this project is just getting underway. It would thus appear that teams of biologists working under some higher organizational scheme will make the next advances in the field of ornithology on Cape Cod, and I have therefore chosen the establishment of the park as the end of the period of ornithology covered in this study.

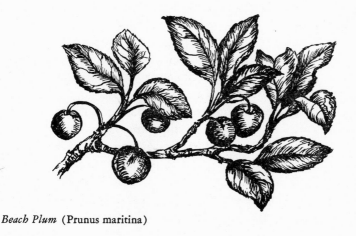

Beach Plum (Prunus maritina)

Sources of Data

THE GATHERING OF DATA for this report has led me through many interesting and stimulating pathways and has proven to be a long and potentially never-ending process. As was noted in the chapter on history, "modern" ornithology on Cape Cod extends back nearly a century, with a few specific items much earlier than this. I have begun with the oldest records and have followed the constantly swelling flood tide of data to the present. Arbitrarily I have cut off the general survey with 1961, which was the year of the establishment of the Cape Cod National Seashore Park; a very few individual items subsequent to this date are, however, included.

The sources of data are: *A.* the museum collections; *B.* the banding records; *C.* the field notes of certain ornithologists; *D.* previously published books and articles in periodicals; and *E.* sight records as printed in "processed" literature.

A. The museum collections: These give a curiously one-sided picture. During the years of the formation of most collections the major interest of local ornithologists was in sea birds, shore birds, game birds, etc. As a result, the collections have splendid series of these groups with many rarities but a real scarcity of the smaller land birds. Furthermore, the recent collecting has been so selective that rarities among the land birds are better represented than are the commoner species. Thus I know of dozens of specimens of various ducks and shore birds, of four specimens of Blue Grosbeak, of two specimens of Slate-colored Junco, and none at all of Downy Woodpecker!

   1) The Museum of Comparative Zoology, Harvard University, Cambridge, Massachusetts, herein abbreviated as MCZ, containing all or parts of the collections of Bangs, Brewster, Bent, Thayer, Allen, Maynard, Mackay, Howe, Kennard, Batchelder, and others, made available to me by Dr. Raymond A. Paynter, Jr. Except for about half a dozen Passerine families, all specimens acquired until about three years ago are listed in a card index. The data on these few Passerine families were extracted from the specimen trays to complete the survey and the more recent acquisitions taken from the catalogue. The skeletal material also includes Cape Cod specimens and has been checked.

   2) The Boston Museum of Science, abbreviated as BMS, formerly the Boston Society of Natural History, containing all or parts of the collections of Bryant, Howe, Shattuck, Brewster, Bangs, Lamb, Durfee, Townsend, Fay, Blaney, Farley, Cobb, Smith, and others; made available by the authorities and checked for Cape Cod

records by Henry M. Parker. This collection now contains specimens, including some rarities, formerly reported in the MCZ. Some recent acquisitions have not
yet been catalogued.

3) The Peabody Museum in Salem, Massachusetts, contains
a few Cape Cod specimens which have been checked by
Miss Dorothy E. Snyder.

4) The British Museum (Natural History), London, contains two large American collections, the H. W. Henshaw collection of 13,326 specimens and the Gerritt S.
Miller collection of 3,737 specimens. I reviewed the
registers of these collections in October 1962 and found:
1) that the Henshaw collection contained very little
from Cape Cod with nothing of importance; and 2)
that the Miller collection contained 616 skins from this
area, largely from North Truro and to a great extent land
birds. The register sheets of this latter collection were
microfilmed for me and this film is deposited in the
MCZ as there is no record of this collection in this country. Individual specimens in the collections were checked
for me through the kindness of Mr. J. D. Macdonald.

5) The collections of the Field Museum of Natural History in Chicago, Illinois, containing the Cory, Conover,
and other collections, include Cape Cod specimens.
These data have been recorded in *A Catalogue of Birds
of the Americas* by Cory and completed by Hellmayr
and Conover; the Cape Cod material was extracted from
these volumes. Individual items were kindly checked by
E. R. Blake and M. D. Maurer.

6) The Massachusetts Audubon Society, abbreviated MAS,
has a small collection containing Cape Cod material.
Part of this is at its headquarters in South Lincoln and
the remainder at the Wellfleet Bay Sanctuary.

7) It has not been possible to check the collections of all

the museums of the country for Cape Cod specimens, though it is known that many are so preserved. Individual specimens are mentioned but mostly as previously published.

B. The banding records:

1) The Austin Ornithological Research Station on the line between North Eastham and Wellfleet. These records began in 1930 and were kept on an almost daily basis until 1957. They were acquired by the Massachusetts Audubon Society with the purchase of the station and are now stored at the headquarters of that organization in South Lincoln, Massachusetts, where they were made available to me by the executive vice-president, Allen H. Morgan. Some data, notably on the terns, have been analyzed and the published papers are referred to in the Systematic List. The land-bird bandings have proven to contain a gold mine of data. I have surveyed these, but a complete analysis has not been attempted so a large field for further research remains. The data from this station were recorded as at North Eastham, though the address of its continuation as the Wellfleet Bay Wildlife Sanctuary is South Wellfleet.

2) Elizabeth Burbank (Mrs. George C. Burbank) was formerly librarian at Sandwich and maintained a banding station there from 1922 to 1954. After her death her records came into the possession of Mrs. Kathleen Anderson of Middleboro, Massachusetts, who kindly loaned them to me. This material has given additional information on the area near the Canal.

3) A few smaller banding stations have had short periods of existence and the data of these as published has been considered.

C. The field notes of certain individual ornithologists, both professional and amateur in status:

1) William Brewster. Notes are preserved in the library
of the MCZ and describe his many trips to various parts
of Cape Cod from 1870 to 1905. Practically nothing of
these has been published; they contain a vast amount
of historically valuable material.

2) Dr. Stanley Cobb. Notes particularly concerning the
Cotuit and Forestdale areas from 1900 on were loaned
to me by Dr. Cobb, who has also related many interesting anecdotes concerning visits to the Chatham Beach
Hotel.

3) Prof. Osborne Earle. Notes chiefly concerning the
Orleans area were reviewed with me by Prof. Earle;
contained in particular many details of changes in status
of Passerine birds.

4) Ludlow Griscom. Many volumes of notes, which are to
be deposited in the Peabody Museum, Salem, Mass.,
were loaned to me by Mrs. Griscom. These contained
detailed observations and counts with full notes on rarities of all Mr. Griscom's vast amount of field work on
Cape Cod during every month of the years from 1929
until illness brought about curtailment of his activities
about 1955. The meticulous detail of these notes, especially with counts and seasonal occurrences, makes them
the backbone of the recent data for the Systematic List.
In spite of the statement regarding "manuscript" in
Griscom and Snyder (1955, page 283), he had assembled only small amounts of data, largely historical,
for Cape Cod; furthermore, he had never organized or
worked up his field notes for this particular project. It
was necessary, therefore, to extract the Cape Cod data
from the mass of notes from other areas and to trans-
scribe them for this study.

5) John P. Bishop. Notes were reviewed after the death
of Mr. Bishop in 1943 by Mr. Griscom, who prepared

an abstract of the significant items of which I have made use.

6) Norman P. Hill. My own notes cover over twenty-five years of observation on Cape Cod including much work at Sagamore as well as many trips in all months of the year to all other areas on the Cape. Since undertaking this project in 1959, a large proportion of my field work has been directed toward specific problems not clearly elucidated from the other assembled data.

D. Previously published books with Cape Cod data are listed in the bibliography with a notation of only author and date at the appropriate place in the text. Periodicals are given a general listing in the bibliography and specific articles are identified by a notation of author, publication, volume, page, and year in the text.

E. The problem of handling sight records and particularly those published in the great volume of "processed literature" has been more difficult. These include *Bulletin of New England Bird-Life, Records of New England Birds*, the regional reports in *Bird Lore* and *Audubon Magazine, Audubon Field Notes*, and the Christmas Count reports. Selected items have been used as it is quickly apparent that the great volume of such data falls into a reproducible pattern so that unusual records can be further investigated if the situation so warrants. I can find no better summation of this matter than that of Witmer Stone in *Bird Studies at Old Cape May*, vol. 1, page iv:

> During the period of my field work at the Cape the greater perfection and more general use of the binocular glass has entirely changed the method of the field ornithologist and there are today no collectors of bird skins . . . The modern glass brings the bird so close to the observer that the experienced student can identify practically all of the birds that he sees at a reasonable distance but the less experienced and less conscientious observer certainly cannot. Unfortunately he is inclined to make identifications in the nonchalant manner that

he is led to think constitutes him an ornithologist while the Christmas and other censuses, into which the spirit of rivalry enters, put a further premium upon unintentionally careless identification as opposed to scientific accuracy. The latter would leave a certain proportion of the birds seen by an observer of limited experience, unidentified. An author is therefore confronted with a mass of "sight records" upon which he has to pass judgement. In all such cases I have considered the personal equation and the experience of others in the same region and acted accordingly.

Doubtless some ornithologists disagreed with some of his decisions as they will with some of mine. Nonetheless, serious ornithologists must remember that popular bird study is here to stay, that it is useless and visionary to expect scientific accuracy from all who participate in this sport, and yet that much faunistic data of great value can be extracted from their material with painstaking screening. From the opposite point of view, these observers must not take personal offense at the elimination of some of their records; they must realize that their approach to bird study is as a sport and they must therefore expect close perusal of their data.

Pitch Pine (Pinus rigida)

Outline of Treatment
for Systematic List

I T HAS BEEN MY INTENTION to record in the Systematic List each and every bird which has been recorded on Cape Cod with any degree of reliability including extinct, extirpated, and introduced species. That some species in this total list cannot be scientifically substantiated is to be expected, but I have elected to list them in their proper sequence rather than in a separate list as a possible guide to future field work.

The treatment accorded to each species is according to the following general outline appropriately modified as needed for the particular species under discussion.

Status—This is the data by which the species is given a place in the avifauna of Cape Cod and is in the following order of decreasing satisfaction:

1) A specimen presently extant in a collection and hence available for inspection.

2) A satisfactory photograph on file and available for inspection of a species sufficiently well marked for such identificacation.

3) A specimen handled by a competent ornithologist but no longer available for inspection, again with due consideration of the critical identification of the species involved. These fall into three categories:

   a) formerly in a museum and so recorded but now lost or destroyed;

   b) found dead or collected and so recorded but not preserved;

   c) banded and released.

4) Presumptive—this indicates a species which, on careful consideration of the evidence, I believe to have been correctly recorded but on the basis of sight records alone.

5) Hypothetical with data—this indicates a species which is probably correctly recorded on the basis of sight identification but which is less acceptable than the above for any of a number of reasons.

6) Hypothetical without data—this indicates a species, the records of which are seriously questionable, again for any of a number of reasons.

7) There are in addition a number of birds of which I have had reports from time to time but which are so improbable and so poorly supported that I have given them no consideration.

Seasonal occurrence—The terms used in this section are largely self-explanatory. It should be noted, however, that the words "Spring," "Summer," "Fall," and "Winter" are used in terms of bird movement rather than in their strict calendar sense. Thus "Spring" indicates the pre-breeding season and especially migration, "Summer" the breeding season with essentially static populations, "Fall" the post-breeding season and especially migration, and "Winter" the non-breeding season with partially static populations.

The figures given under counts indicate the numbers which may be expected on an average day's trip, or sampling in statistical terms. It is important to realize, however: 1) that the total area of the various habitats has never been determined so that samples of breeding and wintering bird counts cannot be projected to give total population figures; 2) that study of images on radar screens show that the recorded sample of migrating birds is an infinitesimal proportion of the total number passing over the Cape; and 3) that there is no proof that the sample, particularly of the migrants, is actually representative of the total. There is necessarily some selection in the counts in terms of habitats, e.g. the average count of White-winged Scoters would not be found in the pine barrens! If there is any significant difference in counts between areas within the Cape it is noted. The terms of occurrence, occasionally qualified, are defined as follows, modified from Robbins and Stewart (1958):

Abundant—found in very large numbers considering habits and conspicuousness.

Common—found in large numbers with the same considerations.

Fairly common—found in moderate or fair numbers with the same considerations.

Uncommon—found in rather small numbers with the same considerations.

Rare—found in small numbers with the same considerations.

Casual—recorded very few times but only a little beyond its normal range.

Accidental—recorded very few times but well beyond its normal range.

Resident—self-explanatory according to the season.

Terminal migrant—a species or population within the species arriving on the Cape and remaining for the following season.

Transient migrant—a species or a population within the species passing through the Cape en route to other areas.

Departure migrant—a species or population within the species departing from the Cape, having been present during the previous season.

Vagrant—wandering individuals or flocks remaining only a short time in any area.

In so far as possible, observers' names are recorded for specific dates and counts. Abbreviations include "C.C." for Christmas Counts and "M.A.S." for the Massachusetts Audubon Society Camp-outs. If any record is based on a specimen its location is noted as well, if on a published note a citation is given, or if on a banding record it is so noted.

Distribution—Brief indications are given of the ecology of the species on the Cape, particularly if it differs from that on the mainland; also general indications of locations over the Cape with differences noted between areas within the Cape or between the Cape and the mainland. There is a constant problem in determining whether differences in reports in different areas reflect a true difference in occurrence or whether it is merely due to concentration of gunners and collectors in the past and field observers at present. Often the availability of suitable habitat is the best clue to this dilemma. Specifically favorable areas have already been described.

History—This is a summary of the data which indicate any change in the status of a species, largely over the last century for sea birds and shore birds but, with only a few outstanding exceptions, only over the past thirty years for land birds. The term "historical period," however, is applied to the century in all cases.

Some attempt is made to correlate the changes in bird populations with changes in ecology.

Subspecies—The concept of subspecies has been minimized in this study. In the few instances where subspecies can be identified in the field or where there are published references to particular ones the data on their occurrence are recorded. Unless specifically noted to the contrary, the Systematic List refers to the species only and not to subspecies. The few hybrids recorded for the Cape are also noted. For some species not racially distinct a study of the data has convinced me that several distinct populations are present on the Cape at different times. Except for one instance, the Mourning Dove, this has not been satisfactorily proven, though I have presented my opinion of the probable pattern; a vast amount of banding studies will be needed either to prove or disprove these hypotheses.

Bayberry (Myrica pennsylvania)

Systematic List

THE SYSTEMATIC LIST is the heart of this report and one important reason for undertaking the entire project. As will be noted, this is more than an abbreviated annotated list but instead as complete a summary as possible for each species, covering its present status, its seasonal occurrence and distribution, its migrational schedule and its history, in short, the biology of that species on Cape Cod.

COMMON LOON
Gavia immer (Brünnich)

STATUS: Represented in MCZ and BMS collections.

SPRING: Common migrant both alongshore and overhead.

Earliest transient date: Uncertain, probably about March 15.

Average migration period: March 30–June 3.

Peak: Prolonged movement with poorly defined peak May 7–20, average 12–30/day, no very high counts.

Latest transient date: Uncertain, probably about June 12.

SUMMER: Regular non-breeding stragglers, often injured or oiled; average 6–8 birds, maximum 49 in 1941 at Monomoy (Maclay).

FALL: Common migrant.

Earliest transient date: Uncertain, probably about August 15.

Average migration period: September 15–December 20.

Peak: Not well marked, probably November 5–25, average 15–30 birds, maximum 375 on November 5, 1940, entering Cape Cod Bay (Benchley).

Latest transient date: Uncertain, probably about January 1.

WINTER: Common resident, though mobile and irregular in numbers which build up after transients have passed; average 10–20 birds, maxima 126 on January 2, 1950, off Monomoy (Griscom) and 120 on March 6, 1957 (Hill), are probably post- and pre-migrational gatherings of local birds.

DISTRIBUTION: Primarily salt water, bays, and estuaries to many miles offshore, also regular in fresh-water ponds and migrating overland. Observed both spring and fall largely on northwest-southeast and north-south routes. Occurs in numbers over entire Cape. Principal migration route both seasons close to mainland crossing Cape near Canal, Mashnee Island in Buzzards Bay being a former favored shooting site. Many also migrate around outer Cape and smaller numbers cross in Barnstable area. Wintering birds in greater numbers to eastward.

HISTORY: By tradition, bred on Cape ponds and estuaries, but specific data are lacking. Marked decrease 1860–1900 because of spring shooting (Forbush, 1912) and no real recovery since as counts have remained stable.

* *

ARCTIC LOON
Gavia arctica (Linnaeus)

STATUS: Hypothetical.
WINTER: Rare but probably regular visitant; only reports of adult birds considered. October 2, 1938, at Monomoy (Griscom & Garrison) to May 31, 1948, at Orleans (Griscom & Emery).
SUMMER: Occasional birds as in 1952 and 1958, often oiled. Recorded from Sandwich, Brewster, Monomoy, Chatham, Orleans, and Eastham.

* *

RED-THROATED LOON
Gavia stellata (Pontoppidan)

STATUS: Represented in MCZ and Chicago collections.
SPRING: Common migrant, occasionally abundant.
Earliest transient date: Uncertain, probably about March 15.
Average migration period: March 23–May 23.
Peak: April 1–30; average 25–50 birds, maximum 1120 on April 28, 1941, at Monomoy (Griscom & Bergstrom).
Latest transient date: Uncertain, probably about May 30.
SUMMER: Scattered stragglers, somewhat irregular but present two out of three years, usually single birds, maximum 8 on July 30, 1945, at Monomoy (Maclay).
FALL: Common migrant, occasionally abundant.
Earliest transient date: Uncertain, probably about September 15.
Average migration period: October 15–December 25.
Peak: November 9–December 1; average 40–100 birds, maximum 1000 in storm on November 30, 1957, at Nauset (Smart).

Latest transient date: Uncertain, probably about January 5.

WINTER: Scattered wintering birds probably every year except for the most severe winters, average 2–6 birds.

DISTRIBUTION: On salt water including open ocean, estuaries and bays, but seldom far offshore, occasionally in migration on freshwater ponds. Considerable number in spring up Buzzards Bay passing along Canal and into Cape Cod Bay; in fall crossing at Canal and in Barnstable area. However, highest counts are reported from Monomoy and Nauset, indicating a heavier flight eastward.

HISTORY: No evidence of change in numbers in historical period presumably due to undisturbed northern breeding range. Recent cycle of mild winters has increased number and success of wintering birds.

* *

RED-NECKED GREBE
Podiceps grisegena (Boddaert)

STATUS: Represented in MCZ collection.

FALL: Rare migrant, sometimes unreported.

Earliest transient date: September 28, 1953, at Eastham (Derby).

Average migration period: October 16–January 2; average 1–2 birds, maximum 5 on October 31, 1954, at Orleans and Chatham (Griscom & Earle).

WINTER: Rather rare and irregular straggler, very rarely a heavy flight appears, e.g. 17+ on February 24, 1934, at Chatham (Richardson).

SPRING: Rare and irregular migrant.

Average migration period: March 1–May 11; average 1–2 birds, maximum 33 on April 2, 1939, at Dennis (Long).

Latest transient date: May 30, 1932, at Monomoy (Griscom & Allen).

DISTRIBUTION: Fresh and salt water including open ocean and

estuaries. More regular and common in Buzzards Bay, decreasing eastward through the Sounds and through Cape Cod Bay to the Wellfleet-Truro area.

HISTORY: No change in numbers reported by Forbush (1912) and no change apparent in past twenty-five years.

* *

HORNED GREBE
Podiceps auritus (Linnaeus)

STATUS: Represented in BMS collection.

FALL: Common to uncommon migrant depending on location.
Earliest transient date: Uncertain, probably about September 14.
Average migration period: October 18–December 10.
Peak: November 15–December 5; see below for counts.

WINTER: Common to uncommon depending on location, see below.

SPRING: Uncommon to rare migrant.
Average migration period: March 10–April 23.
Peak: March 25–April 19; see below for counts.
Latest transient date: Uncertain, disappears from Cape Cod waters earlier than from north of Boston.

SUMMER: Very rare non-breeding straggler.

DISTRIBUTION: Salt-water bays and estuaries, occasionally on open ocean, very rarely on fresh-water ponds on migration. Common migrant and winterer in Buzzards Bay, several hundred in both spring and fall and average 60–80 in winter. Small numbers in Cape Cod Bay west of Barnstable, rare eastward. Decreases steadily eastward in sounds. In Chatham-Orleans area present on migration, average in fall 10–20, maximum 95 on December 28, 1958 (C.C.), usually a few wintering birds and average 3–6 in spring. North of Eastham very few birds recorded.

HISTORY: No information regarding early numbers; Forbush (1912) reported them markedly decreased inland but less so along the coast. Since 1945 there is considerable and fairly consistent increase on the outer Cape, e.g. Christmas Count average of 7/year in the 1930's and 39/year in the 1950's. Also increased in the Falmouth area but proportionately less.

* *

EARED GREBE

Podiceps caspicus (Hablizl)

STATUS: Represented in BMS collection.
Accidental straggler from the West.
SPECIMEN: September 27, 1953, at Monomoy (Morgan).
SIGHT RECORDS: October 13–21, 1951, at Monomoy (Griscom, Drury, Parker, Snyder); March 15, 1952, at Chatham (Griscom, Barry, Morgan).

* *

WESTERN GREBE

Aechmophorus occidentalis (Lawrence)

STATUS: Hypothetical.
One sight record of some species of large black and white grebe on December 28, 1941, at Monomoy (Broun et al.).

* *

PIED-BILLED GREBE

Podilymbus podiceps (Linnaeus)

STATUS: Represented in MCZ and British Museum collections.
SPRING: No evidence of transients; wintering birds usually disappear by late March, latest date April 9, 1949, at Eastham (Griscom & Parker).
SUMMER: Breeding probable but not proven at Monomoy on

either Point Pond, Lighthouse Pond, or both; birds usually present all summer.

FALL: Fairly common migrant, occasionally common.

Earliest transient date: Uncertain, probably about August 16.

Average migration period: September 2–December 20.

Peak: September 20–November 10; counts extremely variable from year to year, minimum 4–6, maximum 90 on October 5, 1952 (Griscom, Bailey, Beattie).

Latest transient date: Uncertain, probably about January 2.

WINTER: Very irregular visitant dependent on the weather, absent if frozen out, up to 5 recorded through February 1954.

DISTRIBUTION: Breeds in rush-margined fresh water, transients on more open ponds moving temporarily to protected salt-water estuaries with freeze-up. Species recorded over entire Cape.

HISTORY: Greatly decreased as a breeding bird since 1850 (Forbush, 1912), though probably never very common on Cape. Counts during historical period show no significant trend, but recent cycle of mild winters has increased the numbers and success of wintering birds.

* *

FULMAR
Fulmarus glacialis (Linnaeus)

STATUS: Specimens obtained but not preserved.

SPECIMENS: September 23, 1912, at Monomoy (Harrington, see Brown, *Auk*, *30*, 105, 1913); December 28, 1918, at Sandwich (Torrey, see Forbush, 1925).

SIGHT RECORDS: Offshore on Georges Banks said to be "Fairly plentiful in winter" (Collins, *Auk*, *1*, 236, 1884), also seen there in July 1955 (Grayce). Inshore, no records until 3 on May 23, 1961, off Chatham (Morgan & Bailey); then 50 on January 28, 1962, also off Chatham (Young, *fide* Bailey).

* *

CORY'S SHEARWATER
Puffinus diomedea (Scopoli)

STATUS: Represented in MCZ, BMS, Chicago and British Museum collections.

SUMMER AND FALL: Uncommon to abundant post-breeding visitant according to local ecological conditions.

Earliest arrival date: July 4, 1944, off Chatham (Griscom).

Average period: August 5–October 1; the last shearwater to arrive and ordinarily the last to depart.

Counts: Irregular in numbers, probably present every year, but counts vary from one to 75, maximum 180 on August 31, 1938; off Monomoy (Hagar) and 1000+ in fall of 1886 in Buzzards Bay (Baird, *Auk*, 4, 71, 1887).

Latest departure date: November 10, 1946, off Chatham (Griscom, Mazzeo, Elkins).

DISTRIBUTION: Pelagic but regularly seen from shore and even entering bays and estuaries. Maximum numbers in warmer waters south of Cape, outnumbering other shearwaters there, extending regularly though usually in smaller numbers to lower Buzzards Bay. Numbers decrease rapidly northward, though there are usually a few off Provincetown and to Stellwagon Bank, particularly when in numbers southward. Still rarer in Cape Cod Bay where recorded at Wellfleet, Billingsgate, and Sagamore. Usually rather solitary, but individuals will join flocks of Greater Shearwaters; will investigate a "slick" but seldom feed from it.

HISTORY: Type specimen of *P. d. borealis* shot October 11, 1880, off Chatham, now in Chicago collection (Cory, *Bull. N.O.C. 6*, 84, 1881). Decrease thereafter attributed to fishermen who used all shearwaters for bait. No evidence of significant change in numbers in past twenty-five years; local counts depend on local bait conditions.

*   *

GREATER SHEARWATER
Puffinus gravis (O'Reilly)

STATUS: Represented in MCZ, BMS, Chicago and British Museum collections.

SUMMER AND FALL: Rare to abundant "wintering" visitant according to local ecological conditions.

Earliest arrival date: April 21, 1911, found dead at Eastham (Cobb), ordinarily rare until July.

Average period: July 28–October 1, migrating later far offshore as 800 on October 27, 1944, off Stellwagon Bank (Drury) and 3700 in storm on November 30, 1957, at Nauset (Smart).

Counts: Irregular in numbers but probably present each year, counts extremely variable; abundant in good fishing years when bait is visible in the water; average 10–100 birds, maximum 1200 on August 20, 1955, off Chatham (Griscom, Bowen).

Latest departure date: November 30, 1957, at Nauset (Smart).

DISTRIBUTION: Most pelagic of the shearwaters but occasionally seen from land. Maximum numbers in colder waters east and north of Cape Cod. Occasionally penetrates Cape Cod Bay to Wellfleet, Barnstable, and Sagamore, usually in small numbers. Much rarer in the warmer waters of the sounds and Buzzards Bay, one shot from flock July 27, 1915, in Buzzards Bay (Cobb), but not present in great flight of 1886. Note reversal of distribution of Cory's Shearwater. In quiet weather gather in flocks which may contain other species. Comes to and feeds regularly at "slicks" and sometimes taken on baited fishhook.

HISTORY: High numbers through 1880's followed by long and marked decline due to persecution by fishermen and a cycle of poor bait years. Return of good bait and decrease in local fishing resulted in an increase after 1949, but local bait conditions always determine local counts.

*   *

SOOTY SHEARWATER
Puffinus griseus (Gmelin)

STATUS: Represented in MCZ, BMS, and Chicago collections.

SUMMER: Uncommon to common "wintering" visitant according to local ecological conditions.

Earliest arrival date: May 23, 1946, off Chatham (Griscom, Bailey, Hill).

Average period: May 30–September 1; usually the first shearwater to arrive and to depart.

Counts: Arrive in loose flocks up to 100 but scatter and join flocks of Greater Shearwaters as some birds depart, e.g. 67 migrating south July 5, 1941, at Monomoy (Griscom & Garrison). Sometimes gone by August, but remain longer and in greater numbers in good bait years, maximum 750 on August 16, 1954, off Chatham (Griscom, Atkins, Kleber, Emery). One light phase bird collected from flock of normals August 11, 1956, off Chatham (Morgan).

Latest departure date: November 30, 1957, in storm off Nauset (Smart).

DISTRIBUTION: Pelagic but regularly seen from beaches, particularly on arrival in May. Maximum numbers to southeast of Chatham, diminishing northward to Provincetown; rarely penetrates Cape Cod Bay to Sagamore and Barnstable (collected October 1916, in MCZ). Enters Nantucket and Vineyard Sounds, decreasing westward, and reached Buzzards Bay only in 1886.

HISTORY: Abundant prior to 1880, decreased by persecution by fishermen. Now increasing steadily, again abundant in good fishing years.

*   *

MANX SHEARWATER
Puffinus puffinus (Brünnich)

STATUS: Represented in MCZ and BMS collections.

SUMMER: Very rare vagrant from eastern Atlantic, see Snyder, *Auk*, 75, 213, 1958. Specimens collected August 9, 1957, on Stellwagon Bank (Burnett) to August 23, 1958, off Chatham (Kleber); total of six specimens, one each in 1953, 1955, 1958, and three in 1957. Sight records extend dates from July 12 to September 27, but small black and white shearwaters are not identifiable with certainty in the field or from photographs.

DISTRIBUTION: Pelagic, parallel to that of Greater Shearwater in colder waters east and north of Cape. Will come to investigate a "slick" and occasionally feed.

HISTORY: Apparently extending its range and increasing in numbers, though possibly only overlooked in the past.

*   *

AUDUBON'S SHEARWATER
Puffinus lherminieri Lesson

STATUS: Represented in MAS collection.
Accidental vagrant from the tropical Atlantic.
One bird, sick or injured, captured on July 28, 1964 at Falmouth (Patten, Garry, in MAS).

*   *

WHITE-FACED PETREL
Pelagodroma marina (Latham)

STATUS: Hypothetical.
One sight record October 1, 1945, "thirty miles off tip of Cape Cod" (Abbott, *Auk*, 63, 251, 1946).

*   *

LEACH'S PETREL

Oceanodroma leucorhoa (Vieillot)

STATUS: Represented in MCZ, BMS, Chicago, and British Museum collections.

Poorly known but probably regular in very small numbers in offshore waters throughout the year. Specimens provide dates in June, July, August, September, October, and December; sight records of this species are always open to question, but May and January can probably be added.

SPRING: Small and ill-defined influx during early May.

SUMMER: Very rare, believed to be birds from the Penikese Island colony.

FALL: Slightly larger influx in September and October.

WINTER: Possibly present.

DISTRIBUTION: Pelagic but seen near or even over land with severe storms and hurricanes, especially in 1954. Most sight records off eastern shore of Cape but occasionally in Cape Cod Bay (specimen from Barnstable, in BMS).

HISTORY: Said to have decreased, but Cape Cod data too fragmentary to be convincing.

*   *

WILSON'S PETREL

Oceanites oceanicus (Kuhl)

STATUS: Represented in MCZ, BMS, Chicago, and British Museum collections.

SUMMER: Common to abundant "wintering" visitant.

Earliest arrival date May 23, 1946, off Monomoy (Griscom, Bailey, Hill).

Average period; June 1–September 1.

Counts: Arrival usually in small scattered groups, 5–50 birds; maximum 2000 on May 27, 1951, off Monomoy (Griscom).

Then scatter and often regather August 5–20; maxima 4000–
5000 on August 6, 1946, on Stellwagon Bank (Curtis) and
5000 on August 11, 1957, off Monomoy (Hill).
Latest departure date: September 24, 1955, off Monomoy
(Griscom & Halbergs); possibly later far offshore.

DISTRIBUTION: Pelagic with greatest number 10–20 miles offshore.
Rarely seen from land except in storms, but may congregate in
Provincetown Harbor and occasionally follows fishing boats in
elsewhere. Feeds regularly over "slicks" at sea. Maximum
numbers along entire eastern shore from Provincetown to
Monomoy, enters both Cape Cod Bay and Buzzards Bay in
small numbers. Usually scattered loose groups, occasionally collecting in massed flocks on the water.

HISTORY: No evidence of significant change in numbers except as
can be accounted for by local ecological conditions from year
to year.

* *

WHITE-TAILED TROPIC-BIRD
Phaëthon lepturus Daudin

STATUS: Represented in BMS collection.
Accidental storm-blown vagrant from the tropical Atlantic.
One bird, injured, picked up alive on April 25, 1944, at Harwich-
port (Baker, in BMS).

* *

WHITE PELICAN
Pelecanus erythrorhynchos Gmelin

STATUS: Specimen obtained but now believed lost.
Accidental vagrant from the West.
One found dead May 12 or 13, 1905, at Sandwich (Kounze, see
Brewster, *Auk*, 26, 185, 1909), formerly in Brewster collection.
Sight record of two birds April 23–24, 1953, at Truro (Howes

et al.) and two birds October 1, 1961, for several weeks at
South Chatham (Drew et al.).

* *

BROWN PELICAN
Pelecanus occidentalis Linnaeus

STATUS: Presumptive.
Accidental vagrant from the South.
SIGHT RECORDS: August 28–30, 1933, at Cataumet (Brooks, *Auk,*
51, 77, 1934) and September 23, 1962, at Monomoy (Hagar);
also probably August 11, 1937, at Monomoy (Kilburn).

* *

BROWN BOOBY
Sula leucogaster (Boddaert)

STATUS: Represented in BMS collection.
Accidental vagrant from the tropical Atlantic.
SPECIMEN: September 17, 1878, on "Cape Cod" and brought to
Boston Market (Brewster, *Bull. N.O.C., 4,* 191, 1879).
SIGHT RECORDS: May 30, 1946 (Griscom, Cottrell), and October
22, 1950 (Griscom, Drury), both at Monomoy. Several other
boobies have been reported but not satisfactorily identified as
to species.

* *

GANNET
Morus bassanus (Linnaeus)

STATUS: Represented in MCZ, BMS, and Chicago collections.
SPRING: Common to abundant migrant.
Earliest transient date: Uncertain, probably about March 23.

Average migration period: March 30–May 30.

Peak: April 9–27; average 100–500 birds from shore, maximum 1800 on April 10, 1949, at Eastham and Orleans (Griscom & Parker).

Latest transient date: Uncertain, probably about June 5.

SUMMER: Occasional non-breeding birds, usually in immature plumage and usually at sea.

FALL: Common to abundant migrant.

Earliest transient date: Uncertain, probably about August 5.

Average migration period: August 25–December 25.

Peak: October 24–December 5; average 100–500 birds, maximum 1000 on December 1, 1946, at Monomoy (Argues).

Latest transient date: Uncertain, probably about January 1.

WINTER: Small number of wintering birds, quite mobile according to the weather and regularly surviving.

DISTRIBUTION: Essentially in the offshore zone, not truly pelagic and approaching shore even to the surf line. Does not enter smaller estuary waters and never over land. Highest counts from Monomoy to Provincetown. Very small numbers in Buzzards Bay at any time. Small numbers in sounds, particularly in spring, and considerable numbers in Cape Cod Bay, particularly in fall; no known records crossing the Cape or along Canal at any time.

HISTORY: Increasing steadily in historic period. Maximum reported 1880–1890 was 100/day; such counts became regular by 1930 and have continued to rise to the present; however, some of this reported increase is probably due to wider use of high-powered telescopes. Migration period has lengthened both spring and fall with the increasing numbers. Recent cycle of mild winters has increased number of wintering birds, though it was always regular off the Cape in contrast to the situation in colder waters northward.

*　*

GREAT CORMORANT
Phalacrocorax carbo (Linnaeus)

STATUS: Found dead, not preserved (Griscom). Sight records carefully screened to avoid confusion with next species.

WINTER: Regular resident, see below for distribution.
Earliest arrival date: October 11, 1942, at Monomoy (Griscom).
Average period: November 1–April 1.
Latest departure date: April 6, 1950, at Nauset (de Windt).

DISTRIBUTION: Rocky coasts and estuaries. Regular and in numbers up to 2000 along Buzzards Bay and in the Woods Hole area (Kelly), but hardly seen east of Nobska Light. Also occurs in Cape Cod Bay at Sagamore but seldom eastward. Rare and irregular on sandy shores elsewhere but probably flying over the outer Cape, e.g. flock of 47 believed to be this species seen arriving from east-north-east on October 19, 1960, at Nauset and going on southwest at great altitude without stopping (Hill).

HISTORY: Steadily increasing parallel with recent changes throughout the Northeast.

* *

DOUBLE-CRESTED CORMORANT
Phalacrocorax auritus (Lesson)

STATUS: Represented in BMS, Chicago, and British Museum collections.

SPRING: Rather uncommon migrant.
Earliest arrival date: April 11, 1955 at Nauset (Earle).
Average migration period: April 25–May 30. No consistent peak period and very irregular in numbers, maximum 190 on April 28, 1941, at Monomoy (Griscom, Morgan).
Latest transient date: Uncertain due to wandering birds from nearby colonies, probably about June 2.

SUMMER: Regular in small numbers around Woods Hole and north through Buzzards Bay from the Weepecket Island colony; also in the Provincetown area from colonies in Boston Harbor, seen regularly crossing the Bay. Only stragglers elsewhere.

FALL: Common to rare migrant, irregular from year to year and dependent on location.

Earliest transient date: Uncertain, probably about July 31.

Average migration period: September 1–November 12.

Peak: September 22–October 31; numbers very irregular, occasionally unrecorded, maximum 140 on September 27, 1947, at Eastham (Griscom & Mazzeo).

Latest departure date: November 16, 1941, at Nauset (Griscom & Curtis).

DISTRIBUTION: Breeds on small rocky islets, on migration in estuaries and occasionally fresh-water ponds, often passing overhead without stopping. No breeding colonies known on Cape Cod, but nearby ones on Weepecket Island off Naushon (10+ pairs in 1960, Hill) and in Boston Harbor supply summer wanderers. Transients, both overhead and on water, are appreciably more common and more regular in Buzzards Bay, crossing the Cape in the region of the Canal and along western shore of Cape Cod Bay; much less regular eastward, an obvious habitat preference.

HISTORY: No data on early historical period. Rare for many years, but rapidly increasing with general increase in the Northeast and re-establishment of adjacent breeding colonies.

* *

MAGNIFICENT FRIGATE-BIRD
Fregata magnificens Mathews

STATUS: Photographed, now on file at Wellfleet Bay Sanctuary. Accidental vagrant from the tropical Atlantic.

Photographed on June 18, 1960, at Chatham (Drew); sight record on June 10, 1936, at North Eastham (Packard, *Auk*, 65, 307, 1948).

* *

GREAT BLUE HERON
Ardea herodias Linnaeus

STATUS: Represented in MCZ and BMS collections.

SPRING: Rather uncommon migrant.

Earliest transient date: Uncertain, probably about March 25.

Average migration period: April 4–May 29.

Peak: April 15–May 15; average 3–4 birds, maximum 8 on April 19, 1940 (Griscom, Alexander, Scott, Bishop).

Latest transient date: Uncertain, probably about June 5.

SUMMER: Scattered non-breeding stragglers, always in immature plumage.

FALL: Fairly common migrant.

Earliest transient date: Uncertain, probably about July 10.

Average migration period: July 30–November 30.

Peak: September 1–October 5; average 20–30 birds, maximum 49 on September 10–11, 1949 (M.A.S.).

Latest departure date: Uncertain, probably about December 10.

WINTER: Uncommon to rare resident depending on severity of weather; wintering numbers build up after mid-December when transients have left, average 10–25, maximum 73 in 1957 (C.C.), some individuals regularly survive.

DISTRIBUTION: Large marsh areas, often solitary, but will gather in small flocks. Seen migrating over Stellwagon Bank from Cape Ann to Cape Cod on August 3, 1947 (Griscom). Found over entire Cape, but concentrates eastward in winter. In general, fewer migrants, but more winterers than on mainland.

HISTORY: No data on early counts, believed to be slightly increased since 1920 (Earle). Winter counts definitely increased recently due to cycle of mild seasons.

SUBSPECIES: Sight record of *A. h. wardi* June 23–August 4, 1946, at Monomoy (Griscom et al.).

* *

GREEN HERON
Butorides virescens (Linnaeus)

STATUS: Represented in MCZ, BMS, Chicago, and British Museum collections.

SUMMER: Rather uncommon and local breeding resident.
Earliest arrival date: April 28, 1953, at South Harwich (Howe).
Average period: May 18–October 1.
Counts: No evidence of transients either spring or fall; scattered pairs only until post-breeding gatherings of 6–10 birds.
Latest departure date: November 26, 1955, at Falmouth (Garry).

DISTRIBUTION: Breeds in secluded wooded areas along streams and swamps, not in colonies; post-breeding gatherings in marshes. Present over entire Cape, 30+ pairs estimated; probably not significantly different in density than on mainland.

HISTORY: Steady reduction in numbers chiefly in the past forty to fifty years due to loss of habitat. In 1914–1918, 10–15/day and in 1950–1960, 4/day in the Cotuit-Mashpee area (Cobb).

* *

LITTLE BLUE HERON
Florida caerulea (Linnaeus)

STATUS: Represented in MCZ collection.

SPRING: Rare and irregular vagrant.
Earliest arrival date: April 9, 1951, at Eastham (Austin).
Average period: April 19–May 10.

SUMMER: Irregular vagrant, not known to nest.

FALL: Uncommon to rare, somewhat irregular, post-breeding wanderer from the South.

Average period: August 5–October 5; average 1–2 birds, maximum 9 in August 1952 at Nauset (Mason).

Latest departure date: October 27, 1951, at Eastham (Mixter).

DISTRIBUTION: Pools in both large and small marshes. Found throughout entire Cape from Sagamore and Falmouth to Chatham and north to Wellfleet.

HISTORY: No data available regarding early status. Very rare or accidental to 1881 when there was a flock of six at Bourne, one collected (Hardy, *fide* Bangs); then irregular to about 1930, since which time it has occurred nearly every year, showing slight increase to present. The flight of 1948 did not reach the Cape in greater than normal numbers, i.e. only ten in three localities (Cottrell, *Bull. Mass. Audubon Soc.*, *33*, 155, 1949).

* *

CATTLE EGRET

Bubulcus ibis (Linnaeus)

STATUS: Specimen shot November 25, 1952, at Truro, now in Hyannis (unknown hunter, *fide* Griscom).

Rare and irregular vagrant from South.

Above specimen remains the only fall record; sight records on April 25, 1956, at Chatham (Brown) and fairly regularly during April since 1960, often associated with southern storms.

* *

REDDISH EGRET

Dichromanassa rufescens (Gmelin)

STATUS: Hypothetical.

One adult seen repeatedly May 30–June 3, 1953, at Monomoy (Griscom, Smart, Drury, Stackpole, et al.).

* *

COMMON EGRET
Casmerodius albus (Linnaeus)

STATUS: Represented in BMS collection.

SPRING: Very rare and irregular vagrant.

Earliest arrival date: March 9, 1942, at Harwich (Cahoon), after a southern storm.

Average period: April 24–May 24.

SUMMER: Rare visitant, somewhat irregular, not known to nest.

FALL: Rather uncommon, rarely common, post-breeding wanderer from the South.

Average period: August 1–September 24.

Peak: Irregular, usually late August, average 3–5 birds, maximum about 150 for entire Cape in flight year of 1948 (Cottrell, *Bull. Mass. Audubon Soc.*, 33, 155, 1949).

Latest departure date: December 14, 1953, at Nauset (Guild).

DISTRIBUTION: Fresh and salt marshes of variable extent, wooded swamps. Occurs over entire Cape, much less frequent than on mainland.

HISTORY: Presumed to have been the "white cranes" reported by the colonists. Became very rare by 1850 and remained so until recovery of significant numbers in South. Steady increase since 1920, and now recorded every year. Moderate penetration to Cape of great flight of 1948.

* *

SNOWY EGRET
Leucophoyx thula (Molina)

STATUS: Represented in BMS collection.

SUMMER: Rare visitant, regular in recent years; casually breeding.

Earliest arrival date: March 12, 1955, at Chatham (Mosher); fairly frequently recorded after southern storms in April.

Average period: April 20–September 10.

Latest departure date: October 13, 1954, at Chatham (Mayo).

DISTRIBUTION: Bred in dense thicket adjacent to marsh in Black-crowned Night Heron rookery in 1955 at Quivet Neck, East Dennis (LeBaron); two young hatched but not known to have survived. Otherwise occurs in fresh and salt marshes, widely scattered from Falmouth and Bourne to Chatham and Provincetown.

HISTORY: Original status unknown. Accidental vagrant from the South until 1948, since then reported every year. Flight of 1948 reached outer Cape where five birds were reported.

* *

LOUISIANA HERON
Hydranassa tricolor (Müller)

STATUS: Hypothetical.
Sight records August 11–September 15, 1946, at Monomoy (Griscom, Rich, Church), August 7, 1961, at Chatham (Gardler) and August 17–18, 1960, at Monomoy (Bailey).

* *

BLACK-CROWNED NIGHT HERON
Nycticorax nycticorax (Linnaeus)

STATUS: Represented in MCZ, BMS, Chicago, and British Museum collections.
SPRING: Uncommon, rarely common.
Earliest arrival date: Uncertain, probably about March 20.
Average resident arrival date: April 1–7.
Counts: Usually no transients, though flocks may be blown in by southern storms as 220 on May 5, 1945, at Nauset (Griscom).
SUMMER: Common breeding resident, locally abundant.
FALL: Common, largely local birds but some transients.
Average departure date: Variable, October 1–November 1.
Peak: Post-breeding gatherings away from colonies in August average 50–100 birds, maximum 250 on August 9, 1940, at

Sagamore (Hill); latest migrating flock October 24, 1943, at Chatham (Griscom).

WINTER: Regular in small numbers, usually surviving.

DISTRIBUTION: Breeds in thickets and low trees near or in swamps, transients in salt marshes and fresh swamps and flying overhead; often along tidal pools on beaches and perching on fish weirs. Formerly bred in many small and a few enormous colonies: at Sandy Neck, Barnstable, since at least 1820, though exact locations shifted from year to year, 2500+ pairs in 1920 (Gross, *Auk*, 40, 1 & 191, 1923); and at Hyannis, 1500 pairs in 1895 (Brewster); both abandoned about 1940. Now nests in smaller but more scattered and shifting colonies at East Dennis, Brewster, Monomoy, Chatham, Mashpee, Provincetown, Pocasset, etc.

HISTORY: Total numbers decreased by loss of great colonies, e.g. daily maxima 250 in 1940, 60 in 1942, 30 in 1948, and 4 in 1961 at Sagamore (Hill). Elsewhere counts have decreased, though to a lesser degree. Smaller colonies much disturbed and some recently destroyed. First winter record in 1894 (Job).

* *

YELLOW-CROWNED NIGHT HERON
Nyctanassa violacea (Linnaeus)

STATUS: Represented in MCZ and BMS collections.

SPRING: Rare and irregular.

Earliest arrival date: April 19, 1891, at Provincetown (Small, in BMS).

Average arrival date: May 10–25; single birds only.

SUMMER: Rare and local; believed to have bred at Provincetown in 1891 (Miller, Small), and nearly fledged young seen at Chatham in 1940 and 1941 (Maclay); suspected elsewhere.

FALL: Uncommon to rare migrant and post-breeding wanderer from the South.

Average departure date: October 1–12.

Counts: Mostly single birds but small flocks of 5–8 occasionally in post-breeding wandering to mid-September. Maximum 8 on September 10, 1949, at Chatham (Griscom).

Latest departure date: January 3, 1955, at Eastham (Griscom).

DISTRIBUTION: Breeds in dense, relatively low trees near water; otherwise seen in fresh and salt marshes. Single birds often associated with Black-crowned Night Herons, but the small flocks tend to stay separate. Recorded over entire Cape.

HISTORY: Probably overlooked in early historical period. Increased reports in past twenty years consistent with increased number of observers familiar with the species. No convincing evidence of a real change in numbers, but now remaining later in the fall.

* *

LEAST BITTERN
Ixobrychus exilis (Gmelin)

STATUS: Represented in Mass. Audubon Society, BMS, and British Museum collections.

SPRING: Collected in May 1892 at North Truro (Miller & Bangs, in BMS and British Museum) and nesting at Pilgrim Lake at that time, unreported there since and not found in special searches in 1958 and 1961 (Hill). Also seen May 17, 1941, at Falmouth (Jones).

FALL: Very rare and irregular migrant; recorded from July 18, 1953, at West Dennis (Whiting) to September 6, 1934, at North Eastham (Low).

* *

AMERICAN BITTERN
Botaurus lentiginosus (Rackett)

STATUS: Represented in MCZ, BMS, and Chicago collections.

SPRING: Arrival of residents, no evidence of transients.

Earliest arrival date: March 27, 1938, at Chatham (Bishop).

Average arrival date: April 15–20; singles and pairs only.

SUMMER: Formerly bred abundantly at Pilgrim Lake, North Truro, thirteen pumping at once in 1891 (Brewster); none found there in special searches in 1958 and 1961 (Hill). Now rare and local breeding resident, known at Pamet River in Truro, Chatham, Monomoy, Mashpee, and probably occurs at a few other places.

FALL: Uncommon transient.

Average migration period: September 15–November 15.

Peak: October 1–25; average 1–3 birds, maximum 6 on October 17, 1954, at Monomoy (Griscom).

WINTER: Very rare, local and irregular straggler; only occasionally survives the season.

DISTRIBUTION: Breeds in fresh-water reedy margins and rarely salt marshes. Transients more often in salt marshes. Much less common on Cape than on mainland, but no apparent difference between areas on the Cape.

HISTORY: See above regarding former colony at Pilgrim Lake, North Truro; their occurrence in this area was due to the development of extensive reed beds in a newly created pond; these beds are now choked with peat and relatively dry due to a drop in the water level, leaving essentially no emergent vegetation. Otherwise counts over the rest of the Cape have shown no significant trend.

* *

GLOSSY IBIS

Plegadis falcinellus (Linnaeus)

STATUS: Represented in MCZ and BMS collections.

Accidental straggler from the South, characteristically found after southern storms in spring.

COLLECTED: one on May 4, 1878, Eastham (Denton, see Cory & Allen, *Bull. N.O.C.*, 3, 152, 1878) and two on May 5, 1878, at Orleans (Brewer, *Bull. N.O.C.*, 3, 151, 1878).

SIGHT RECORDS: one at Provincetown (Austin) and two at Chatham (Eldredge) April 20–27, 1952; one at Chatham on May 1–3, 1958 (Frey).

* *

MUTE SWAN
Cygnus olor (Gmelin)

STATUS: Presumptive.

Introduced species; an irregular straggler from breeding colonies in Rhode Island and Westport, Mass. Recorded from April 7 to December 31.

DISTRIBUTION: Shallow ponds and estuaries. Has bred irregularly at Falmouth; recorded from Sandwich and Falmouth east to Chatham and Wellfleet.

HISTORY: All reports are since the early 1940's when the above-mentioned colonies began a marked increase.

* *

WHISTLING SWAN
Olor columbianus (Ord)

STATUS: Specimen obtained, now presumed lost.

FALL: Very rare vagrant: two shot about 1840 at Centerville (Baxter, *fide* Brewster); 28 on October 28, 1917, at Eastham (Blaney); one shot on November 3, 1939, at Barnstable (unknown hunter, bird seized by warden); and two seen November 8–December 31, 1948, at Eastham and Orleans (many observers).

HISTORY: Traditionally common transient spring and fall in colonial times, but rapidly reduced and became very rare by 1850 (Forbush, 1912). Now believed to be increasing slowly.

* *

CANADA GOOSE

Branta canadensis (Linnaeus)

STATUS: Represented in MCZ and BMS collections. Three separate populations involved: 1) breeding; 2) transient; and 3) terminal winter; individual birds and flocks not always assignable to particular population.

1) BREEDING: Traditionally nested in small numbers throughout Cape; no details on numbers or exact locations. Scattered pairs still breed, whether feral or truly wild.

2) TRANSIENT:

SPRING: Common migrant.

Average migration period: March 6–May 20.

Peak: March 15–April 15; average 200–800, occasionally to 1000.

Latest transient date: Uncertain, probably about May 30.

FALL: Common migrant.

Earliest transient date: Uncertain, probably about September 25.

Average migration period: October 5–November 30.

Peak: October 10–November 20; average flocks 50–500, rarely to 2000.

DISTRIBUTION: Sand and mud flats, marshes; often resting offshore in daytime; regularly in fresh-water ponds or grazing in uplands. Spring flocks from south go partly up Buzzards Bay, cross Cape at Canal and go due north offshore, and partly further east, both crossing the Cape in the Hyannis-Barnstable area and passing along eastern shore line. Fall migration route more confined in strip 35–40 miles wide, running slightly west of south, eastern edge of which reaches Canal and includes the Sandwich-Mashpee area (Philips, *Auk*, 27, 263, 1910, and 29, 390, 1912). Highest fall counts occur in this area, but some flocks deflected eastward by offshore winds to outer Cape; in general, fewer eastward in fall than in spring.

HISTORY: Enormously abundant according to colonial records, decreasing steadily to low point 1880–1910 (Forbush, 1912). Fairly marked increase to 1920 and slower increase since then.

3) TERMINAL WINTERING: Common to abundant resident.

Average period: December 5–March 5.

Counts: Increase steadily during December after transients have decreased, final increments to January 5. Average 3000–5000 birds, then decrease according to severity of season. Start departing with first mild weather in February.

DISTRIBUTION: Habitat as with transient population, but route very different. Observed both arriving and leaving on an east-north-east course which is compass-true to Cape Sable, Nova Scotia (Richardson). Wintering grounds virtually confined to the Monomoy-Wellfleet-Brewster triangle.

HISTORY: This population probably never as heavily shot out as others but fluctuates widely according to the severity of the season, e.g. 1800 of 6000 survived in 1948; there is, however, some evidence that geese are more mobile than ducks and that at least some will move rather than starve. The recent cycle of mild winters has caused an increase.

SUBSPECIES: Small individuals of this species are reported as casual visitants, possibly more common in the past. Race involved is not determinable.

* *

BRANT

Branta bernicla (Linnaeus)

STATUS: Represented in MCZ, BMS, and Chicago collections.

SPRING: Common migrant.

Earliest transient date: Uncertain, probably about February 20.

Average migration period: March 1–May 15.

Peak: March 25–April 20; see below for counts.

Latest transient date: Uncertain, probably about May 30.

SUMMER: Scattered non-breeding stragglers.

FALL: Common migrant, locally abundant.

Earliest transient date: Uncertain, probably about October 10.

Average migration period: October 18–December 20.

Peak: November 1–30; see below for counts.

Latest transient date: Uncertain, probably about January 5.

WINTER: Irregularly absent to fairly common. Winter range of species is limited on the north by ice (Philips, *Auk*, *49*, 445, 1932), so Cape Cod is sometimes excluded by the weather. Flocks up to 800 in mild years.

DISTRIBUTION: Shallow salt water of bays and estuaries. In spring, most flocks from southwest to a main gathering point at Monomoy (this area known for good Brant shooting in spring but never in fall). Smaller flocks up Buzzards Bay, cross along Canal and go north out of Cape Cod Bay or cross Cape in Hyannis-Barnstable area to join wintering flocks at Brewster. On leaving, all fly north to Bay of Fundy, not east to Nova Scotia. In fall, flocks come down Bay of Fundy, some going east of Cape and pass southward mostly without stopping, though a few appear at Monomoy; other flocks enter Cape Cod Bay, often seen off Manomet, swing east and congregate in Bay mostly off Brewster, though a few cross the Cape and continue southward (Lewis, *Auk*, *54*, 73, 1937). Wintering flocks remain at Brewster, Barnstable, Nauset, Pleasant Bay, Waquoit, Poponesset, etc.

HISTORY: Formerly abundant, 90 per cent reduced and restricted to Cape Cod and the islands by 1850 (Forbush, 1912), but still 25,000–40,000 at Chatham in spring (Philips, *Auk*, *49*, 445, 1932). Then slow decrease until eelgrass blight in 1931 caused widespread starvation, e.g. counts of 1000 on April 20, 1931 (Richardson), and 50 on April 4, 1932 (Low), both at Eastham; also 1630 on December 20, 1931, and 4 on December 23, 1932 (C.C.). Flocks mostly under 100 thereafter until 1939, slow increase to 1948, and more rapid increase to 1961 to levels comparable to 1930, e.g. 1000–3000 birds at height of migration. Since 1945 flocks have reappeared widely over entire Cape. Prior to 1931 only stragglers remained later than April 25; now regular into May.

*   *

BLACK BRANT
Branta nigricans (Lawrence)

STATUS: Specimens obtained, now lost.

Accidental vagrant, whether Pacific species or an unspecified dark race of eastern bird not clear.

SPECIMENS: At Monomoy, spring of 1883 (Cory, *Auk*, *1*, 96, 1884) and April 15, 1902 (Carey, see Fay, *Auk*, *27*, 336, 1910), seen by Brewster but since lost.

SIGHT RECORDS: On November 23–24, 1947, October 28, 1951, and February 28, 1953, all at Brewster (Griscom); one trapped and banded on November 9, 1952, at Monomoy (Smith).

*   *

BARNACLE GOOSE
Branta leucopsis (Bechstein)

STATUS: Represented in BMS collection.

Accidental from Old World. One shot from a flock of 3–4 on November 1, 1885, at North Eastham according to specimen label or North Chatham according to *O & O*, *11*, 16, 1886 (Dill). Record on September 20, 1920 (Peters), is considered to have been an escaped bird.

*   *

WHITE-FRONTED GOOSE
Anser albifrons (Scopoli)

STATUS: Represented in BMS collection.

Very rare vagrant from Mississippi flyway; one shot from flock of seven on November 1, 1923, in North Truro (Peters); two spent winter of 1937 at Monomoy with Canada Geese (Griscom), and one seen January 1, 1949, at Nauset (Griscom).

* *

SNOW GOOSE
Chen hyperborea (Pallas)

STATUS: Represented in BMS collection.

SPRING: Rare and irregular, occasionally locally common.

Earliest arrival date: March 9, 1954, at Brewster (Hill).

Average migration period: March 10–April 15.

Counts: Irregular, average 10–15 birds, maximum 600 at Brewster on March 9, 1954 (Hill).

Latest transient date: April 29, 1936, at Eastham (Brewer).

FALL: Uncommon migrant.

Earliest transient date: October 2, 1938, at Monomoy (Griscom & Garrison).

Average migration period: October 25–November 30.

Counts: Average 4–10, maximum 40 on November 27, 1948, at Brewster (Griscom, Cottrell, Elkins, Emery).

Latest transient date: Uncertain, probably about December 27.

WINTER: Very rare straggler, usually not surviving.

DISTRIBUTION: Usually associates with Brant on flats, also in marshes and seen migrating past without stopping. Has been recorded over entire Cape.

HISTORY: By tradition, an abundant migrant both spring and fall in colonial times but rare by 1850 (Forbush, 1912). Now increasing steadily and recorded annually; rarely appears in large numbers.

SUBSPECIES: Both *C. h. hyperborea* and *C. h. atlantica* have been collected on Cape Cod. Circumstances are seldom so favorable as to be able to separate them in the field.

* *

BLUE GOOSE
Chen caerulescens (Linnaeus)

STATUS: Represented in the Chicago collection.
Very rare vagrant from the Mississippi flyway.
SPRING: One shot April 1, 1883, at Monomoy (in Chicago).
FALL: One shot October 30, 1920, at Mashpee (Wright, see Lamb, *Auk, 38,* 109, 1921); 12 seen October 31, 1938 (Eaton), and 3 seen November 12, 1950 (Smith), both at Barnstable; one shot November 6, 1934, at Harwich (LeClair) and December 9, 1934, at Yarmouth (Pulsifer), see Cottam, *Auk, 52,* 432, 1935.

* *

MALLARD
Anas platyrhynchos Linnaeus

STATUS: Represented in MCZ and BMS collections.
SPRING: Probably no transients, records attributable to wintering or feral birds.
SUMMER: Scattered breeding feral pairs.
FALL: Uncommon migrant, occasionally common.
   Earliest transient date: Uncertain, probably about August 25.
   Average migration period: September 10–December 20.
   Counts: Average 3–8 birds, occasional marked invasions as 150 on November 8, 1952, at Eastham (Mixter).
   Latest transient date: Uncertain, probably about January 5.
WINTER: Scattered birds winter regularly, usually surviving.
DISTRIBUTION: All types of fresh water, also salt marsh and salt

bays. Usually associated with Black Duck flocks. Recorded over entire Cape.

HISTORY: Marked decrease 1880–1910, but always commoner on Cape than on mainland (Forbush, 1912). Recent increase probably due largely to feral birds, and the species is now less common on the Cape than on the mainland. Several Black x Mallard hybrids have been collected.

* *

BLACK DUCK
Anas rubripes Brewster

STATUS: Represented in MCZ, BMS, Chicago, and British Museum collections. Three populations involved: 1) breeding; 2) transient; and 3) terminal winter. Individual birds and flocks not always assignable to particular population. See also Hagar, *Bird-Banding, 17,* 97, 1946.

1) BREEDING: Common nesting species throughout Cape Cod in wide variety of both fresh- and salt-water habitats. Local birds gather after nesting by late July, often at Monomoy, average 100–200 birds, and then merge with next population.

2) TRANSIENT:
SPRING: Common migrant.
Earliest transient date: Uncertain, probably about February 25.
Average migration period: March 5–May 24.
Peak: March 15–April 20; average 500–1000 birds, occasionally to 2000.
FALL: Abundant migrant.
Average migration period: August 20 (when gatherings of local birds show marked increase) –November 30.
Peak: October 1–November 16; average 500–1000 birds; maximum 5000 on November 12, 1948, at Brewster (Griscom).

3) TERMINAL WINTER: Common to abundant resident.

Average period: December 1–March 5.

Counts: Increase steadily through December after counts of transients have dropped, final arrivals not until early January; average 7000–8000, maximum 10,000 (Hagar, l.c.). Decrease due to winter mortality according to severity of season. Start departing with mild weather in late February.

DISTRIBUTION: Breeds in salt- and fresh-water marsh, swamp and pond habitats. Gathers in marshes, estuaries, mud flats, and occasionally protected salt water. Found in numbers over entire Cape. Density of wintering birds increases eastward due to decreasing severity of weather. Transient population routes show a few from northwest, more from north, and at least part of the terminal wintering population come directly from Nova Scotia (see Mendall, 1958).

HISTORY: Formerly very abundant, decreasing markedly to a low point about 1908 when prohibition of spring shooting allowed recovery (Forbush, 1912). Fluctuates rather widely from year to year for no apparent reason, downward trend during early 1950's now appears reversed. Winter population often markedly weather-killed.

*   *

GADWALL

Anas strepera Linnaeus

STATUS: Represented in MCZ collection.

FALL: Rare migrant.

Earliest transient date: September 9, 1959, at Provincetown (Gammell).

Average migration period: September 19–December 15.

Counts: Usually 1–2 birds only, maximum 3 on November 11, 1954, at Monomoy (Griscom).

Latest transient date: January 2, 1949, at Brewster (C.C.).

WINTER: Very rare and irregular straggler, sometimes in small flocks as 4 on February 6, 1937, at Falmouth (Minot).

SPRING: Very rare and irregular migrant, no spring specimens.

Earliest transient date: March 5, 1930, at Eastham (Beston).

Average migration period: March 20–April 20; single birds, rarely a pair.

Latest transient date: April 26, 1959, at Orleans (Bigelow).

DISTRIBUTION: Associated with Black and other river duck flocks in fresh and salt marshes and ponds. Thinly scattered over entire Cape.

HISTORY: Allegedly "not uncommon" to 1850, but rare thereafter (Forbush, 1912). Appears to have increased since 1930; this may be an artifact due to increased observation. Furthermore, it may be more common than reported, as females and immatures are easily overlooked in flocks of other species.

* *

PINTAIL

Anas acuta Linnaeus

STATUS: Represented in MCZ and BMS collections.

FALL: Uncommon migrant.

Earliest arrival date: August 11, 1943, at Monomoy (Griscom & Curtis).

Average migration period: September 15–December 1.

Peak: October 12–November 12; average 5–10 birds, maximum 18 on October 13, 1951, at Monomoy (Griscom, Parker, Drury).

Latest transient date: Uncertain, probably about December 10.

WINTER: Rare and irregular resident except on Monomoy where present in small numbers unless frozen out, usually survives the season.

SPRING: Rather rare migrant.

Earliest transient date: Uncertain, probably about February 22.

Average migration period: March 10–April 28; mostly pairs, maximum 6 on April 6–7, 1940 (Hill).

Latest transient date: May 20, 1938, at Monomoy (Bishop).

DISTRIBUTION: Fresh and salt marshes, estuaries, ponds, etc., usually associating with Black Ducks. Recorded over entire Cape.

HISTORY: Reported as "abundant" at Eastham to about 1860 but rare by 1908 (Swan), though always less common on the coast than interior (Forbush, 1912). Increased moderately since 1912, still less common than on mainland, and by no means abundant now.

*   *

COMMON TEAL

Anas crecca Linnaeus

STATUS: Represented in BMS collection.
Accidental vagrant from Old World.

SPECIMEN: About February 22, 1896, at Sagamore (Philips, in BMS, see Brewster, *Auk*, *18*, 135, 1901).

SIGHT RECORDS OF DRAKES: April 7, 1938, at Chathamport (Bishop); April 7, 1940, at Eastham (Richardson); April 18–19, 1943, at Eastham (Long); December 9, 1950, at Monomoy (Griscom, Elkins, Smart).

*   *

GREEN-WINGED TEAL

Anas carolinensis Gmelin

STATUS: Represented in MCZ, BMS, and British Museum collections.

SPRING: Rather uncommon, sometimes rare, migrant.
Earliest transient date: Uncertain, probably about March 25.
Average migration period: March 30–May 20.
Peak: April 5–25; average 5–10 birds, maximum 24 on April 9, 1949 (Griscom, Crain, Parker, Mason).
Latest transient date: Uncertain, probably about May 31.

SUMMER: Very local and probably irregular breeding resident in ponds on Monomoy, 2+ pairs with young in 1960 and 1961; possibly formerly at North Truro (Miller).

FALL: Uncommon migrant.

Earliest transient date: Uncertain, probably about August 18.

Average migration period: August 25–December 10.

Peak: October 1–November 25; average 10–30, maximum 80 on November 27, 1959, at Nauset (Fox, Smart).

Latest transient date: Uncertain, probably about January 2.

WINTER: Occasional small groups on Monomoy ponds and single birds elsewhere.

DISTRIBUTION: Fresh and brackish ponds, less often in marshes, and rarely in salt-water estuaries. Much less common on Cape than on mainland, but no difference between areas on Cape.

HISTORY: Reportedly "plentiful" up to 1860 and then a rapid decrease to 1910 (Forbush, 1912); some increase since, more rapid since 1945. Increased wintering 1950–1959 due to cycle of mild winters.

* *

BLUE-WINGED TEAL
Anas discors Linnaeus

STATUS: Represented in MCZ and BMS collections.

SPRING: Arrival of residents, no evidence of transients.

Earliest arrival date: March 27, 1960, at Orleans (Fox).

Average arrival period: April 3–10; almost invariably in pairs.

SUMMER: Breeds at Monomoy (5–6 pairs), probably at Wellfleet, Harwich, Falmouth, Sandwich, and perhaps elsewhere.

FALL: Uncommon migrant.

Earliest transient date: Uncertain, probably about August 14.

Average migration period: August 22–October 12.

Peak: August 28–September 21; average 10–20 birds, maximum 120 on September 7, 1941, at Monomoy (Griscom, Eliot, Kraus, Clement).

Latest departure date: November 17, 1945, at Brewster (Griscom & Garrison).

WINTER: Casually attempts to winter, but never known to have survived.

DISTRIBUTION: Breeds in fresh and brackish ponds with rush margins. On migration in wider selection of ponds and marshes. Recorded over entire Cape, but much less numerous than on the mainland north and west of Boston. Occasionally occurs in marked flights as in 1907, 1938, 1941, 1953, etc.

HISTORY: Formerly "plentiful," but becoming uncommon (Forbush, 1912). Now increasing steadily with adequate protection; breeding re-established 1936–1940 and pairs increasing slowly since then.

* *

EUROPEAN WIDGEON
Mareca penelope (Linnaeus)

STATUS: Represented in BMS collection.

FALL: Rare and irregular migrant.

Earliest arrival date: September 5, 1954, at Monomoy (Griscom).

Average migration period: September 30–November 20; single birds, rarely two drakes or a presumed pair.

Latest transient date: January 16, 1946, at Brewster (Griscom & Curtis).

WINTER: Known to winter at Falmouth each year 1952 to 1955, disappearing March 22–28.

SPRING: Casual, one record, a male on April 16, 1944, at Eastham (Griscom & Cottrell).

DISTRIBUTION: Associates with American Widgeon flocks and recorded chiefly at Eastham Great Pond, Monomoy, and Falmouth. Probable hybrid of European x American Widgeon seen October 18, 1960, at Falmouth (Hill), a drake with brown

Ludlow Griscom, 1890–1959

Allen H. M‹

Air view, north over the Monomoy Shorebird Flats

body, gray head but bright yellow crown, not the described pale buffy variant of the American.

HISTORY: Probably no long-term change. First collected in 1921. A drake shot in November 1927 at Eastham was banded in Iceland.

* *

AMERICAN WIDGEON
Mareca americana (Gmelin)

STATUS: Represented in MCZ, BMS, Chicago, and British Museum collections.

FALL: Fairly common migrant.

Earliest arrival date: August 27, 1958, at Falmouth (Garry).

Average migration period: September 10–December 10.

Peak: October 15–November 30; see below for counts.

Latest transient date: Uncertain, probably about December 25.

WINTER: Regular in small flocks to 18 birds on outer Cape and to 80 birds at Falmouth; flocks very mobile and shift to salt water temporarily with freezing weather or cross to Nantucket or Martha's Vineyard. Winter residents disappear April 15–25.

SPRING: Rare and often irregular migrant.

Average migration period: March 14–April 20; average 3–7 birds.

Latest departure date: April 29, 1954, at Falmouth (Cobb).

DISTRIBUTION: Brackish and fresh ponds with heavy vegetation, moves to salt water during freezes. Recorded in greatest numbers at Falmouth, Monomoy, and Eastham with smaller numbers at Brewster, Wellfleet, Dennis, Sandwich, etc.

HISTORY: Formerly "common" but decreasing rapidly after 1870 (Forbush, 1912), always more common on Cape Cod than on mainland, though fewer than on the islands. Relatively rare 1930–1947, up to 12–15 birds. Marked increase began in 1948, and this now stabilized with maximum about 300–400 birds.

More recent history obscured by release of wing-clipped adults in 1952 at Monomoy.

* *

SHOVELER
Spatula clypeata (Linnaeus)

STATUS: Represented in BMS collection.

FALL: Rare and irregular migrant.

Earliest arrival date: September 29, 1951, at Monomoy (Griscom, Emery, Barry).

Average migration period: October 10–November 15; single birds and pairs.

Latest transient date: Uncertain, probably about December 30.

WINTER: Very rare and irregular straggler, survived to April 4, 1940, at Chathamport (Long).

SPRING: Casual, three records, March 25, 1948, at Chatham (Griscom, Mazzeo, Harris); April 7, 1909, at Eastham (Blaney, in BMS); April 21, 1931, at Orleans (Richardson).

DISTRIBUTION: Shallow fresh-water and brackish ponds. Records scattered over Cape according to habitat. Species much rarer than on mainland.

HISTORY: Allegedly much reduced after 1860 (Forbush, 1912), but Cape Cod data incomplete and unconvincing, probably never very common here though reputed to have nested as near as No Man's Land in 1602 (Gosnold). Very rare until 1950, possibly a slight increase since then.

* *

WOOD DUCK
Aix sponsa (Linneaus)

STATUS: Banded at Austin Station.

SPRING: Arrival of residents; as a transient very rare and irregular at Canal and casual eastward.

Earliest arrival date: March 24, 1939, at Harwich (Bishop).
Average arrival period: April 2–22, almost invariably in pairs.
SUMMER: Rare, breeding locally at Brewster, female and young
seen in 1923 (Earle) and 1955 (Smart); Harwich, female and
young seen in 1961 and 1962 (Hill); Yarmouth, female and
young seen in 1951 (Caldwell); Dennis; Sandwich, and probably elsewhere.
FALL: Rare migrant.
Average migration period: September 10–October 20; average
1–2 birds, maxima 12 on October 1, 1938, at Harwich (Gris-
com) and October 10, 1959, at Falmouth (Garry).
Latest departure date: November 26, 1949, at Brewster
(Keenan).
WINTER: Casual straggler, surviving only if fed artificially.
DISTRIBUTION: Breeds in relatively secluded ponds with forested
shores. In migration in more open ponds and occasionally
brackish marshes. Much less common on Cape than on main-
land and fewer eastward on Cape.
HISTORY: No data on very early period when Cape was wooded.
Rare and local throughout historical period. Has nested in boxes
placed in swamps. No convincing evidence of increasing numbers in spite of increasing forests on Cape Cod.

*   *

REDHEAD

Aythya americana (Eyton)

STATUS: Represented in BMS collection.
FALL: Uncommon migrant.
Earliest arrival date: October 6, 1923, at Eastham (Great Pond
Shooting Record).
Average migration period: October 28–December 25.
Peak: November 8–December 8; average 2–8 birds, maxima 15
on November 11, 1952, at Monomoy (Griscom, Bailey,

Beatties) and 250 on December 1, 1955, at Falmouth (Kelly).

Latest transient date: Uncertain, probably about January 4.

WINTER: Irregularly present, shifting location according to freeze-up; average 1–4 birds, maximum 9 in 1950 and 1954. Usually depart by April 1.

SPRING: Rare and irregular migrant.

Earliest transient date: Uncertain, probably late February.

Average migration period: March 5–April 7; average 1–2 birds but occasionally absent, maximum 14 on March 10, 1955, at Brewster (Ford).

Latest departure date: April 19, 1952, at Monomoy (Whiting).

SUMMER: Casual, usually crippled birds as August 8, 1903, at Waquoit (Cobb).

DISTRIBUTION: Very particular as to ecological conditions, shallow fresh or brackish ponds with abundant plant growth. Recorded from Falmouth east to Chatham and north to Eastham. Probably reaches Cape Cod from west or even southwest as this is the northeasternmost area where it is reasonably regular.

HISTORY: General decrease prior to 1908, not as marked on Cape Cod as on mainland but more so than on islands (Forbush, 1912). Since then fluctuations can be attributed to local ecological conditions rather than a basic change in numbers. Increased wintering birds since about 1949, but no apparent change in spring and fall transients.

*   *

RING-NECKED DUCK

Aythya collaris (Donovan)

STATUS: Represented in BMS collection.

SPRING: No transients, locally wintering birds depart in April.

SUMMER: Breeds casually, female and five young seen on July 16, 1958, at Falmouth (Crompton).

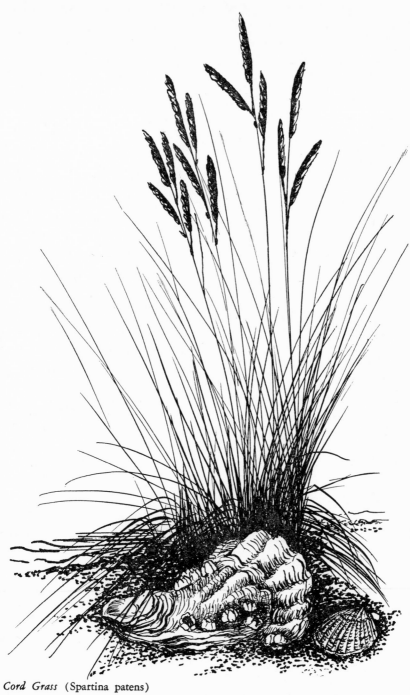

Cord Grass (Spartina patens)

FALL: Regular transient westward at Pocasset and Falmouth, terminal migrants eastward.

WINTER: Largely a terminal wintering population, variable in numbers.

Earliest arrival date: October 26, 1949, at Eastham (Hill).

Average period: November 11–April 19.

Peak: November 25–January 1; see below for counts.

Latest departure date: April 28, 1941, at Eastham (Griscom, Mason, Bergstrom).

DISTRIBUTION: Fresh-water ponds and brackish or salt estuaries. Recorded in small numbers all over Cape north to Wellfleet, but main concentration areas are Falmouth, Brewster, and particularly Eastham Great Pond; move to salt water temporarily when frozen out. Main flight believed to come from the north and to be an eastern segment of the flight from Maine that appears in Lakeville, Mass.; some may come direct from Nova Scotia (Mendall, 1958). Always less common on Cape than on mainland on migration but more success in wintering, though even here there is often considerable mortality.

HISTORY: Formerly very rare vagrant, only early record is single female collected October 28, 1903, at Eastham (Blaney, see Allen, *Auk*, 25, 234, 1908). Then one bird each year in 1930, 1933, 1936; six in 1937; 76 in 1938, and present in varying numbers every year since to maximum count of 175 on November 16, 1958, at Falmouth (Garry); outer Cape maxima lower averaging 15–30 birds. This rise is consistent with that elsewhere in state and with the build-up of the eastern breeding population, but note that this rise did not appear on Cape Cod until several years later than on the mainland. See Mendall, 1958, and *Auk*, 55, 401, 1938; also Griscom, *Auk*, 56, 134, 1939.

* *

CANVASBACK
Aythya valisineria (Wilson)

STATUS: Represented in BMS collection.

FALL: Rare as transient, mostly terminal migrants.
Earliest arrival date: October 12, 1951, at Monomoy (Whiting).
Average migration period: November 8–December 25; see below for counts.

WINTER: Irregularly wintering in small flocks, maximum 9 in 1937 at Falmouth (Minot); usually surviving season by moving to salt water with freeze-up.

SPRING: No convincing evidence of transients, gatherings represent regrouping of successful wintering birds; usually gone by April 12, latest date April 28, 1940, at Eastham (Hill).

DISTRIBUTION: Fresh and brackish ponds with adequate vegetation, ecological conditions nearly as critical as with Redhead. Recorded from Falmouth east to Monomoy and north to Truro.

HISTORY: Original status unknown, but reported as "little more than a straggler" by 1860 and remained so until 1907 (Forbush, 1912), though probably subject to small flights as seven specimens in 1874 from Cape Cod to Boston Market (Baird, Brewer, and Ridgway, 1884). Increased about 1908 and thereafter (see Fay, *Auk*, 27, 369, 1910), many shot, maximum 75 seen on November 8, 1908, at Harwich (Nickerson). Recent counts much less but have been reasonably stable, 1940–1960, average 1–4 birds, maximum 12 on November 26–27, 1955, at Falmouth (Garry) on migration; fewer on outer Cape.

* *

GREATER SCAUP
Aythya marila (Linnaeus)
STATUS: Represented in MCZ collection.

* *

LESSER SCAUP
Aythya affinis (Eyton)

STATUS: Represented in BMS collection.

NOTE: The comparative status of the two species of Scaup Duck is impossible to determine accurately; see Griscom and Snyder, 1955. There is reason to believe that the situation has changed since wide-spread collecting was in fashion, at which time the Lesser was reasonably common. It is recommended that these two species be listed simply as "Scaup" except in the rare and exceptional instances when a more definite identification is possible. On Cape Cod their occurrence is parallel throughout the year in contrast to the mainland where, though parallel in the fall, the Lesser has a later spring flight. The dates given below apply to both species.

FALL: Fairly common transient.
   Earliest arrival date: September 17, 1949, at Eastham (Griscom, Cottrell, Morgan).
   Average migration period: October 25–December 5; average 100–300 birds, maximum 2500 on December 1, 1955, at Falmouth (Kelly).
   Latest transient date: Uncertain, probably about December 25.

WINTER: Uncommon to common resident, maximum 700 at Waquoit on January 5, 1933 (Griscom).

SPRING: Uncommon to common, transients sometimes lacking.
   Average migration period: March 5–April 25; average 50–150 birds, maximum 500 on April 19, 1940 (Griscom & Scott).
   Latest departure date: May 30, 1932, at Monomoy (Griscom & Eliot).

SUMMER: Occasional non-breeding stragglers, usually cripples, reported about one year in five.

DISTRIBUTION: In the early historical period it seems clear that the Greater Scaup was the bird of the salt estuaries and bays and the Lesser of the ponds. A survey of stringently screened sight records since 1935 reveals that the Lesser is still exclusively found on fresh water, notably Mill and Cliff ponds in Brewster, Eastham Great Pond, at Falmouth, and occasionally in Monomoy Point Pond. There is no completely convincing record of this species in salt water though such should probably occur temporarily immediately after a freeze-up. On the other hand, the Greater now occurs in both salt and fresh water, making up 100 per cent of the salt-water flocks and in the vicinity of 50 per cent of the fresh-water flocks. These species reported over entire Cape, transient flocks more common westward, crossing between Cape Cod Bay and Buzzards Bay along the Canal and also at Mashpee and Falmouth. Wintering flocks more common eastward. In general less common than on the mainland.

HISTORY: Decreased 25 to 50 per cent on Cape prior to 1908 (Forbush, 1912). The Lesser has continued to decrease with a marked drop about 1923–1927, but the Greater has responded to protection with a rise to about 1930 and now essentially stable numbers. This shift in proportion probably accounts for the change in geographical habitat noted above, i.e. increased numbers of Greaters simply expanded into unoccupied niche of the diminished Lessers. First began wintering in 1898 at Barnstable (Shattuck, see Howe, *Auk*, *15*, 189, 1898) and increasing steadily since.

* *

TUFTED DUCK
Aythya fuligula (Linnaeus)

STATUS: Hypothetical.
Accidental vagrant from the Old World. Sight record of a drake on January 21–29, 1962, at Falmouth (Garry) and a pair there throughout the winter of 1962–1963.

* *

COMMON GOLDENEYE
Bucephala clangula (Linnaeus)

STATUS: Represented in MCZ, BMS, and Chicago collections.

FALL: Very common migrant.

Earliest arrival date: October 13, 1951, at Monomoy (Griscom, Drury, Parker).

Average migration period: November 12–January 1.

Peak: Requires cold weather to bring in main flight, so December 5–31; average 300–800, maximum 2561 on January 1, 1950 (C.C.).

WINTER: Common; a terminal population averaging 300–700 birds remains after transients have moved on, decreases according to severity of season with an apparent mortality of 25 to 30 per cent.

SPRING: Very common migrant.

Earliest transient date: Uncertain, probably about February 27.

Average migration period: March 5–April 15.

Peak: March 15–April 5; average 500–900 birds, maximum 1340 on April 3–4, 1942 (Hill).

Latest migration date: Uncertain, probably about May 29.

SUMMER: Crippled or oiled non-breeding birds nearly every year.

DISTRIBUTION: Chiefly broad estuaries and bays, some on open ocean; regular in ponds on migration. Transient flocks both spring and fall over entire Cape though relatively more westward in spring, often heard at night crossing overhead. Cross in numbers at Canal, 315 in fifteen minutes on March 31, 1951 (Hill); also cross in Hyannis-Barnstable and Orleans-Brewster areas. Late fall transients and wintering birds concentrate eastward in Pleasant Bay and southward along the sounds.

HISTORY: Marked decrease 1850–1900 but less on Cape than inland (Forbush, 1912). Slow and steady increase since then. Counts of 20–200 in 1906–1907 (Cobb) and of 200–400 in 1950–1955 at Eastham.

* *

BARROW'S GOLDENEYE
Bucephala islandica (Gmelin)

STATUS: Represented in MCZ and BMS collections.

SPECIMENS: "Cape Cod" in 1872, month and collector unknown, in MCZ; December 11, 1908, at Eastham (Luce, in BMS); December 1, 1911, at South Orleans (Smith, in BMS); December 23, 1914, at Eastham (Peck, in BMS). Earlier records expunged by Brewster, *Auk*, 26, 153, 1909.

SIGHT RECORDS: Only drakes considered, extend dates of occurrence through January and February, once to April 3, 1960, at Chathamport (Mayo). Note that this species arrives later and departs earlier than the Common Goldeneye.

DISTRIBUTION: Ordinarily associated with rocky shores and hence only casual along sand beaches of Cape Cod. On Cape usually reported in salt estuaries but once in Cliff Pond, Brewster. Recorded from Wianno to Chatham and north to Wellfleet; not yet reported in Buzzards Bay.

HISTORY: No evidence of change in status. Increase in records reflects increase in observers.

*   *

BUFFLEHEAD
Bucephala albeola (Linnaeus)

STATUS: Represented in MCZ collection.

FALL: Fairly common migrant.
Earliest arrival date: Uncertain, probably about September 18.
Average migration period: October 26–January 1.
Peak: December 1–25; average 100–175 birds, maximum 885 on December 28, 1958 (C.C.).

WINTER: Uncommon resident, average 35–50 birds, maximum 75 on February 23, 1946 (Griscom). Apparently little winter mortality.

SPRING: Fairly common migrant.

Average migration period: March 1–April 20.

Peak: Usually March 15–30 but variable, sometimes as early as March 3–8 or as late as mid-April. Average 90–200, maximum 250 on March 15, 1955 (Hill).

SUMMER: Casual as non-breeding straggler, presumably crippled.

DISTRIBUTION: Typically protected salt water of estuaries and bays, rarely on open ocean, into fresh water regularly on migration. Found over entire Cape; transient flocks cross at Canal and widely in Harwich-Brewster-Chatham area. Chief wintering grounds in this latter area and less common north of Wellfleet. Fairly common in lower Buzzards Bay. In general, less common than on mainland.

HISTORY: Numbers held up reasonably well to about 1875 and then showed a marked decrease, though not as much on the Cape as on the mainland (Forbush, 1912). Increase began with prohibition of spring shooting and is still continuing, e.g. C.C. average of 64/year in the 1930's and 300/year in the 1950's. Wintering flocks increasing since about 1945.

* *

OLDSQUAW

Clangula hyemalis (Linnaeus)

STATUS: Represented in MCZ, BMS, and Chicago collections.

FALL: Abundant migrant.

Earliest arrival date: October 12, 1941, at Monomoy (Snow).

Average migration period: October 24–December 10.

Peak: November 9–December 1; average 5000–15,000 birds, maximum 40,000–50,000 on November 12, 1939, at Monomoy (Griscom, Scott, Garrison, Bradford).

WINTER: Common resident, average less than 1000 inshore and 1000–3000 offshore on shoals, maximum 10,000 on February 2, 1939, off Monomoy (Griscom, Bishop, Parker, Robbins).

SPRING: Common migrant.

Earliest transient date: Uncertain, probably about March 10.

Average migration period: March 20–May 5.

Peak: April 1–20; average 200–1200 birds, maximum 2000 on April 19, 1940, at Monomoy (Griscom, Scott, Bishop, Alexander).

Latest transient date: Uncertain, probably about May 30.

SUMMER: Non-breeding stragglers, frequently oiled, reported nearly every year.

DISTRIBUTION: Shallow offshore waters with sandy bottoms with mussel beds. Greatest counts on Monomoy shoals and high counts in alongshore areas of outer Cape; smaller numbers in larger estuaries and harbors west to and including Buzzards Bay. Proportionately more eastward in fall migration and winter and more westward in spring migration. Rarely in fresh water on migration.

HISTORY: Less decrease on Cape Cod than elsewhere (Forbush, 1912), probably because this population more remote and never shot out rather than because birds were driven to this area as a refuge. Nonetheless, there was some decrease in the last century. More recently there was a cycle of high counts, 1938–1943; lesser counts since are believed due to shifting of offshore mussel beds, though there may also be a decrease in numbers.

*   *

HARLEQUIN DUCK
Histrionicus histrionicus (Linnaeus)

STATUS: Represented in MCZ and BMS collections.

WINTER: Rare and irregular visitant.

Earliest arrival date: October 22, 1950, at Monomoy (Griscom, Drury, Bowen).

Average period: November 20–April 15; one, two, or rarely three birds.

Latest departure date: May 30, 1940, at Monomoy (Griscom, Eliot, Stackpole).

DISTRIBUTION: Characteristically found on rocky coasts, so rarity on Cape is an obvious habitat preference; occurs chiefly about the few rocky areas as at East Orleans, Falmouth, Woods Hole, in Cape Cod Bay from Sagamore to Manomet, and at man-made jetties and breakwaters, rarely with flocks of other sea ducks along sandy shores.

HISTORY: No data available regarding original status. On the basis of specimens in the past there has probably been no real change, the recent increase in reports reflecting the increase in observers.

* *

LABRADOR DUCK

Camptorhynchus labradorium (Gmelin)

EXTINCT: Traditionally said to have occurred on Cape Cod, but no specimens or satisfactory records are extant. Collected in Vineyard Sound but apparently closer to Martha's Vineyard than to Cape Cod (Daniel Webster).

* *

COMMON EIDER

Somateria mollissima (Linnaeus)

STATUS: Represented in MCZ, BMS, Chicago, and British Museum collections.

FALL: Abundant migrant, mostly a terminal population arriving on Monomoy shoals, but some transients moving past to Nantucket and Vineyard shoals.

Earliest arrival date: Uncertain, a few seen with scoter flocks in late September.

Average arrival period: October 16–December 8.

Peak: Counts rise rapidly through November to maximum at end of migration; see below for numbers.

WINTER: Abundant resident. See below for counts.

SPRING: Abundant migrant, mostly departure migrants.

Average departure period: March 15–April 25.

Peak: March 25–April 15; flocks of 500–1000 seen moving north offshore.

Latest departure date: Uncertain, probably about May 28.

SUMMER: Many non-breeding stragglers, small groups and flocks up to 100; almost entirely in immature plumage, but drakes can be watched molting into adult plumage during the late summer.

DISTRIBUTION: Shallow offshore waters with sandy bottoms and mussel beds. Greatest counts on shoals off Monomoy, sometimes to 10–20 miles offshore. Smaller number in Cape Cod Bay from Barnstable to Wellfleet and fewer westward to Sagamore; still fewer westward from Monomoy through the sounds to Woods Hole and into Buzzards Bay. Migration routes to north and northeast, mostly along eastern shore to Provincetown, but some enter Cape Cod Bay in fall; these cross Cape in region of Eastham.

HISTORY: Forbush (1912) chronicled a marked decrease prior to 1900, but this seems to apply only to the mainland and Cape Cod Bay flocks, as counts about 1890 on Monomoy shoals (Mackay, *Auk*, 7, 315, 1890) were of same order of magnitude as about 1940, suggesting that the remoteness of this population protected it. Bay flocks now increasing, 40–50 in 1894 (Nutter) to 12,000 on January 2, 1954 (Griscom, Hill, Snyder, Morgan, Beattie), both off Wellfleet; 2500 inside Barnstable Harbor on February 17, 1960 (Hill). Also gradual increase of great flock off Monomoy but with wide fluctuations due to oil disasters; in following table, note almost geometric increase from 1940 to 1950:

December 15, 1940   15,000
December 27, 1942   40,000
December 1, 1946   80,000
December 20, 1947 300,000

November 27, 1949 450,000
December 29, 1951 500,000, oil disaster in March 1952
December 27, 1952 150,000
December 2, 1960 500,000.

SUBSPECIES: Very rarely specimens approaching *S. m. borealis* have been picked up; well over 99 per cent of population is *S. m. dresseri*.

* *

KING EIDER

Somateria spectabilis (Linnaeus)

STATUS: Represented in MCZ and Chicago collections.

WINTER: Rare and irregular visitant.

Specimens: Four in November, one in December, and one in April. Sight records confined to adult and sub-adult drakes so species may be more numerous than reported.

Earliest arrival date: October 12, 1944, at Nauset (Griscom, Cahoon, Maclay).

Average period: November 20–April 15; single birds, occasionally a presumed pair.

Latest departure date: May 30, 1937, at Monomoy (Griscom).

SUMMER: Casual non-breeding stragglers, mostly oiled or crippled birds.

DISTRIBUTION: Ordinarily found along rocky shores, so rarity on Cape is due in part to habitat preference. Recorded and collected in lower Buzzards Bay and Woods Hole (Brooks, *Auk*, *30*, 107, 1913) but more regularly along western shore of Buzzards Bay; also collected several times in Cape Cod Bay off Manomet (Job, *Auk*, *13*, 203, 1896). Species believed to reach area from west rather than north. Off the sandy shores eastward, it is much rarer, reported at Monomoy, Chatham, Brewster, Orleans, and Eastham.

HISTORY: No data.

* *

WHITE-WINGED SCOTER
Melanitta deglandi (Bonaparte)

STATUS: Represented in MCZ, BMS, and Chicago collections.

FALL: Very abundant migrant, mostly transient but some terminal migrants.

Earliest arrival date: August 13, 1952, at Sagamore (Hill), seen arriving from the north.

Average migration period: August 25–December 10; adults only until September 10.

Peak: October 2–15 for migrants entering Cape Cod Bay; average 30,000–40,000 in ten-day period; November 1–20 for gatherings; average 100,000–200,000, maximum 400,000 on November 14, 1943, off Monomoy (Griscom).

Latest arrival date: Uncertain, probably about December 25.

WINTER: Common resident; counts drop to average of 10,000–20,000 in January and February, maximum 40,000 on February 2, 1939, at Monomoy (Griscom, Bucheister, Bishop).

SPRING: Abundant migrant.

Earliest transient date: Uncertain, probably about March 15.

Average migration period: March 25–June 1.

Peak: April 5–25; maxima 10,000 on April 6, 1944, at Falmouth (Emerson) and 4000 on April 19, 1940, at Chatham (Griscom). Occasionally a late May flight.

SUMMER: Regular non-breeding individuals and small flocks.

DISTRIBUTION: Shallow salt water from estuaries to open ocean, rarely on fresh-water ponds on migration. Fall arrival: 1) from north low over the water both into Cape Cod Bay and past Provincetown, former crossing at Canal, at Barnstable, and at Orleans (Job, *Auk*, *13*, 197, 1896); and 2) from northwest flying high overland into both Cape Cod Bay and lower Buzzards Bay. Greatest late migrational gathering off Monomoy; wintering flocks there and widely scattered in estuaries, bays, and offshore waters elsewhere, generally fewer but still common westward in Cape Cod Bay and in the sounds to Buzzards Bay. Fall flocks often contain all three scoters, Eiders and Oldsquaws; in spring the species tend to stay separate. April and early May flights from the south generally go up Buzzards Bay, crossing to Cape Cod Bay, and in smaller numbers northeast through the sounds, rounding the outer Cape, e.g., 9000 in two hours on April 26, 1964 at Sagamore migrating high overhead to the northeast. A later flight moves west through the sounds to Rhode Island and Connecticut and thence overland northwest (Mackay, *Auk*, 8, 279, 1891). The two well-marked migration routes both spring and fall are evidence for two separate populations which mingle in the winter.

HISTORY: Forbush (1912) presented evidence of a considerable decrease of all three species of scoters, perhaps 50 per cent from 1840 to 1890, probably less on outer Cape than in bays. Counts by Mackay around Monomoy about the same as today's, so this species stabilized by 1890, except that the late-spring flight to the west reported at 10,000 then is now much smaller. Nonetheless, the White-winged is now much the most numerous of the three scoters throughout the area and numbers have been essentially stable for the past twenty-five years.

*   *

SURF SCOTER
Melanitta perspicillata (Linnaeus)

STATUS: Represented in MCZ, BMS, and Chicago collections.

FALL: Common migrant.

Earliest transient date: August 16, 1941, at Chatham (Griscom).

Average migration period: September 1–December 5; adults only until late September.

Peak: September 25–October 8 for migrants entering Cape Cod Bay, average 10,000–20,000 in ten-day period; October 15–

November 15 for gatherings, average 5000–10,000, maximum 20,000 on October 29, 1959, off Monomoy (Bailey).

WINTER: Rather uncommon resident; average 20–50 birds, maximum 400 on January 17, 1949, in sound west of Monomoy (Griscom, Curtis).

SPRING: Fairly common migrant.

Average migration period: March 28–May 28.

Peak: April 2–20; average 500–1000, maximum 2500 on April 2, 1944, at Monomoy (Griscom, Cahoon); occasionally a late May flight.

Latest transient date: Uncertain, probably about June 3.

SUMMER: Non-breeding stragglers, somewhat irregular.

DISTRIBUTION: Shallow salt water from estuaries to open ocean, rarely on fresh water during migration. Fall arrival from north down inner coast, no apparent overland flight, crossing largely in Barnstable-Centerville area as well as at Canal, relatively few swing eastward. Main wintering flocks in lower Buzzards Bay, secondary and much smaller flocks on Monomoy shoals and small groups elsewhere. In spring, April flights from south go eastward, rounding the outer Cape, as well as through Buzzards Bay, crossing into Cape Cod Bay; later flights almost always take the inner route. Now little or no overland flight, though old records refer to such.

HISTORY: Forbush (1912) following Mackay (*Auk*, 8, 279, 1891) considered this the most numerous of the scoters "although the White-wing is a close second." Population collapsed after 1915, cause not known; now generally present in only about 10 to 20 per cent of former numbers and thus far below White-winged. At present it is the second commonest scoter along the inner coast and the least common on the outer Cape. Recent counts not entirely convincing, but there may now be a small increase appearing.

* *

COMMON SCOTER

Oidemia nigra (Linnaeus)

STATUS: Represented in MCZ, BMS, Chicago, and British Museum collections.

FALL: Common migrant.

Earliest transient date: August 23, 1890, at North Truro (Miller, in British Museum).

Average migration period: September 8–December 10; adults only until early October.

Peak: October 2–15 for migrants entering Cape Cod Bay, average 3000 in ten-day period; November 1–December 1 for gatherings, average 5000–10,000, maximum 40,000 on November 9, 1952, off Monomoy (Griscom, Emery, Barry, Bailey).

WINTER: Rather uncommon resident, greatest number on Monomoy shoals, average 500–1000, maximum 1600 on January 2, 1950 (Griscom, Parker, Cottrell); much smaller numbers elsewhere.

SPRING: Common migrant.

Average migration period: March 25–May 30.

Peak: April 2–28; average 500–1500, maximum 10,000 on April 13, 1947, off Chatham (Griscom); rarely a late May flight detected.

Latest transient date: Uncertain, probably about June 4.

SUMMER: Rare but fairly regular non-breeding straggler.

DISTRIBUTION: Shallow salt water from offshore shoals to estuaries, rarely on ponds in migration. Fall migration through Massachusetts Bay into Cape Cod Bay and also down outer coast. This species averages 5 per cent of White-winged counts on Monomoy shoals; also scattered smaller flocks in Cape Cod Bay, Buzzards Bay, and throughout the sounds. In spring, as with Surf Scoter, April flights go eastward through the sounds, rounding the outer Cape, whereas later flights tend to go up Buzzards Bay, crossing along Canal.

HISTORY: Forbush (1912), while admitting lack of specific evidence, believed that this species had decreased proportionately more than the other two scoters. If so, however, the decrease was prior to 1890, as Mackay's figures (*Auk*, 8, 279, 1891) are quite close to recent ones. At present this is the second commonest scoter on the outer Cape and the least common along the inner coast. Counts have now been stable for about twenty-five years, 1935–1960.

*   *

RUDDY DUCK
Oxyura jamaicensis (Gmelin)

STATUS: Represented in MCZ, BMS, Chicago, and British Museum collections.

FALL: Uncommon migrant.

Earliest transient date: Uncertain, probably about September 29.

Average migration period: October 8–December 20.

Peak: November 20–December 10; see below for counts.

WINTER: Variable number up to 240 (December 28, 1952, C.C.) at beginning of winter but with considerable mortality.

SPRING: No evidence of transients. Small gatherings are probably regrouping of successful wintering birds.

Average departure period: April 12–24.

Latest departure date: Uncertain, probably about April 28.

SUMMER: Formerly bred at North Truro 1890 and 1891 (Miller, *Auk*, 8, 117, 1891, and Brewster) and by tradition for twenty years previously; none there at present. See under American Bittern for information on ecological changes. Recently breeding suspected at Monomoy Point Pond. Otherwise only scattered casual reports of wandering birds.

DISTRIBUTION: Ponds, fresh or brackish, with considerable vegetation. Appears in all suitable ponds particularly in Eastham, Orleans, Brewster, Monomoy, Falmouth, etc. Seldom if ever on salt water until wintering flocks frozen out. No data on migration routes.

HISTORY: Abundant to 1885, gunners killed 20–30/day on Cape, then 60 per cent decrease to 1908 (Forbush, 1912). Rather low numbers through 1920's, rising steadily since as indicated by maximum counts: 40 in 1930, 129 in 1938, 241 in 1944, 400 in 1953, and 850 (550 at Brewster plus 300 at Falmouth) in 1955.

* *

HOODED MERGANSER
Lophodytes cucullatus (Linnaeus)

STATUS: Represented in Chicago collection.

FALL: Rather rare migrant, chiefly arrival of a terminal population.

Earliest arrival date: October 10, 1944, at Eastham (Griscom).

Average migration period: October 25–December 25; average 1–7 birds, maximum 23 on December 29, 1963, at Brewster (Kenneally, Hill). Late movements apparently in response to freezing of mainland ponds.

WINTER: Uncommon, formerly irregular, now apparently regular, average 3–6 birds. Survival rate usually good.

SPRING: No evidence of transients. Early spring gatherings are probably regrouping of successful wintering birds.

Average departure period: April 1–8.

Latest departure date: April 28, 1940, at Eastham (Hill).

SUMMER: Casual, non-breeding; several late August records at Monomoy.

DISTRIBUTION: May appear in any relatively secluded pond from Woods Hole and Pocasset to North Truro. Rarely in more open ponds or salt water. Absence of deep woods limits habitat and is factor in the much lower numbers on the Cape as compared with the mainland.

HISTORY: No data regarding this species in the early colonial days when the Cape was wooded. Habitat factor mentioned above probably limited numbers thereafter, although Jones (see Forbush, 1912) reported it as "plentiful" at Waquoit; correct identification of species must be questioned, however. No data at hand shows any increase on Cape in spite of an increase on the mainland.

*   *

COMMON MERGANSER
Mergus merganser Linnaeus

STATUS: Represented in MCZ and Chicago collections.

FALL: Fairly common migrant, arrival of a terminal population.
Earliest arrival date: November 6, 1938, at Brewster (Griscom, Curtis, Richardson).
Average migration period: November 25–December 30; arrive in numbers only with cold weather inland.

WINTER: Common resident with little mortality; average 50–300 birds, maximum 1128 on December 30, 1951 (C.C.). Very mobile, shifting on and off Cape and to and from salt water according to weather.

SPRING: No transients; wintering birds leave as soon as mainland ponds open.
Average departure period: March 1–April 15.
Latest departure date: April 28, 1939, at Dennisport (Taber, Stackpole).

SUMMER: Casual straggler, one record on August 11, 1936, at North Eastham (Austin Station).

DISTRIBUTION: Mostly on larger ponds, moving to salt water in freezes. Found over entire Cape, concentrating eastward in more severe weather.

HISTORY: Said to have decreased in past (Forbush, 1912). Slow increase apparent on Cape since 1935.

*   *

RED-BREASTED MERGANSER
Mergus serrator Linnaeus

STATUS: Represented in MCZ, BMS, and Chicago collections.

FALL: Common migrant.

Average migration period: October 18–December 25.

Peak: November 9–December 10; average 200–500, maximum 1300 on November 12, 1949, from Chatham to Eastham (Griscom, Parker).

WINTER: Fairly common resident, average 50–100 birds.

SPRING: Common migrant.

Average migration period: March 1–May 15.

Peak: April 3–25; average 100–500 birds, maximum 2500 on April 10, 1949, from Chatham to Eastham (Griscom, Crain, Parker).

Latest transient date: Uncertain, probably about May 30.

SUMMER: Has nested regularly at Monomoy since 1877, nests and young found (Bearse, *in litt.* to Bangs), young seen regularly to present. Nests at least sporadically along Nantucket Sound at Great Island (Cory, Brewster), Poponesset (Cobb), Waquoit (Jones), and Falmouth (Brewster); also along Cape Cod Bay at Sagamore (Hill), Barnstable (Hill), Wellfleet (Haven), and probably elsewhere. Also some scattered non-breeding stragglers.

DISTRIBUTION: Almost exclusively in salt water, usually in estuaries and inshore rather than in deep water. Essentially equal numbers over entire Cape.

HISTORY: Forbush (1912) reported a decrease, perhaps as much as 50 per cent from 1885 to 1908. Irregularly cyclic since for no known reason, but no evidence of long-term change.

*   *

TURKEY VULTURE

Cathartes aura (Linnaeus)

STATUS: Represented in BMS and British Museum collections.
SUMMER: Rare and irregular vagrant from the South.
Earliest date: April 19, 1958, at East Orleans (Earle).
Latest date: November 19, 1929, at Chatham (Eldredge, in
BMS, *Auk*, 47, 250, 1930).
DISTRIBUTION: Wide-ranging over all types of habitat; records
scattered and erratic from Woods Hole to Provincetown. Individuals range widely, as presumed same bird reported April
through June 1958 from Centerville to Orleans.
HISTORY: Five records of which three were specimens 1888 to
1929. Then recorded in ten of twenty-two years 1939 to 1960
inclusive, at least thirteen birds, one specimen. This reflects
changes elsewhere in the Northeast (Bagg & Parker, *Auk*, 68,
315, 1951).

*   *

BLACK VULTURE

Coragyps atratus (Bechstein)

STATUS: Represented in BMS collection.
Very rare vagrant from South, no seasonal pattern of occurrence.
SPECIMENS: March 31, 1923, at Chatham (Brooks, in BMS, *Auk*,
41, 164, 1924) and February 16, 1947, at South Harwich
(Hardacker, in BMS).
SIGHT RECORDS: one each in April, May, June, August, and September, scattered from Woods Hole to Orleans. All records but
the first specimen noted above made since 1941 and hence coincident with the increase in observers.

*   *

GOSHAWK
Accipiter gentilis (Linnaeus)

STATUS: Presumptive.

WINTER: Very rare and irregular visitant.

Earliest arrival date: September 24, 1939, at Monomoy (Griscom).

Average period: October 15–April 1; almost invariably single birds.

Latest departure date: April 21, 1959, at Wellfleet (Bailey).

DISTRIBUTION: Records mostly in wilder areas of Sandwich moraine east to Brewster and Dennis, occasional at Monomoy and north to Wellfleet.

HISTORY: No evidence that great fall flights of past penetrated to Cape Cod, though scattered birds were presumably overlooked; all records are since 1936 and hence coincident with the increase in observers.

* *

SHARP-SHINNED HAWK
Accipiter striatus Vieillot

STATUS: Represented in MCZ, BMS, and British Museum collections.

SPRING: Arrival of breeding birds, no evidence of transients.

Average arrival period: March 30–April 19.

SUMMER: Rare and local breeding resident, widely but thinly distributed in suitable extensive woods and often irregular in any given locality, recorded from Sandwich, Cotuit, and Mashpee to Chatham, Orleans, and Wellfleet; possibly less numerous east of Barnstable.

FALL: Uncommon, occasionally abundant, migrant.

Average migration period: August 27–November 20.

Peak: September 4–17; average 3–10/day, maximum 120 on
September 4, 1939, at Chatham (Elkins).

WINTER: Rather uncommon and somewhat irregular though usually
present; usually survives the season.

DISTRIBUTION: See above for breeding pairs. Transients and wintering birds scattered over all types of country, transients often
along outer beaches and rarely even at sea. Recorded over entire
Cape.

HISTORY: Little detail in older records but apparently decreasing,
particularly the breeding population.

*   *

COOPER'S HAWK

Accipiter cooperii (Bonaparte)

STATUS: Represented in British Museum collection.

SPRING: Arrival of breeding birds, no evidence of transients.
Average arrival period: March 28–April 19.

SUMMER: Rare and local, widely but thinly distributed in woods
of mixed growth, irregular from year to year in any given
locality. Has nested at Wellfleet, Chatham, Mashpee, Falmouth,
etc.

FALL: Rather uncommon migrant.
Average migration period: August 25–November 25.
Peak: September 3–25; average 1–2 birds, maximum 4 on
September 10–11, 1949 (Griscom).

WINTER: Rare and irregular, less so since 1949, but survives only
occasionally.

DISTRIBUTION: See above for breeding distribution. As transient
and winterer, widely distributed in most habitats with woods
and thickets, less along outer beaches than Sharp-shinned
Hawk. Recorded over entire Cape.

HISTORY: Decreasing steadily as throughout New England.

*   *

RED-TAILED HAWK
Buteo jamaicensis (Gmelin)

STATUS: Represented in MCZ collection.
Fairly common permanent resident, a few transients spring and fall.
DISTRIBUTION: Widely scattered through pitch pine woods, estimate of 20+ pairs over entire Cape, most common hawk on
Cape and more common than on mainland. The breeding adults
are essentially non-migratory and account for most of the
records throughout the year. Transients rather rare, irregularly
augment the local population but are difficult to detect, probably
March 20–April 10 and in mid-October.
HISTORY: No data on early period; scarce in early historical period
when land was mostly cleared; recovered with reforestation and
probably still increasing.

*   *

RED-SHOULDERED HAWK
Buteo lineatus (Gmelin)

STATUS: Presumptive.
SUMMER: Very rare and local breeding species; pair with nest and
young June 22, 1960, at Mashpee (Hill) and probably pairs at
Sandwich (Burbank), Woods Hole (Freeland), and Brewster
(Bailey). Dates of arrival and departure unknown.
Otherwise a rare and irregular migrant along Canal and at Sagamore during April and again in September and October, but
only a casual straggler elsewhere, decreasing eastward where
most records are of single birds from November to February.
HISTORY: Formerly absent except as a very casual vagrant, now increasing slowly and gradually moving eastward as woods develop proper mixture of deciduous growth. Has not replaced
the Red-tailed as on the mainland.

*   *

BROAD-WINGED HAWK
Buteo platypterus (Vieillot)

STATUS: Banded at Austin Station.

SPRING: Arrival of breeding residents, very rare and irregular as transient.

> Average arrival period: April 23–May 20, extreme dates not satisfactorily known; usually single birds, maximum 5 on May 10, 1953, at Provincetown (Whiting).

SUMMER: Rare and local breeding resident in mixed pine and oak woods. Recorded at North Eastham (Austin, Low), Brewster (Hill), Wianno (Eaton), and possibly at Wellfleet and Cotuit.

FALL: Rather uncommon migrant.

> Earliest transient date: July 27, 1959, at Eastham (Bailey).
> Average migration period: August 25–September 27; usually only 1–2 birds.
> Latest departure date: November 18, 1957, at Wellfleet (Bailey).

DISTRIBUTION: See above for breeding bird distribution. Migrants widely scattered over all types of country including occasionally along outer beaches. No apparent differences within areas on Cape.

HISTORY: No data. All records are coincident with the increase in observers in the past thirty years.

*   *

SWAINSON'S HAWK
Buteo swainsoni Bonaparte

STATUS: Hypothetical.

Species suspected twice, late August and mid-September of different years at Chatham and Eastham.

*   *

ROUGH-LEGGED HAWK
Buteo lagopus (Pontoppidan)

STATUS: Represented in MCZ, BMS, and British Museum collections.

WINTER: Rather uncommon but regular resident, no evidence of transients either spring or fall.

Earliest arrival date: October 17, 1953, at Nauset (Mason).
Average period: November 1–April 1.
Counts: Average 1–2 birds, maximum 6 on December 19, 1937 (C.C.).
Latest departure date: May 16, 1959, at Orleans (Lund).

DISTRIBUTION: Open uplands and salt marshes over entire Cape, occasionally soaring or migrating high over woodlands. More numerous on Cape than on mainland, but less so than on islands. Observed migrating high from northwest to southeast on November 20, 1960, at Sagamore (Hill).

HISTORY: Formerly most common in pine barrens from Bourne to Falmouth, but decreasing as elsewhere in New England (Forbush, 1925). No significant change in numbers apparent in past two decades.

*   *

GOLDEN EAGLE
Aquila chrysaëtos (Linnaeus)

STATUS: Presumptive.

WINTER: Very rare and irregular visitant, constantly wandering and not remaining for entire season.

Earliest arrival date: November 8, 1948, at Chatham (Griscom), adult seen arriving from northwest.
Average period: November 29–January 15; always single birds.
Latest departure date: February 17, 1946, at Brewster (Hill).

DISTRIBUTION: Roosts in deeper woods near ponds and feeds in marshes and estuaries. Has been recorded only from the Chatham-Orleans-Brewster area.

HISTORY: No data. All known records are 1942 to 1948.

*   *

BALD EAGLE
Haliaeetus leucocephalus (Linnaeus)

STATUS: Represented in MCZ collection. Three populations involved: 1) breeding; 2) summering; and 3) wintering. Some individuals are not assignable to a specific population, but there is a well-marked hiatus in records in April and again in October which presumably marks the dividing point between wintering and summering birds.

1) BREEDING: Subspecies unknown and now extinct. Only specific record is of a nest at Bear Hollow near Snake Pond, Sandwich, 1900–1905 (Cobb); traditionally nested at a number of other locations (Brewster); nothing is known regarding numbers, exact locations, dates, etc.

2) SUMMERING: Southern nesting, *H. l. leucocephalus,* uncommon and sometimes irregular visitant, mostly immature birds.
Earliest arrival date: May 4, 1943, at Osterville (Eaton).
Average period: May 30–September 1.
Peak: June 15–July 31; see below for counts.
Latest departure date: September 30, 1950, at Chatham (Griscom).

DISTRIBUTION: Collects at herring runs in June and then scatters widely over entire Cape. An immature banded May 20, 1938, at Bombay Hook, Delaware, was found August 25, 1938, at Chatham.

HISTORY: Decreasing throughout historical period. This population plus some nesting birds once common from Bourne to Mashpee and Falmouth. At Cotuit and Mashpee, ten seen June 25, 1918, three in 1940, and only single birds since (Cobb).

Brush moorland, Wellfleet

Air view, Sandy Neck and Great Marshes at Barnstable

Dunes along North Beach, Chatham

Salt marsh, Wellfleet

3) WINTERING: Northern nesting, *H. l. alascanus,* uncommon and sometimes irregular visitant.

Earliest arrival date: November 8, 1952, at Brewster (Griscom, Bailey).

Average period: December 15–March 15.

Peak: After cold weather on mainland, usually mid-January, often present for very short time; average 1–4 birds, maximum 9 on December 21, 1947 (C.C.).

Latest departure date: March 30, 1947, at Brewster (Griscom).

DISTRIBUTION: Scattered over entire Cape, concentrating eastward in cold weather where seen on ice in bays and estuaries feeding on dead and dying ducks.

HISTORY: Very little data on early status. Counts during 1930's and 1950's essentially equal but with a cycle of higher counts 1946–1949; apparently decreasing now.

* *

MARSH HAWK
Circus cyaneus (Linnaeus)

STATUS: Represented in MCZ, BMS, Chicago, and British Museum collections.

SPRING: Arrival of residents, rare as transient.

Average migration period: March 25–May 1.

Peak: April 1–20; average 5–8 birds, maximum 15 on April 6–7, 1940 (Hill).

SUMMER: Rather uncommon and local as breeding species, estimated 8–10 pairs on Cape, reported at Monomoy, Eastham, Orleans, Truro, Barnstable, Falmouth, etc.

FALL: Fairly common migrant.

Earliest transient date: Uncertain, probably about August 8.

Average migration period: August 20–November 15.

Peak: September 6–October 15; average 5–10 birds, maximum 25 on October 13, 1951, at Monomoy (Griscom, Parker, Drury).

WINTER: Rare but regular resident, average 1–2 birds, maximum 4 on January 17, 1937 (Griscom); usually survives the season.

DISTRIBUTION: Breeds in salt and brackish marshes. Ranges over same and open rolling country generally, occasionally soaring over woods. Found over entire Cape but less common westward in midwinter.

HISTORY: Decreased since Small reported 50 on several occasions between 1885 and 1890 at North Truro; no evidence of change, however, since 1935.

*   *

OSPREY

Pandion haliaetus (Linnaeus)

STATUS: Represented in MCZ, BMS, and Chicago collections.

SPRING: Rare migrant.

Earliest arrival date: March 24, 1943, at Sandwich (Burbank).

Average migration period: April 20–May 30; no peak dates and usually single birds.

SUMMER: Very rare and local as breeding bird, irregular in any given locality; reported at North Falmouth, Waquoit, Mashpee, and Harwich since 1900. In addition, there are wandering single birds which range widely and appear fairly frequently.

FALL: Rather uncommon migrant.

Average migration period: August 12–October 12.

Peak: September 1–30; average 1–2 birds, occasionally three.

Latest departure date: October 28, 1950, at Eastham (Griscom, Smart, Mason).

DISTRIBUTION: Breeding known only along sound shores and decreasing eastward. Wandering and migrant birds reported over entire Cape.

HISTORY: The breeding pairs at the southwestern extremity of the Cape are probably an overflow from the Narragansett Bay population and are decreasing parallel to it. No evidence of change in numbers of migrant birds.

* *

GYRFALCON
Falco rusticolus Linnaeus

STATUS: Presumptive.

FALL: Very rare but probably regular migrant (see Richardson, 1955, pages 12–17 and 117–119).

Earliest arrival date: September 30, 1951, at Monomoy (Bailey).

Average migration period: October 4–November 7; over half of all records fall between October 4 and 22, always single birds.

WINTER: Very rare and irregular vagrant.

SPRING: Very rare and irregular, no transients.

Average departure date: Mid-March.

Latest departure date: June 8, 1948, at Eastham (Richardson).

DISTRIBUTION: Primarily found in open country, marshes, and outer beaches; hence mostly reported from Eastham to Monomoy, rarely west to Barnstable. All three color phases occur, black much the most frequent.

HISTORY: All records are since 1939, thus reflecting increased numbers of experienced observers and not a real change in occurrence. Nonetheless, the species is reported more on Cape Cod than on the mainland.

* *

PEREGRINE FALCON
Falco peregrinus Tunstall

STATUS: Represented in MCZ, BMS, and British Museum collections.

FALL: Uncommon migrant.

Earliest transient date: August 14, 1937, at Barnstable (Eaton).

Average migration period: September 8–November 20.

Peak: October 5–10; usually 1–2 birds, maximum 9 on several occasions at Monomoy (Griscom).

WINTER: Rare straggler, widely ranging and so intermittently present throughout the season.

SPRING: Uncommon migrant.

Average migration period: April 17–May 30; usually single birds, maximum 5 on April 27, 1949, at Nauset (A. Griscom).

Latest departure date: May 31, 1954, at Monomoy (Griscom, Ross, Beattie).

DISTRIBUTION: Primarily open country, marshes, and outer beaches. Concentrates in areas occupied by shore birds, i.e. Monomoy, Nauset, Barnstable, etc., but recorded from entire Cape.

HISTORY: No evidence of any change in numbers.

* *

PIGEON HAWK
Falco columbarius Linnaeus

STATUS: Represented in MCZ, BMS, PM, and Chicago collections.

FALL: Uncommon migrant, occasionally fairly common.

Earliest arrival date: August 11, 1943, at Monomoy (Griscom & Curtis).

Average migration period: August 28–November 5.

Peak: September 9–28; usually 4–6 birds, maximum 16 on September 9–10, 1949 (M.A.S.).

Latest transient date: Uncertain, probably about November 17.

WINTER: Very rare and irregular, may survive entire season.

First recorded in 1941 and collected in 1950.

SPRING: Rare but regular migrant.

Earliest transient date: April 1, 1945, at Chatham (Griscom).

Average migration period: April 12–May 25; no peaks, usually single birds, occasionally two.

Latest departure date: May 30, 1958, at Nauset (Fox).

DISTRIBUTION: Largely open country with thickets, also marshes and along outer beaches. Recorded over entire Cape but more common in spring around Canal than eastward; more evenly distributed in fall except for concentrations along outer beaches.

HISTORY: No evidence of significant change in numbers.

*   *

SPARROW HAWK
Falco sparverius Linnaeus

STATUS: Represented in MCZ, BMS, and British Museum collections.

SPRING: Common migrant.

Average migration period: April 1–30.

Peak: April 10–24; average 5–10 birds, maximum 33 on April 24, 1954, at Monomoy (Griscom, Elkins).

SUMMER: Fairly common breeding resident over entire Cape, number of pairs not known.

FALL: Uncommon migrant.

Earliest transient date: Uncertain, locally raised young increase counts in August.

Average migration period: September 8–December 10.

Peak: No marked peak, average 3–6 birds, occasionally to 10–12. Note lower counts in fall than in spring in contrast to other falcons.

WINTER: Rather uncommon resident, average 2–5 birds; survives season successfully.

DISTRIBUTION: Open and brushy areas, also dunes adjacent to salt marshes. Widely distributed over entire Cape without marked concentration, second in numbers to Red-tailed Hawk and more numerous than on mainland.

HISTORY: Status prior to 1900 not clear; definitely increasing since then with a marked increase since 1950, especially of wintering birds.

*   *

RUFFED GROUSE
Bonasa umbellus (Linnaeus)

STATUS: Represented in MCZ and Chicago collections.
Rare and local permanent resident.

DISTRIBUTION: Essentially confined to and breeding in mixed forests of the Falmouth-Sandwich moraine from Falmouth north to Bourne, east to Orleans, and south to Chatham. Stray birds occasionally to south shore or north to Eastham. Pairs widely scattered in summer, gathering in loose flocks in early winter, maximum 8 on December 19, 1943, at Brewster (Griscom).

HISTORY: Formerly common but reduced by shooting and destruction of forest (Forbush, 1912). None east of Harwichport and Brewster by 1888 (Cahoon). Slowly extending eastward since 1900, reached Orleans in 1916 (Earle) and Chatham in 1937 (Bishop). Numbers increasing gradually without evidence of marked fluctuation.

*   *

HEATH HEN
Tympanuchus cupido (Linnaeus)

EXTINCT: Believed to have been common, but no specimens are extant. Inhabited open and brushy plains, not woods. In 1849 the Wellfleet oysterman told Thoreau of killing "wild hens," presumably this species, in Orleans, Eastham, and Wellfleet eighty years previously, i.e. about 1770. Seen about 1812 on Cape Cod by Eliza Cabot (Brewster, 1906, page 173). Specimen killed in 1855 on Cape Cod but was believed to have flown over from Martha's Vineyard as no birds were then known locally.

ADDENDUM: Attempts were made in 1877 and 1891 and possibly earlier to introduce the Prairie Chicken from the West; nearly

300 birds were brought in but did not persist, though they probably account for some records reported as Heath Hen.

* *

BOBWHITE
Colinus virginianus (Linnaeus)

STATUS: Represented in MCZ, Chicago, and British Museum collections.
Common permanent resident.
DISTRIBUTION: Brushy pasture and uplands with thickets and wood edges. Widespread over entire Cape, but fewer north of Wellfleet. Often coming to feeding stations in winter.
HISTORY: Became abundant in colonial times as forests were cleared, reduced after 1800 by overshooting. Also heavy wet snows and cold rainy springs caused local disasters. Original stock on Cape exterminated about 1857 by wet snow, repopulated with less hardy and smaller birds from South by Fay (Forbush, 1912). Another large local loss in 1898, but escaped in 1905 when badly reduced elsewhere. Increased since 1909 due to decrease in foxes, also releasing of raised birds. Much favored by mild winters in 1950–1960 and now present in high counts, e.g., average on Christmas Counts of 10–15 in the 1930's, rising steadily from 1951 on to maximum of 214 on January 3, 1959. Much more numerous than on mainland.

* *

RING-NECKED PHEASANT
Phasianus colchicus Linnaeus

STATUS: Represented in MCZ and Chicago collections.
Introduced species; rather uncommon and local permanent resident.
DISTRIBUTION: Brushy fields and uplands, occasionally into marsh

edges. Found throughout the Cape but in no great numbers and definitely less than on mainland.

HISTORY: First introduced between 1895 and 1900. Species unable to maintain itself against both fall hunting pressure and winters with heavy snow, so additional birds are raised locally and released each year.

*   *

CHUKAR
Alectoris graeca (Meisner)

Introduced species, apparently unsuccessful. Seen in summer of 1957 at Sagamore (Hill).

*   *

TURKEY
Meleagris gallopavo Linnaeus

EXTIRPATED: no specimens preserved. Probably common in original forest as reported to Champlain in 1605; present thereafter according to tradition. Very rapidly diminished by shooting and destruction of forests; rare by 1672 (Josselyn, see Forbush, 1912), but actual date of disappearance not known.

*   *

SANDHILL CRANE
Grus canadensis (Linnaeus)

STATUS: Presumptive.

One bird in partially immature plumage present in Orleans and ranging to adjacent towns from September 1 to October 24, 1955 (Islieb, Griscom, Morgan, et al.).

ADDENDUM: A specimen of the Saras Crane, *Grus antigone*, native to India, superficially similar to Whooping Crane, was kept on the Whittemore Estate in Falmouth and was allowed to roam;

it was reported widely 1916–1926 over Falmouth and out to Naushon and Martha's Vineyard (Jones, *Auk*, *45*, 203, 1928).

* *

KING RAIL
Rallus elegans Audubon

STATUS: Represented in MCZ and BMS collections.

SPRING: Casual; specimen on June 1, 1921, at Harwich (Weeks, in BMS) and banded on May 15, 1933, at North Eastham (Brown); two sight records of large rails flushed in late May probably pertain to this species.

SUMMER: Casually breeding, pair with brood about 1880 at Sandwich (Jones, see Forbush, 1925); also a single bird recorded from June 20 on, 1924, at Eastham (Earle).

FALL: Rare migrant, probably much overlooked, so extreme dates are meaningless.

Average period: September 20–December 30; most specimens taken in late September and October.

WINTER: Casual straggler, not surviving season. Recorded twice in January and taken twice in February, caught in trap in 1892 at North Truro (Miller, *Auk*, *9*, 396, 1892) and February 14, 1919, at Sandwich (Higgins, see Forbush, 1925).

DISTRIBUTION: Migrant and wintering birds characteristically in salt marshes, reported mostly from outer Cape. No details available on breeding record in Sandwich.

HISTORY: No evidence of any change in numbers.

* *

CLAPPER RAIL
Rallus longirostris Boddaert

STATUS: Represented in MCZ and BMS collections.

SPRING: Casual; presumably only the successful wintering birds, no evidence of migrants. Three records, April 12 to May 11, and all on the bay shore of Eastham.

SUMMER: Breeds locally at Barnstable, Yarmouthport, Nauset, and possibly elsewhere. Successful wintering birds apparently augmented by very late arrivals from off Cape, dates unknown.

FALL: Uncommon and local.

Average period: August 25–December 30.

Peak: September 10–October 25; average 1–3 birds, maximum 7 on October 11, 1953, at First Encounter Beach, Eastham (Snyder).

WINTER: Very rare, apparently surviving most seasons in very small numbers.

DISTRIBUTION: Extensive salt marshes. Nests located in wetter areas in *Spartina alterniflora*. Range widely through marsh and even to edge of uplands on high tides. Recorded from Sagamore and Cotuit to Monomoy and Wellfleet.

HISTORY: Reports of frequent occurrence in past not confirmed, though it probably occurred erratically and in very small numbers throughout the historical period; collected in 1895 (Rodgers, see Brewster, *Auk*, *18*, 136, 1901), twice in 1923 (Bent, in MCZ, and Burbank, see Forbush, 1925), and seen year after year prior to 1916 at Dennis (Crowell, see Forbush, 1925), also in 1939 at Sagamore and Wellfleet. Beginning in 1949, the species suddenly increased markedly so that the above seasonal reports apply to 1949 to 1961. First appeared in early fall in 1949 at Eastham and Orleans; next extended season into early winter, becoming fairly regular on Christmas Counts after 1951; by 1952 extended range south to Monomoy, west to Barnstable and Cotuit, and north to Wellfleet. First nest, ten eggs, found June 17, 1956, at Barnstable, hatched July 3 (Hill), since then nests or broods of young found at Nauset and Yarmouthport. Range and numbers now remaining fairly stable, 1–3 birds at each of 4–8 locations. Much more numerous on Cape than on mainland of Massachusetts.

*   *

VIRGINIA RAIL
Rallus limicola Vieillot

STATUS: Represented in MCZ, BMS, and British Museum collections.

SPRING: Recently no transients, three or four records to May 30 of successful wintering birds; no data on arrival at North Truro except for pair collected May 21, 1892 (Miller, in British Museum).

SUMMER: Formerly bred "commonly" at North Truro 1891–1895 (Brewster) and possibly as late as 1939 or 1940, but none found in 1958 or 1961 (Hill); see under American Bittern for information on ecological changes. Bred at North Eastham in 1933 (Austin Station); probably breeding at West Harwich, three pairs but no nest found, June 10, 1961 (Hill, Fox), and possibly elsewhere.

FALL: Rather rare but regular migrant.
Earliest transient date: August 22, 1953, at Monomoy (Bailey). Average migration period: September 10–November 15; no peaks, mostly single birds, maximum of 5 on November 11, 1952, at Monomoy (Griscom, Emery, Barry, Beattie).

WINTER: Rare and local but regular along open brooks, average 1–3 on Christmas Counts, a few usually survive.

DISTRIBUTION: See above regarding North Truro. The marsh of Herring River at West Harwich is fresh to brackish in the upper reaches and full of *Typha* sp. Transients found in both salt and fresh marshes and wintering birds along swift brooks and springs, especially Mill Brook, Brewster. Recorded over entire Cape but, except in winter, less common than on mainland.

HISTORY: No evidence of change except at North Truro. Known to winter back at least to 1877 (Brewster).

*   *

SORA

Porzana carolina (Linnaeus)

STATUS: Represented in MCZ, BMS, Chicago, and British Museum collections.

SPRING: Very rare transient in late April at Sagamore, even rarer eastward, banded in April 1932 at North Eastham (Austin Station).

SUMMER: Formerly bred "very commonly" at North Truro 1891–1895, nest with fifteen eggs found June 1, 1895 (Brewster); not found there since. Nest found May 18, 1894, at Barnstable (Brewster). No other summer records.

FALL: Uncommon migrant.

Earliest transient date: August 6, 1955, adult found dead at Chatham (Fuller).

Average migration period: August 30–November 11.

Peak: September 15–30, not marked; average 1–3 birds, maximum "dozens" on September 19–20, 1937, at Harwich (Garrison).

WINTER: Casually attempts to winter, possibly surviving rarely, known to have persisted to February 12, 1919, at Sandwich (Torrey) and to March 3, 1940, at Brewster (Hill, Parker); found dead March 22, 1958, at Eastham (Gardler).

DISTRIBUTION: See above regarding North Truro. Transients found in salt and fresh marshes and often killed flying into buildings, etc. Wintering at springs and along open brooks. Recorded over entire Cape, less numerous than on mainland except in winter.

HISTORY: No evidence of change except at North Truro.

* *

YELLOW RAIL

Coturnicops noveboracensis (Gmelin)

STATUS: Represented in MCZ and BMS collections.

SPRING: Recorded but not satisfactorily confirmed.

FALL: Rare and little-known migrant, special techniques required to record this species other than fortuitously.

Specimens: Total of four, taken from September 14, 1891, at Monomoy (Marsden, in MCZ) to November 25 or 27, 1911, at Chatham (Bearse, in BMS), see Fay, *Auk*, *29*, 237, 1912.

Sight records: Extend above dates through December to early January and once to February 21, 1954, at Nauset (Morgan), so may possibly survive in mild winters.

DISTRIBUTION: Grassy fresh and salt marshes; recorded from Barnstable, Monomoy, Chatham, Nauset, and Brewster.

HISTORY: No evidence of any change in numbers.

* *

BLACK RAIL

Laterallus jamaicensis (Gmelin)

STATUS: Hypothetical.

One heard July 1889 and June 1890 at Falmouth (Brewster) and two heard August 15, 1948, at Chatham (Griscom). Nesting record of 1885 at Chatham (Baker, see Allen, 1886) not satisfactory.

* *

PURPLE GALLINULE

Porphyrula martinica (Linnaeus)

STATUS: Specimens obtained, but present location unknown.

SPRING: Rare and irregular vagrant occurring after southern storms.

Specimens: One found dead March 30, 1952, at Monomoy (Smith); one caught in trap April 1890 at Chatham (see Farley, *Auk*, *18*, 190, 1901); one from "Cape Cod" April 1870 (Brewster, see Baird, Brewer and Ridgway, *1*, 385); one shot April 1902 at Sandwich (see Farley, *Auk*, *22*, 409, 1905); one killed by cat April 18, 1932, at Wellfleet (May).

Sight records: April 17, 1932, at North Truro (Brown) and June 22, 1947, at Yarmouth (Thatcher).

FALL: Single sight record, immature bird on October 5, 1946, at Monomoy (Griscom).

* *

COMMON GALLINULE
Gallinula chloropus (Linnaeus)

STATUS: Represented in BMS and British Museum collections.

SPRING: No data regarding arrival dates at North Truro; only recent record on April 17, 1960, at Orleans (Mayo).

SUMMER: Formerly bred "abundantly" at North Truro (Miller, immature collected June 3, 1891, in British Museum, see *Auk*, 8, 118, 1891), 15–20 pairs in June 1891 and 20 heard May 19–20, 1895 (Brewster); none reported since. No recent evidence of breeding anywhere on Cape, though wandering birds appear throughout the season.

FALL: Rare but regular migrant.

Average migration period: September 20–November 12.

Peak: September 27–October 8; average 1–2 birds, flight in 1953 to 10+ in late September at Monomoy (Griscom).

Latest departure date: January 29, 1963, at Falmouth (Garry).

DISTRIBUTION: See above regarding North Truro. Otherwise fresh and brackish ponds with emergent vegetation; occasionally salt marshes and rarely found exhausted on sand dunes. Recorded at Falmouth, Sandwich, and on outer Cape from Monomoy north to Provincetown.

HISTORY: No evidence of change in numbers except at North Truro.

* *

AMERICAN COOT
Fulica americana Gmelin

STATUS: Represented in MCZ, Chicago, and British Museum collections.

FALL: Fairly common migrant.

Earliest arrival date: August 14, 1952, at Provincetown (Gammell).

Average migration period: September 20–December 20.

Peak: November 5–December 5; average 15–50 birds, maximum 244 on November 11, 1952, at Monomoy (Griscom, Bailey, Barry, Beattie).

WINTER: Uncommon but regular at beginning of season, successful in mild years.

SPRING: Rare transient, recently in increased numbers; most records probably refer to successful wintering birds.

Average migration period: April 1–19; rarely to 3–4 birds.

Latest departure date: May 21, 1950, at Monomoy (Bailey).

DISTRIBUTION: Fresh and brackish ponds and marshes with considerable vegetation. Found over entire Cape, but concentrating eastward in colder weather.

HISTORY: Formerly very common, marked decrease after 1870 (Forbush, 1912). Now increasing steadily and extending dates of migration.

* *

AMERICAN OYSTERCATCHER

Haematopus palliatus Temminck

STATUS: Represented in BMS collection.

Very rare vagrant from South usually after storms.

SPRING: Collected in late April 1885 at Monomoy (Nye, see Brewster, *Auk, 2,* 384, 1885) and May 29, 1955, at Chatham (Morgan, in BMS). Sight records in May 1959, May 1961, and March 1963.

FALL: Collected in August 1899 at Chatham (Hardy, in BMS, see Brewster, *Auk, 18,* 136, 1901); seen September 10, 1924, at Nauset (Richardson) and September 21–23, 1936, at Monomoy (Hagar, Griscom).

* *

SEMIPALMATED PLOVER
Charadrius semipalmatus Bonaparte

STATUS: Represented in MCZ, BMS, Chicago, and British Museum collections.

SPRING: Uncommon migrant.

Earliest arrival date: April 12, 1955, at Eastham (Hill, Petty).

Average migration period: May 5–June 2.

Peak: May 20–30; average 20–30 birds, maximum 50 on May 30 on several occasions.

SUMMER: Rare scattered non-breeding stragglers.

FALL: Common to abundant migrant.

Earliest transient date: Uncertain, probably about July 6.

Average migration period: July 20–October 15.

Peaks: August 1–10 for adults, average 300–500, maximum 5000 on August 4, 1955 (Griscom); also August 23–September 1, average same, maximum 2300 on August 23–24, 1941 (Griscom); either peak may exceed the other or fail entirely

Latest departure date: November 20, 1953, at Barnstable (Pratt).

DISTRIBUTION: Feeds on wet flats and roosts on higher beaches at high tide. Maximum numbers on outer Cape at Monomoy, Nauset, Wellfleet, and Provincetown with smaller numbers at Barnstable, Sagamore, Woods Hole, etc. No data regarding migration routes.

HISTORY: Not shot until latter half of nineteenth century after decrease of larger shore birds, but diminished after 1880 (Forbush, 1912). Increasing since 1910 with protection, and probably now as numerous as ever in past as counts have been essentially stable for twenty-five years.

*   *

PIPING PLOVER
Charadrius melodus Ord

STATUS: Represented in MCZ, BMS, and Chicago collections.

SPRING: Fairly common, both arrival of local birds and transients.
Earliest arrival date: March 11, 1956, at Eastham (Hill).
Average migration period: March 30–April 30.
Peak: April 10–20; average 15–25 birds, maximum 52 on April
16, 1944, at Monomoy (Griscom, Cottrell).

SUMMER: Fairly common breeding bird on nearly all beaches, 15
pairs at Monomoy, 5–6 pairs at Nauset, 7 pairs around Cotuit,
8 pairs at Centerville, 5 pairs at Sagamore, etc.

FALL: Fairly common migrant.
Average migration period: July 25–September 28.
Peak: August 3–September 1; average 10–25 birds, maximum
56 on August 6, 1949, at Monomoy (Griscom, Fuller, Kellogg).
Latest transient date: Uncertain, probably about October 16.

WINTER: Casual straggler, collected February 22, 1954, at Chatham (Morgan, in BMS); probably surviving in mild seasons.

DISTRIBUTION: Nests and feeds on drier whiter sand of upper
beaches. Recorded on all suitable shore line of entire Cape,
maximum numbers on more extensive beaches of outer Cape.

HISTORY: Formerly "abundant" (Thoreau, 1849), but decreased
later parallel to Semipalmated Plover. Equally rapid recovery, is
again threatened by loss of beaches to summer cottages and
disturbance of those remaining by "beach buggy" travel.

SUBSPECIES: Massachusetts is on the border line between *C. m.*
melodus and *C. m. circumcincta*; most specimens are the former,
but some of the latter are extant (Griscom & Snyder, 1955).

*   *

WILSON'S PLOVER
Charadrius wilsonia Ord

STATUS: Represented in MCZ collection.
Accidental vagrant from the South.
SPECIMEN: Male collected June 26, 1929, at North Truro (Austin, in MCZ, *Auk*, 46, 538, 1929).
SIGHT RECORD: One on May 29, 1954, at Nauset (Griscom, Verry, Goodridge). Other sight records and old specimens no longer extant are not satisfactory.

*   *

KILLDEER
Charadrius vociferus Linnaeus

STATUS: Represented in MCZ, BMS, Chicago, and British Museum collections.
SPRING: Rare migrant.
Earliest transient date: Uncertain, probably about March 15.
Average migration period: April 1–May 30; almost invariably single birds.
SUMMER: Breeds very locally at Woods Hole and possibly at Barnstable; scattered non-breeding birds appear occasionally elsewhere.
FALL: Rare to locally not uncommon migrant.
Earliest transient date: Uncertain, probably July 26, 1961, at Sagamore, migrating high to southeast (Hill).
Average migration period: August 1–November 15; see below for counts.
WINTER: Very rare and irregular eastward, recently increasing around Woods Hole. Probably surviving very rarely.
DISTRIBUTION: Breeds in upland pastures, golf courses, airports, etc. Transients in same places, also on flats and around fresh and brackish ponds. Generally less regular and fewer birds east-

White Cedar (Chamaecyparis thyoides) in swamp. Fern fiddleheads in fore-
ground

ward, increasing westward, but still much less numerous than on mainland.

HISTORY: Reported as abundant summer resident 1832–1835 (Cabot) and common summer resident 1849–1855 (Thoreau). Rapidly decreased after 1850 to status of very rare spring and fall migrant (Cahoon). Immense flight (see Chadbourne, *Auk*, 6, 255, 1889) on November 25–26, 1888, in violent easterly gale; birds came in from the sea in flocks of hundreds, greatest number at Provincetown to Chatham, but also west to Marstons Mills; numbers decreased steadily through December, but many persisted through January and a few survived the winter. This flight did not change their status in subsequent years. Since protection in 1915, the increase on the mainland has been reflected in a steady but slow increase in the scattered stragglers, mostly since 1940; e.g. single birds to 1940, up to 10 by 1948, and to 25 by 1953 in late summer and early fall. Re-established as breeding bird in Falmouth-Woods Hole area by 1953 and probably at Barnstable about the same time.

* *

MOUNTAIN PLOVER
Eupoda montana (Townsend)

STATUS: Represented in BMS collection.
Accidental straggler from the West.
Collected fortuitously on October 28, 1916, at Chatham (Crowell, in BMS, see Brooks, *Auk*, *34*, 86, 1917).

* *

AMERICAN GOLDEN PLOVER
Pluvialis dominica (Müller)

STATUS: Represented in MCZ, BMS, Chicago, and British Museum collections.
SPRING: Very rare migrant, never regular.
Recorded from May 1 to 30, always single birds.

SUMMER: Very rare and irregular non-breeding straggler.

FALL: Rare to uncommon migrant.

Earliest transient date: Uncertain, probably about August 12.

Average migration period: August 20–October 20.

Peak: Oceanic flight of adults August 20–September 9, so a heavy easterly gale at that time may bring them in; flocks may land, and if so will remain after storm, or may simply fly past. Young birds which come overland produce a secondary and variable peak in mid-September. See below for counts.

Latest departure date: November 24, 1931, at Nauset (Richardson).

DISTRIBUTION: Spring birds reported only with the great shorebird concentrations of outer Cape. Fall adults which come in from the sea also concentrate on outer Cape, fewer westward to Canal. Regularly land in pastures and uplands as well as on flats. Young birds more evenly distributed over entire Cape.

HISTORY: Remarkably abundant every fall and not uncommon in spring to about 1850; thereafter occurred in sporadic flights as in 1863, 1867, 1870, 1873, 1881, 1882, 1883, 1886, 1889, 1890 (Mackay, *Auk*, 8, 17, 1891), all dependent on easterly gales at the proper time. Descriptions of the density of birds in these flights are staggering, described as "raining plover" and "flying so fast and low" that one was "in danger of being struck" (see Forbush, 1912). Ninety per cent decrease before 1900 (Forbush, l.c.) and in very low numbers thereafter. Slow increase now apparent. Average counts in past twenty-five years have been 5–15 birds, maxima 200 on August 30, 1935 (Hagar), and 60 on August 25, 1945 (Griscom, Rich, Maclay), both at Nauset, flying south in storm. Also a small recent increase in spring records.

*   *

BLACK-BELLIED PLOVER
Squatarola squatarola (Linnaeus)

STATUS: Represented in MCZ, BMS, Chicago, and British Museum collections.

SPRING: Abundant migrant.

Average migration period: April 20–June 3.

Peak: May 20–25; average 1000 birds, maximum 3500 on May 21, 1943, at Monomoy (Griscom, Hill, Bishop).

SUMMER: Most regular and common of non-breeding shore-bird stragglers.

FALL: Abundant migrant.

Earliest transient date: Uncertain, probably about July 10.

Average migration period: July 25–October 25.

Peak: August 15–25 for adults, average 800–1500 birds, maximum 2500 on August 25, 1945, at Nauset (Griscom, Rich, Maclay); also September 5–October 1, average 1500–2000 birds, maximum 3000 on September 30, 1950, at North Beach (Bailey).

WINTER: Regular in small numbers, average 1–5, and often surviving successfully.

DISTRIBUTION: Feeds on tidal sand flats and roosts on higher beaches. Greatest numbers at Monomoy, North Beach, Nauset, Wellfleet, and Barnstable and fewer at Provincetown; much lower numbers but invariably present on south coast and around Canal where largest counts occur in September after arrival of young birds. No data concerning migration routes; has been seen flying across Cape in West Barnstable (Cobb).

HISTORY: Originally not as numerous as Golden Plover, but also showed a marked decrease in mid-nineteenth century. Definite increase noted on Cape when spring shooting was prohibited and a marked increase with full protection. Counts have been fairly stable for over twenty-five years and are essentially as reported a hundred and thirty years ago, so apparently full recovery has taken place.

* *

RUDDY TURNSTONE
Arenaria interpres (Linnaeus)

STATUS: Represented in MCZ, BMS, Chicago, and British Museum collections.

SPRING: Very common migrant.

Earliest transient date: April 13, 1940, at Eastham (Curtis).

Average migration period: May 12–June 4.

Peak: May 20–30; average 500–1000 birds, maximum 2500 on several occasions.

SUMMER: Rather uncommon non-breeding straggler.

FALL: Common migrant.

Earliest transient date: Uncertain, probably about July 18.

Average migration period: July 28–October 12.

Peak: August 5–20; average 100–400 birds, maximum 1000 on August 6–11, 1951, at Monomoy (Griscom, Meade). Young birds appear about September 1, but no high counts.

Latest transient date: Uncertain, probably about December 1.

WINTER: Very rare at beginning of season, seldom if ever surviving.

DISTRIBUTION: More partial to pebbly beaches than other shore birds, but also on flats. Widespread in moderate numbers over entire Cape, highest concentration at Monomoy.

HISTORY: Formerly abundant, then decreased to uncommon, but rapidly increased with protection, never as much shot as the larger species. No significant change in numbers in past twenty-five years, so apparently at or near original numbers.

SUBSPECIES: The European race, *A. i. interpres*, was reported as collected at Monomoy (Bishop, *Auk*, *23*, 335, 1906); identification now considered incorrect (Griscom & Snyder, 1955).

* *

AMERICAN WOODCOCK
Philohela minor (Gmelin)

STATUS: Represented in MCZ collection.

SPRING: Arrival of residents, very few transients.

Earliest arrival date: February 27, 1954, at Woods Hole (Kelly).

Average arrival period: March 1–25; transients recorded into early May.

SUMMER: Rare and local breeding resident; requires special habitat of fresh-water ponds and bogs with muddy soil, will not occupy sandy soil. Very scattered pairs from Woods Hole and Sagamore decreasing eastward to Chatham, Orleans, and Brewster but probably not further north.

FALL: Rather uncommon migrant.

Average migration period: October 5–December 5; usually single birds.

Peak: Flights occur but rarely and then usually in early November.

WINTER: Casual and very local around a few spring holes, seldom surviving.

DISTRIBUTION: See above regarding breeding birds. Spring migrants chiefly near Canal. Fall migrants regular from Canal east to Barnstable-Hyannis area and south to Woods Hole; small number regularly at Provincetown and Truro with occasional storm-borne flights; always less numerous from Wellfleet to Chatham. Generally much fewer than on mainland.

HISTORY: Breeding birds much reduced by summer shooting, forest fires, and especially conversion of swamps to cranberry bogs. Transient birds slowly and steadily decreasing (Forbush, 1912). Storm-borne flights recorded in 1868, 1908, and 1923. No apparent change in either breeding or migrant populations since 1935.

*   *

COMMON SNIPE
Capella gallinago (Linnaeus)

STATUS: Represented in MCZ, BMS, and British Museum collections.

FALL: Uncommon migrant.

Earliest arrival date: August 16, 1948, at Sagamore (Hill).

Average migration period: September 12–November 30.

Peak: Not well marked, late October and early November; see below for counts.

WINTER: Rare and local along swift brooks and at springs, a few usually surviving the winter.

SPRING: Very rare migrant, possibly only successful wintering birds.

Average migration period: March 27–May 10; usually single birds.

DISTRIBUTION: Frequents meadows with muddy soil. Transients mostly around Canal in spring when only casual on outer Cape. In fall storm-borne flights strike outer Cape from Provincetown to Chatham, possibly from an overwater migration route, e.g. 32 on October 12, 1933, at Eastham (Low), also see Forbush, 1912; less common westward in fall. Generally less numerous than on the mainland except in winter.

HISTORY: "Common migrant" to 1888, 40 flushed in a few hours at Grassy Pond, Harwich (Cahoon), but decreasing even then. Continued decrease chronicled by Forbush (1912). Recent counts of migrants average 1–4 birds, maximum 7 on November 11, 1952, at Monomoy (Griscom) and early winter maximum of 18 on December 30, 1956 (C.C.).

* *

LONG-BILLED CURLEW
Numenius americanus Bechstein

STATUS: Represented in BMS collection.

SPECIMEN: One found on June 14, 1938, at West Chatham (Bishop) and collected next day (Griscom, in BMS, *Auk*, 56, 332, 1939). Several recent unconfirmed sight records.

HISTORY: Said to have been a common fall migrant particularly on the plains of Eastham prior to 1850 (Hatch), in flocks of 15–20 in 1870 (Samuels), but rare by 1888 (Cahoon). Though many were shot, none were preserved, and there remains the possibility of error in identification as there is disagreement on relative numbers of this and the Whimbrel. There seems no doubt that some Long-billed Curlew were present, but some of the birds reported as such may have been misidentified Whimbrel.

*   *

WHIMBREL
Numenius phaeopus (Linnaeus)

STATUS: Represented in MCZ, BMS, Chicago, and British Museum collections.

SPRING: Rare and irregular migrant.
Earliest arrival date: Early April 1890 at Monomoy (Cahoon).
Average migration period: April 20–June 1; mostly single birds.

SUMMER: Rare and irregular non-breeding stragglers.

FALL: Common migrant.
Earliest transient date: Uncertain, probably about July 5.
Average migration period: July 12–September 28.
Peak: July 22–August 5 for adults, average 50–80 birds, maximum 150 on July 22, 1954, at Monomoy (Griscom, Elkins); September 8–17 for young, average same, maximum 95 on September 17, 1937, at Monomoy (Griscom). Numbers very erratic and either peak may fail entirely.

Latest transient date: October 27, 1937, at Barnstable (Aylward).

DISTRIBUTION: Occupies uplands, especially *Hudsonia* dunes, also upper beaches and mud flats. In spring most migrants leave the Atlantic coast south of Cape Cod; the small numbers recorded have been in the Chatham-Orleans-Eastham area. In fall the main flight is offshore (Taverner, *Wilson Bull.*, *54*, 3, 1942), the maximum numbers on outer Cape from Provincetown to Monomoy and in fewer numbers westward to Canal.

HISTORY: As stated under Long-billed Curlew, there is some disagreement as to relative numbers of these species; the Whimbrel was generally said to have been rare, but Mackay (*Auk*, 9, 345, 1892) disagreed, at least as regards Nantucket. "Fairly common" in spring, "common" in fall by 1888 (Cahoon), but decreased to 1908 (Forbush, 1912). Slight increase thereafter, but counts have now been stable for about twenty years.

SUBSPECIES: An individual of some white-rumped race of the species seen September 7–9, 1951, at Monomoy (Bailey) and a week later at Hyannis (Coolidge, see *Bull. Mass. Audubon Soc.*, *35*, 392, 1951).

*   *

ESKIMO CURLEW
Numenius borealis (Forster)

STATUS: Represented in MCZ, BMS, Chicago, and British Museum collections.

EXTIRPATED: approaching extinction.

SPRING: Formerly very rare; shot in April 1890 at Chatham (Gould, in MCZ) and May 1873 at Wellfleet (Denton); perhaps transients, but survival of crippled birds suspected.

FALL: Formerly very irregular, from absent to abundant.

Average migration period: July 15 (Cahoon)–mid-November (Forbush).

Peak: Oceanic flight of adults August 25 on and of young September 8 on; great flights fell from August 25 to September 5 and required an easterly storm, more severe weather being needed to bring in this species than the Golden Plover; birds sometimes alighted and remained a week or so and sometimes passed without stopping.

DISTRIBUTION: Occurred in uplands and pastures rather than on beaches. Recorded from outer Cape and west to Hyannis.

HISTORY: Apparently regular and abundant to about 1800. Then came irregularly in immense flights gradually more and more widely spaced. Great ones recorded include 1863, 1872 (when two gunners killed 5000 birds), and 1883. Mackay chronicled the decrease, gradual in the 1880's and rapid thereafter (*Auk*, 9, 16, 1892). Last record, one shot on September 5, 1913, at East Orleans (Rogers, see Lamb, *Auk*, 30, 581, 1913).

*   *

UPLAND PLOVER
Bartramia longicauda (Bechstein)

STATUS: Represented in MCZ, BMS, Chicago, and British Museum collections.

FALL: At present known as rare and irregular migrant at this season only.

Earliest transient date: July 30, 1951, at Chatham (Griscom, Maclay).

Average migration period: August 16–September 6; usually only 1–2 birds, not recorded every year.

Latest transient date: September 9, 1954, at Chatham (Crompton).

DISTRIBUTION: Pastures, moors, dunes, rarely if ever on flats and beaches. Has occurred over entire Cape.

HISTORY: Presumed to have been rare and local until forests were cleared, but then became common breeding bird on plains of

Eastham, Wellfleet, and Truro (Thoreau, 1849–1855) and as a transient (Forbush, 1912). Cahoon (1888) reported it fairly common spring and fall, giving as dates April 12–May 10 (collected April 22, 1889 at North Truro, Miller, in British Museum) and late July to September 12; believed a few nested. Decreased rapidly since due to regrowth of forest and excessive shooting. No breeding since at least 1900.

* *

SPOTTED SANDPIPER
Actitis macularia (Linnaeus)

STATUS: Represented in MCZ, Chicago, and British Museum collections.

SPRING: Arrival of breeding residents, no evidence of transients.
Earliest arrival date: May 5, 1962, at Sagamore (Hill).
Average arrival period: May 10–30.

SUMMER: Uncommon and rather local breeding species on many beaches and some inland ponds. At present, 5–8 pairs on Monomoy, 2–3 pairs at Nauset, 2 pairs at Falmouth, 4–6 pairs at Provincetown, 3 pairs at Cotuit, 5–6 pairs at Barnstable, 2–3 pairs at Sagamore, etc.

FALL: Uncommon transient, lingering local birds.
Earliest transient date: Uncertain, probably about July 7.
Average migration period: July 25–September 1; no peaks, average 5–10 birds, maximum 20 on August 5, 1941, at Monomoy (Hill).
Latest departure date: November 20, 1961, at Provincetown (Bailey).

DISTRIBUTION: Occupies clean sand beaches and feeds along wrack line, also sand-bordered inland ponds, less often in mud. See above for distribution of breeding birds; transients found over entire Cape without evidence of concentration.

HISTORY: Formerly abundant, e.g., 50–100 pairs at Monomoy (Cahoon, 1888). Since bird was little shot as game, the marked decrease is presumably due to disturbance in its habitat.

* *

SOLITARY SANDPIPER
Tringa solitaria Wilson

STATUS: Represented in MCZ and Chicago collections.

SPRING: Formerly fairly common, now very rare and irregular migrant.

Earliest arrival date: April 18, 1931, at Eastham (Richardson).

Average migration period: May 1–20.

Latest transient date: May 24, 1877, at Monomoy (Deane).

FALL: Formerly fairly common, now rare migrant.

Earliest transient date: July 27, 1952, at Barnstable (Cobb).

Average migration period: August 20–October 2; mostly single birds, maximum 4 on September 11, 1948, and September 21, 1950 (Griscom).

Latest transient date: November 11, 1941, at Eastham, found dead (Williston).

DISTRIBUTION: Small inland ponds with muddy edges and along ditches, rarely on marshes. Cape Cod is far east of normal migration route; no difference in counts from west to east on Cape, much less common than on mainland.

HISTORY: Cahoon (1888) considered it fairly common spring and fall; no other data available.

* *

WILLET
Catoptrophorus semipalmatus (Gmelin)

STATUS: Represented in MCZ, BMS, and Chicago collections (both subspecies). Two populations involved which are separable as subspecies and which are ordinarily distinguishable in the field.

1) *C. s. semipalmatus,* Eastern.

SPRING: Uncommon transient.

Earliest arrival date: March 19, 1959, at Chatham (Wellman).

Average migration period: April 18–May 30.

Peak: April 26–May 26; average 2–5 birds, maximum 22 on May 21, 1933, at Chatham (Griscom).

Latest transient date: Probably June 15, 1888, at Monomoy (Cahoon).

SUMMER: Very rare straggler, not known to nest in recent years.

FALL: Rare migrant.

Earliest arrival date: July 3, 1945, at North Chatham (Griscom).

Average migration period: July 20–September 5; scattered single birds.

Latest departure date: October 29, 1877, at Orleans (collector unknown, in BMS).

HISTORY: Originally breeding abundantly all along coast but rapidly extirpated, remained at Monomoy to about 1875 (Brewster). Then very rare until afforded protection and slowly increasing to present, but not yet re-established as a breeding species. The fact that it is much more common spring than fall lends credence to the theory that birds from Nova Scotia go south in fall by an oceanic route.

2) *C. s. inornatus,* Western.

SPRING: Accidental; collected April 21, 1937, at Monomoy (Smith, in BMS); also one sight record.

FALL: Uncommon to rare migrant.

Earliest arrival date: July 1, 1953, at Nauset (Earle).

Average migration period: July 25–September 30.

Peak: Small peak July 25–August 5, average 3–5 birds, and larger peak August 25–September 17, average 5–12 birds, maximum 57 at Nauset on September 12, 1936 (Griscom).

Latest departure date: November 9, 1941, at Nauset (Griscom & Hill).

HISTORY: Subspecies not separated until 1912; occurs in small numbers each year with marked flights recorded on Cape Cod in 1936, 1939, 1940, 1944, 1949, and 1950. Definitely fewer records since 1950.

DISTRIBUTION (both subspecies): Salt marsh pools, sand and mud flats, occasionally beaches. Eastern subspecies tends to remain more in marshes. Recorded over entire Cape, but concentrates at Monomoy and Nauset.

* *

GREATER YELLOWLEGS
Totanus melanoleucus (Gmelin)

STATUS: Represented in MCZ, BMS, and Chicago collections.

SPRING: Uncommon migrant.

Earliest arrival date: March 19, 1938, at Monomoy (Smith).

Average migration period: April 8–June 1.

Peak: May 1–25; average 5–15 birds, occasionally to 30.

Latest transient date: Uncertain, probably about June 5.

SUMMER: Rare non-breeding straggler.

FALL: Fairly common migrant.

Earliest transient date: Uncertain, probably about July 4.

Average migration period: July 10–November 10.

Peak: Early peak poorly marked and occasionally lacking, August 1–8, average 30–70 birds, maximum 100 on August 4, 1951, at Monomoy (Griscom, Smart, Cottrell, Snyder); more regularly a peak August 25–September 10, average 75–200 birds, maximum 400 on September 5, 1939, at Nauset (Hill). Occasionally a marked very late flight as 700 on October 24, 1940, at Nauset (Benchley).

WINTER: Very rarely and irregularly remains to early winter, e.g., January 19, 1941, at Monomoy (Cottrell); survival never proven.

DISTRIBUTION: Primarily in marsh pools and mud flats, numbers partially dependent on mowing of meadows. Occurs in suitable habitat over entire Cape with greatest concentrations in larger marshes as at Barnstable and Nauset. Has been observed crossing Cape at West Barnstable (Cobb) and along Canal (Hill).

HISTORY: Decreased from abundant to common with shooting (Forbush, 1912). Cahoon (1888) reported only 30 as largest flock; increase began about 1906, reached present levels by 1935, and has remained essentially constant since. Pattern of migration has changed in that both Cahoon and Forbush reported it more common in spring than in fall, whereas the reverse is true now. Lingering into January began about 1931.

* *

LESSER YELLOWLEGS
Totanus flavipes (Gmelin)

STATUS: Represented in MCZ, BMS, Chicago, and British Museum collections.

SPRING: Rare and irregular; extreme dates meaningless. Occasionally in numbers after a southern storm as in April 1921 (Forbush, 1925).

Average migration period: April 28–May 28; average 1–4 birds, often not recorded.

SUMMER: Very rare and irregular non-breeding straggler.

FALL: Uncommon to rare migrant.

Earliest transient date: Uncertain, probably about July 4.

Average migration period: July 12–November 1.

Peak: July 26–August 18, variable in time of arrival and in numbers, from absent to maximum of 200+ on August 15, 1921, at Barnstable (Cobb); second peak may develop in early September to maximum of 250 on September 2, 1940 (Griscom). Occasionally almost complete failure of flights.

WINTER: Very rarely and irregularly remains into early winter, January 12, 1937, at Nauset (Hagar, in BMS).

DISTRIBUTION: As with the Greater Yellowlegs, this species appears in marsh pools and mud flats, rarely on outer beaches, more dependent than larger species on mowing of meadows. Greatest numbers at Barnstable and Nauset, smaller numbers elsewhere in proper habitat.

HISTORY: Formerly ranking with Golden Plover and Knot in abundance, diminished by gunning (Forbush, 1912), but never to critical levels, so increased rapidly with protection, though not to original numbers. The decrease since 1942 is believed due to failure to mow the meadows and thus produce the proper habitat. Tendency to remain later than October 1 has developed since 1930.

*   *

KNOT
Calidris canutus (Linnaeus)

STATUS: Represented in MCZ, BMS, and Chicago collections.

SPRING: Common migrant.

Earliest arrival date: May 3, 1945, at Nauset (Griscom).

Average migration period: May 10–June 2.

Peak: Usually May 20–30; average 50–200 but maximum of 5000+ on June 5, 1953, at Monomoy (Morgan).

SUMMER: Uncommon non-breeding straggler.

FALL: Common migrant.

Average migration period: July 10–November 10.

Peak: July 22–August 10, with second rise from mid-September into early October; average 100–800, see below for maxima.

Latest transient date: Uncertain, probably about November 18.

WINTER: Irregular in small flocks, occasionally surviving.

DISTRIBUTION: Usually on sand flats and beaches, prefers extensive areas, so greatest concentrations are at Nauset, Monomoy, Wellfleet, Barnstable, and Provincetown. In general less common on inner coast, but if flats are destroyed flocks move elsewhere, as in 1959 when there were ten times as many at Scituate as on Cape Cod. Local on south side of Cape, has been observed crossing along Canal.

HISTORY: One of the most abundant of the shore birds until 1850. Twenty-five thousand seen (not shot) at Billingsgate and many killed, often by "fire-lighting," rapid decrease so same observer at same place saw only 100/year by 1890 (Barrett, see Mackay, *Auk*, *10*, 30, 1893). Similarly, a 75 percent decrease at Chatham (Eldredge), a 95 percent decrease at North Eastham (Swan), and none left at North Truro (Small) during same period (see Forbush, 1912). Decrease halted with prohibition of spring shooting; very slow increase with complete protection and now accelerating, cf. maximum summer counts of 300 in 1929, 1000 in 1937, 1500 in 1941, followed by apparent decrease for eight years, then 2400 in 1951, 5000 in 1954. Wintering since 1879 (Mackay, l.c.).

* *

PURPLE SANDPIPER

Erolia maritima (Brünnich)

STATUS: Represented in MCZ collection.

WINTER: Rare and local visitant, no evidence of transients.

Earliest arrival date: September 8, 1877 (Jeffries, see Brewer, *Bull. Boston Soc. Nat. Hist.*, 1878, page 306).

Average period: November 15–March 15.

Latest departure date: May 18, 1955, at Woods Hole (Fordyce).

DISTRIBUTION: Normally occurs on rocky coasts and is casual on sand beaches. Found in boulder-strewn areas on north side of Cape and along Buzzards Bay to Woods Hole; also on breakwaters there and elsewhere.

HISTORY: Original numbers not known; reported as "irregular" in 1888 (Cahoon). With the recent increase on the New England coast it is appearing more frequently and now perhaps regularly on breakwaters and boulders around east end of Canal and along Buzzards Bay.

* *

PECTORAL SANDPIPER
Erolia melanotos (Vieillot)

STATUS: Represented in MCZ, BMS, Chicago, and British Museum collections.

SPRING: Very rare and irregular.

Specimens: Total of six, taken from March 20, 1888, to April 30, 1889, all from Monomoy (Cahoon).

Recent sight records extend latest date to May 29, 1960, at Chatham (Gardler).

FALL: Uncommon migrant, somewhat irregular in numbers.

Earliest arrival date: July 16, 1934, at North Eastham (Low).

Average migration period: July 24–October 24.

Peak: Rarely a peak in early August, maximum of 40 on August 3, 1935, at Monomoy (Griscom); more often a peak September 16–October 16, occasionally to 20, maximum 75 on September 22, 1936, at Nauset (Griscom).

Latest departure date: November 13, 1883, at Osterville (Townsend, in BMS).

DISTRIBUTION: Muddy pools and grassy meadows; like Lesser Yellowlegs, favorable habitat depends on mowing of meadows. Occurs where conditions are right at any marsh over entire Cape but probably less common eastward given equal conditions, Barnstable being known as best area in past.

HISTORY: Formerly abundant but always local due to habitat requirements, decreasing from 1870 on (Forbush, 1912). Little evidence of increase since protection (Cobb); this may be real or may merely reflect changed environment so birds simply move through and fail to congregate. Apparent decrease since 1940

certainly due to decreased mowing, recent local increase at
Monomoy Point due to special management.

* *

WHITE-RUMPED SANDPIPER
Erolia fuscicollis (Vieillot)

STATUS: Represented in MCZ, BMS, Chicago, and British
Museum collections.

SPRING: Rather uncommon migrant.

Earliest arrival date: May 21, 1933, at Monomoy (Griscom).

Average migration period: May 24–June 2; average 1–5 birds,
maximum 32 on June 3, 1941, at Chatham (Hill).

SUMMER: Rare and irregular non-breeding straggler.

FALL: Uncommon to fairly common migrant.

Earliest transient date: Uncertain, probably about July 11.

Average migration period: July 28–November 1; average 5–25
birds, occasional marked flights but dates not consistent, e.g.,
235 on September 9, 1942 (Mason), and 75 on September
30, 1950 (Griscom), both at Monomoy.

Latest departure date: December 11, 1935, at Monomoy (Hagar,
Auk, 54, 389, 1937).

DISTRIBUTION: Feeds on marsh flats, roosts on sand beaches. No
critical habitat requirements. Found over entire Cape.

HISTORY: Original status uncertain, decreased in period of un-
limited shooting (Forbush, 1912), but has now increased again.
No significant change in numbers between 1940 and 1960.

* *

BAIRD'S SANDPIPER
Erolia bairdii (Coues)

STATUS: Represented in BMS collection.

FALL: One of the rarest and probably *the* most misidentified shore
bird on the Cape.

Specimens: Total of six, five taken from August 24, 1896, at

Chatham (Paine) to September 14, 1908, at Eastham (Cobb, in BMS), and one on the later date of October 18, 1910, at Monomoy (Jump, *Auk*, *28*, 110, 1911).

Sight records (stringently screened):

Earliest arrival date: July 16, 1938, at Monomoy (Griscom, Garrison).

Average migration period: August 20–September 20; almost always single birds.

Latest departure date: October 30, 1948, at Eastham (Meade).

DISTRIBUTION: Prefers grassy brackish pools with muddy margins in marshes. Recorded over entire Cape.

HISTORY: No significant data. Apparently overlooked in the past and no detectable change from 1935 to 1961.

* *

LEAST SANDPIPER
Erolia minutilla (Vieillot)

STATUS: Represented in MCZ, BMS, Chicago, and British Museum collections.

SPRING: Fairly common migrant.

Earliest arrival date: May 6, 1868, at Orleans (Allen, in MCZ).

Average migration period: May 10–May 30.

Peak: May 20–25; average 50–200 birds, maximum 700 on May 21, 1943, at Monomoy (Griscom, Hill, Bishop).

SUMMER: Very rare non-breeding straggler.

FALL: Common migrant.

Earliest transient date: Uncertain, probably as early as June 28.

Average migration period: July 4–October 1.

Peak: July 13–30; average 100–300 birds, maximum 1000 on both July 13, 1952, and July 29, 1953, at Monomoy (Griscom).

Latest departure date: November 1, 1954, at Nauset (Kleber, in BMS).

DISTRIBUTION: Normally in marshes and meadows so in greatest numbers at Nauset, Monomoy, Barnstable, Dennis, etc., and in smaller numbers in smaller marshes elsewhere throughout the Cape.

HISTORY: Formerly abundant as never shot for game until supply of larger species diminished, then pursued and began to decline. Never seriously diminished, has shown slight increase in past twenty-five years.

* *

CURLEW SANDPIPER
Erolia ferruginea (Pontoppidan)

STATUS: Represented in BMS collection.
Very rare vagrant from the Old World.
SPECIMENS: Two extant and in BMS, May 10, 1878, exact locality on Cape not known (Deane, *Bull. Nuttall Ornith. Club*, 4, 124, 1879), and August 4, 1940, at Monomoy (Griscom, *Auk*, 58, 95, 1941); also collected July 1892 at Chatham (Rogers, see *Shooting and Fishing*, 12, 345) and August 26, 1889, at Chatham (formerly in Plummer collection).
SIGHT RECORDS (stringently screened):
Spring: May 29, 1949, at Chatham (Griscom, Eliot, Crain, Morgan, Mason, Elkins).
Fall: Total of five records from August 21, 1955, at Monomoy (Griscom) to October 31, 1948, at Nauset (Meade).

* *

DUNLIN
Erolia alpina (Linnaeus)

STATUS: Represented in MCZ, BMS, Chicago, and British Museum collections.
SPRING: Common migrant.
Average migration period: April 1–June 6.
Peaks: April 12–May 5, probably regrouping of birds wintering

on Cape and relatively nearby; average 200–400 birds, maximum 1600 on May 3, 1945, at Nauset (Griscom); also May 26–June 1, a different population in high breeding plumage, counts extremely variable, average 2–50, maximum 500 on May 28, 1941, at Monomoy (Snyder).

SUMMER: Uncommon non-breeding straggler.

FALL: Abundant migrant.

Earliest transient date: Uncertain, probably about August 23.

Average migration period: September 15–December 1.

Peak: October 15–November 20; average 500–1500 birds, see below for maxima.

WINTER: Recently regular, see below for counts, moderately successful except in most severe seasons.

DISTRIBUTION: On rather extensive sand and mud flats, found over entire Cape. Highest counts at Brewster, Nauset, Monomoy, Barnstable, and Wellfleet. Irregular numbers in the later spring flight presumably due to flocks leaving the Atlantic Coast south of New England for the Northwest, cf. Whimbrel.

HISTORY: Formerly abundant, reduced after 1890 to occasional flocks (Forbush, 1912), fairly rapid recovery with protection. Fall concentrations and particularly wintering flocks have shown a continuous increase in past twenty-five years, this antedating the cycle of mild winters. Maximum fall migratory counts are 1700 in 1937, 2000 in 1941, 3000 in 1945, 5500 in 1949, and stable since. Christmas Count figures reflect the milder seasons and show in 1930's a maximum of 414 and missed on three years, in 1950's a maximum of 1800 and never missed.

SUBSPECIES: Small, short-billed Dunlin, not assignable to *E. a. sakhalina*, have been collected from time to time. Though several specimens cannot be assigned to a particular subspecies, the following have been recorded (Griscom, *Auk*, 54, 70, 1937): *E. a. arctica* on August 11, 1900, at Monomoy (Cochrane, in BMS), and *E. a. alpina* on August 8–16, 1936, at Monomoy (Griscom, in BMS).

*   *

SHORT-BILLED DOWITCHER
Limnodromus griseus (Gmelin)

STATUS: Represented in MCZ, BMS, Chicago, and British Museum collections.

SPRING: Common migrant, occasionally rare.

Earliest arrival date: May 1, 1888 (Cahoon).

Average migration period: May 10–June 1.

Peak: May 20–25; average 200 birds, maximum 400 on May 21, 1943, at Monomoy (Griscom, Hill, Bishop). Flight may fail entirely.

SUMMER: Rather uncommon non-breeding straggler.

FALL: Abundant migrant.

Earliest arrival date: Uncertain, probably about July 2.

Average migration period: July 8–September 25.

Peak: July 20–August 3; see below for counts.

Latest departure date: Uncertain due to confusion with next species, certainly to October 14, 1895, at Orleans (Lamb, in MCZ).

DISTRIBUTION: Feeds on extensive muddy flats and inner beaches; largest counts at Monomoy, Nauset, Wellfleet, and Barnstable, smaller numbers over entire Cape. In spring numbers variable as flocks may leave Atlantic coast for northwest south of New England, cf. Whimbrel and Dunlin. In fall flocks strike coast further north and move southward.

HISTORY: Abundant to about 1860, then 75+per cent decrease by 1900 and slower further decrease to 1912. Bags of 100+ in 1870, of 18 by 1908, and only three seen in 1909 (Forbush, 1912). Slow increase at first with protection, more rapid recently, e.g., maximum counts at Monomoy of 1000 in 1937, 1700 in 1947, 5000 in 1953, and 6000 in 1958. Counts lower, but increases essentially parallel in other locations.

SUBSPECIES: See Griscom & Snyder (1955) for discussion. The separation of the two species, *griseus* vs. *scolopaceus*, presents problems with specimens in the hand, so separation of sub-species of *griseus* in the field is obviously unconfirmable.

* *

LONG-BILLED DOWITCHER
Limnodromus scolopaceus (Say)

STATUS: Represented in MCZ and BMS collections.

FALL: Rare migrant, details of occurrence poorly known due to confusion with previous species, particularly counts and early dates.

> Specimens: Total of five, taken from August 29, 1888, at Monomoy (Cahoon, in MCZ) to November 2, 1878, at East-ham (Tileston, in BMS). Unconfirmed sight records earlier than above and satisfactory sight record to November 22, 1953, at Nauset (Griscom, Emery, Beattie). All counts meaningless.

* *

STILT SANDPIPER
Micropalama himantopus (Bonaparte)

STATUS: Represented in MCZ, BMS, Chicago, and British Museum collections.

SPRING:No spring specimens; one sight record of adult on May 26, 1951, at Monomoy (Griscom, Eliot, Ross, Garrison).

FALL: Uncommon to rare migrant, occasionally absent.

> Earliest arrival date: July 5, 1885, at Monomoy (Carpenter, in MCZ).

> Average migration period: July 18–September 10.

> Peak: August 10–20; average 3–8 birds, maximum 30 on August 14, 1943, at Monomoy (Griscom); flight may fail in any given year.

> Latest departure date: September 20, 1903, at Chatham (Brooks, *Auk*, 24, 437, 1907).

DISTRIBUTION: Found in salt marshes and pools, less on beaches, often in company of Yellowlegs. Greatest numbers at Barnstable, Monomoy, Nauset, and Orleans, but has been collected north to Wellfleet and west to Sandwich and Sagamore. Apparently rare on south side of Cape.

HISTORY: No early data as bird was overlooked in New England until 1868. Presumed to have decreased with the other species (Forbush, 1912), but 103 were shot in 1901 at Chatham. Since 1935 numbers have been much lower than this; this may be a habitat factor as with Lesser Yellowlegs and Pectoral Sandpiper.

* *

SEMIPALMATED SANDPIPER
Ereunetes pusillus (Linnaeus)

STATUS: Represented in MCZ, BMS, Chicago, and British Museum collections.

SPRING: Abundant migrant.
Earliest arrival date: April 18, 1952, at Osterville (Johnson).
Average migration period: May 5–June 2.
Peak: May 25–30; average 5000–12,000 birds, maximum 25,000 on May 30, 1937, at Monomoy (Griscom).

SUMMER: Uncommon non-breeding straggler.

FALL: Abundant migrant.
Average migration period: July 6–October 20.
Peak: July 22–August 18; average 2000–5000 birds, maximum 11,000 on August 5, 1941 (Hill); no clear-cut second peak.

WINTER: Casual through December and early January to February 4, 1939, at Nauset (Benchley). No proven survival for entire season.

DISTRIBUTION: Sand and mud flats along bays and marshes, less on outer beaches. Occurs in numbers over entire Cape with highest counts at Monomoy, Nauset, Wellfleet, Barnstable, and Provincetown and smaller counts elsewhere.

HISTORY: There is some discrepancy in reports of former numbers; said to have been "abundant" (Forbush, 1912) but in flocks not as "many as 1000" by 1860 (Griscom & Snyder, 1955). If this figure applies to the Cape, this species was markedly decreased earlier than others of its size and prior to heavy market gunning of small birds. Never seriously diminished, however, and recovered rapidly with protection. Numbers essentially stable for past twenty-five years, so complete recovery has apparently been accomplished.

* *

WESTERN SANDPIPER

Ereunetes mauri Cabanis

STATUS: Represented in BMS and Chicago collections.

SPRING: No specimens, but reported as very rare and irregular migrant from May 24 to 30.

FALL: Uncommon to rare migrant.

Earliest transient date: July 4, 1943, at Monomoy (Griscom, Maclay).

Average migration period: July 20–October 10.

Peak: Rarely a peak August 1–10, more regularly September 1–15; average 2–10 birds, maximum 50+ on September 2, 1945, at Nauset (Griscom, Cottrell).

Latest departure date: November 12, 1954, at Nauset (Kleber, in BMS).

DISTRIBUTION: Occurs with Semipalmated Sandpipers on mud and sand flats and in marsh pools. Recorded over entire Cape.

HISTORY: Not separable from Semipalmated Sandpiper with sufficient accuracy to detect any significant change in counts.

* *

BUFF-BREASTED SANDPIPER
Tryngites subruficollis (Vieillot)

STATUS: Represented in MCZ, BMS, and Chicago collections.
FALL: Very rare and irregular migrant.
> Earliest arrival date: August 12, 1959, at Monomoy (Freeland).
> Average migration period: August 24–September 10; mostly single birds, rarely two.
> Latest departure date: October 3, 1878, from "Cape Cod" (collector unknown, in MCZ).

DISTRIBUTION: Found typically in mowed meadows and marshes, also around brackish pools. A few said to accompany the September flight of the Pectoral Sandpiper (Fay, *Auk*, 27, 219, 1910). So rare that distribution of reports reflects only distribution of gunners in the past and of observers at present.
HISTORY: Occurred annually in small numbers to about 1900, then essentially unreported until 1937. Very irregularly since then, but with increasing frequency.

*   *

MARBLED GODWIT
Limosa fedoa (Linnaeus)

STATUS: Represented in MCZ, BMS, and Chicago collections.
SPRING: Single record, one shot May 19, 1885, at Chatham (Whitcomb).
FALL: Rare but regular migrant.
> Earliest arrival date: July 12, 1959, at Chatham (Maclay).
> Average migration period: July 25–November 5.
> Peak: Maximum numbers in September but no real peak; average 1–4 birds, maximum 8 on September 23, 1950, at Monomoy (Griscom, Meade, Parker).
> Latest departure date: December 17, 1935, at Nauset (Richardson).

DISTRIBUTION: Prefers extensive mud and sand flats so essentially confined to a few favorable areas such as Monomoy, Nauset, etc., but collected north to Wellfleet and west to Sandwich.

HISTORY: Formerly common migrant spring and fall; rapidly reduced by both shooting and loss of western breeding grounds to agriculture, becoming very rare by 1880 (Forbush, 1912). Began to show increase between 1930 and 1940 and now regular, occurring earlier in the summer since 1955.

* *

BAR-TAILED GODWIT
Limosa lapponica (Linnaeus)

STATUS: Represented in MCZ and BMS collections.
Accidental vagrant from the Old World.

SPECIMENS: September 14 or 15, 1907, from "Cape Cod" (Boston Market specimen, in MCZ) and July 26, 1937, at Nauset (Peters & Hagar, in BMS, *Auk, 54,* 537, 1937). At least one additional unconfirmed sight record.

* *

HUDSONIAN GODWIT
Limosa haemastica (Linnaeus)

STATUS: Represented in MCZ, BMS, Chicago, and British Museum collections.

SPRING: Formerly very rare migrant, April 29–May 25 (Cahoon); now hardly more than casual vagrant with only two recent records, May 31, 1954 (Hill), and June 3, 1953 (Morgan), both at Monomoy.

FALL: Uncommon to rare migrant.
Earliest arrival date: July 1, 1953, at Nauset (Bigelow).
Average migration period: July 15–November 3.
Peak: August 3–15 for adults arriving in breeding plumage; see

below for counts. Occasionally a flight August 20–September 5, rarely to October 1, associated with a severe easterly storm; see below for counts.

Latest departure date: December 4, 1939, at Monomoy (Walcott & Peabody).

DISTRIBUTION: Midsummer adults concentrate in areas of extensive flats, especially at Monomoy, also Nauset, Brewster, etc. Later flight birds which come in from the sea and which depart before the storm abates concentrate from Eastham to Monomoy, though in great flights it has been collected north to Wellfleet, south to Yarmouthport, and west to Sandwich (Fay, *Auk*, *28*, 257, 1911).

HISTORY: Originally rare in spring (Cahoon, 1888), then absent until 1953. In fall "formerly very common" but "now tolerably common" (Cahoon, 1888) with greatest numbers noted September 25–October 10, later than recent dates. Counts decreased steadily to 1910, then only sporadic reports to 1935, with midsummer adults appearing from 1937 on—2 in 1937, 5 in 1943, 12 in 1950, 52 in 1952, 62 in 1958. The late-August and September flights were always irregular, even when the bird was common, and depended on severe easterly gales; great flights recorded include: 1903 (7 shot on August 29); 1907 (50–75 reported); 1910 (25 shot August to October) (Fay, l.c.); more recently August 30, 1935, with 82 at Nauset (Hagar) and 150+ at Monomoy (Eldredge) with unconfirmed reports of 400–500 at latter locality (Hagar, *Auk*, *53*, 330, 1936).

* *

RUFF

Philomachus pugnax (Linnaeus)

STATUS: Represented in Peabody Museum collection.
Accidental vagrant from the Old World.

FALL: Discrepancy in published dates of specimen, the label reads

September 15, 1890 (*fide* Snyder), at Chatham (Churchill, to Plummer collection to Peabody Museum). Sight records are September 3, 1954, at Nauset (Griscom, Maclay); September 4, 1954, at Provincetown (Gammell); September 6–9, 1955, at Nauset (Mason) and in July 1964, at Monomoy (Harrington, Forster).

* *

SANDERLING
Crocethia alba (Pallas)

STATUS: Represented in MCZ, BMS, Chicago, and British Museum collections.

SPRING: Abundant migrant.

Average migration period: May 15–June 6.

Peak: May 25–June 1; average 5000–20,000 birds, maximum 27,000 on May 30, 1952, at Monomoy (Griscom, Ross, Emery, Smart, Snyder).

SUMMER: Fairly common non-breeding straggler.

FALL: Abundant migrant.

Average migration period: July 15–November 10.

Peak: July 22–August 12; average 500–3000 birds, maximum 10,000 on July 22, 1954, at Monomoy (Griscom, Tramontano); poorly marked peak of immatures in late September and early October.

WINTER: Regular though uncommon resident, usually successful.

DISTRIBUTION: The most characteristic bird of the outer beaches, flocking and feeding at the edge of the surf and roosting on higher sand, seldom on mud. Appears over entire Cape in flocks directly proportional to the extent of the sand beaches and inversely proportional to disturbance by humans.

HISTORY: Recorded as abundant from colonial days and maintained numbers to about 1870, then decreased moderately, though probably less on the Cape than elsewhere; began to increase about 1908 (Forbush, 1912). Counts fairly stable from 1929 to 1943, then the midsummer adult flight began to increase, e.g., 2000–2500 in 1929–1941, 5000 in 1946, 8000 in 1952, 10,000 in 1953. Early-winter Christmas Count figures markedly increased since 1950 with cycle of mild seasons.

* *

AMERICAN AVOCET

Recurvirostra americana Gmelin

STATUS: Represented in BMS collection.
Accidental vagrant from the West.
SPECIMEN: September 11, 1935, at Sagamore (Griscom, in BMS, see Hagar, *Auk*, 53, 330, 1936).
SIGHT RECORD: One bird in late summer and early fall of 1960 at Nauset and Wellfleet (Bailey).

* *

RED PHALAROPE

Phalaropus fulicarius (Linnaeus)

STATUS: Represented in MCZ, BMS, Chicago, and British Museum collections.
SPRING: Rare to occasionally common migrant.
Earliest transient date: April 8, 1930, at Chatham (Eldredge).
Average migration period: April 15–May 30.
Peak: Not confined as to date but dependent on easterly storm; great flights include 1000 on April 19, 1938, at Monomoy (Griscom, Tousey, Bishop, see Griscom, *Auk*, 56, 185, 1939); 2000+ on May 23, 1892, at Provincetown and more south to Chatham (Mackay, *Auk*, 9, 296, 1892, and Miller, *ibid.*, 298); 1000 and 500 on May 26, 1940, at Provincetown (Allen) and Monomoy (Hill, Davis, Watson, Nash, Drury) respectively.

Latest transient date: June 2, 1892, at North Truro (Miller, in MCZ).

FALL: Rare to uncommon migrant, sight records carefully screened.

Earliest transient date: July 24, 1891, off Chatham (Greenwood, collected).

Average migration period: August 15–December 1.

Peak: Poorly marked inshore peaks from late September to mid-November (Griscom, l.c.); maximum 300 on November 16, 1959, at Wellfleet (Bailey).

Latest transient date: Uncertain, probably about December 15.

WINTER: Probably rare and irregular straggler but increasing recently, 150+ on December 11, 1954, at Barnstable Harbor (Romaine) and specimen taken on January 2, 1961, at North Beach (C.C.). There are additional reports of unidentified winter phalaropes.

DISTRIBUTION: Much the most pelagic of the phalaropes and seldom seen from shore; most inshore records are from Provincetown to Monomoy. Rare west to Falmouth (Jones, collected May 8, 1937), Woods Hole, and into Buzzards Bay in spring but not fall; occasionally in Cape Cod Bay in fall but very rare in spring.

HISTORY: No evidence of any change in numbers, but an increased tendency to linger into late fall and winter.

*   *

WILSON'S PHALAROPE

Steganopus tricolor Vieillot

STATUS: Banded at Austin Station.

FALL: Rare but probably regular migrant.

Earliest arrival date: August 4, 1940, at Monomoy (Griscom).

Average period: August 15–September 6; occurs singly.

Latest departure date: October 5, 1935, banded at North Eastham (Austin Station).

DISTRIBUTION: Marsh pools with grass margins, occasionally salt creeks. Recorded only from Monomoy north to Wellfleet.

HISTORY: Not recorded until 1935, increased reports since due to increased recognition as 1–4 are reported annually.

* *

NORTHERN PHALAROPE
Lobipes lobatus (Linnaeus)

STATUS: Represented in MCZ, BMS, Chicago, and British Museum collections.

SPRING: Rare migrant.

Earliest arrival date: April 14, 1940, at Monomoy (Curtis).

Average migration period: May 1–27.

Peak: May 20–25; average 10–40 birds, no great flights; species has made up only 5 to 6 per cent of total in the phalarope flights of 1892 and 1940.

Latest departure date: June 1, 1943, at Orleans (Hill).

FALL: Uncommon migrant.

Earliest arrival date: July 24, 1938, off Chatham (Griscom, Curtis, Garrison, Scott).

Average migration period: August 1–October 12.

Peak: August 20–September 15; average 20–500 in inshore waters, maximum 1000+ and 400 on September 7, 1953, in easterly gale at Nauset (Snyder) and Monomoy (Griscom) respectively.

Latest transient date: November 11, 1940, off Chatham (Poor, in BMS). Later dates unconfirmed as to species involved.

DISTRIBUTION: Less pelagic than Red Phalarope, considerable numbers in inshore waters and thus more often seen from land. Spring records mostly from Chatham to Provincetown. In fall, in addition, considerable numbers collect off Provincetown and enter Cape Cod Bay, being recorded frequently to Sagamore and Barnstable; also small numbers in Nantucket Sound to Hyannis and rarely to Buzzards Bay (September 15, 1883, Austin, in MCZ).

HISTORY: No evidence of any change in numbers.

* *

POMARINE JAEGER

Stercorarius pomarinus (Temminck)

STATUS: Represented in MCZ, BMS, Chicago, and British Museum collections. Sight records of jaegers are often unconfirmable as to species.

SPRING: No specimens; apparently a rare migrant and poorly known, particularly early in the season.

Average migration period: May 26–June 18; only singles and pairs.

SUMMER: Rare scattered non-breeding birds at sea.

FALL: Rather uncommon migrant.

Average migration period: July 29–September 30.

Peak: August 25–September 17; average 3–5 birds, maximum 10 on September 10, 1934, off Monomoy (Griscom), flight years not well marked.

Latest transient date: November 13, 1884, at Provincetown (Miller, in British Museum). Unidentified jaegers have been seen later in fall; no satisfactory winter records, though reported as "occasional in small numbers" (Collins, *Auk*, *1*, 236, 1884).

DISTRIBUTION: Seen regularly from outer shores but more pelagic than Parasitic Jaeger. Records are nearly all from easternmost areas—Stellwagon Bank and Provincetown south to Monomoy and its shoals; rare in Cape Cod Bay where collected September 14, 1908, at Barnstable (Jones, in BMS), no Nantucket Sound records except in the immediate vicinity of Monomoy, but penetrated Buzzards Bay in fall of 1886 (Baird, *Auk*, *4*, 71, 1887).

HISTORY: Reported as abundant offshore in 1882 (Job) and 1886

(Bangs); also twice as many Pomarine as Parasitic collected 1888–1891 at Provincetown (Miller, in British Museum). By no means abundant now and averages about a quarter as many as Parasitic; no data indicates any change in numbers since 1935, however.

*   *

PARASITIC JAEGER
Stercorarius parasiticus (Linnaeus)

STATUS: Represented in MCZ, BMS, Chicago, and British Museum collections.

SPRING: Uncommon migrant.

Earliest transient date: May 6, 1875, at Monomoy (Brewster).

Average migration period: May 23–June 1; usually in pairs, occasionally in flocks to seven.

SUMMER: Rare scattered non-breeding birds at sea.

FALL: Fairly common migrant.

Average migration period: July 28–September 30.

Peak: August 23–September 18; in average years up to about twenty per day either from shore or boat; in flight years up to forty per day, maximum 80 on August 21, 1954, at sea off Chatham (Griscom, Earle, Parker, Bowen, Morgan, Kleber).

Latest transient date: October 8, 1883, off Chatham (Bangs, in BMS); sight records attributed to this species to December 28, 1941, at Wellfleet (Brown).

DISTRIBUTION: Pelagic but enters inshore waters much more than other two species of jaeger. Most frequent from Stellwagon Bank and Provincetown to Monomoy and its shoals, but regular in small numbers in Cape Cod Bay to Sagamore, Barnstable, and Eastham; also Nantucket Sound west to and into Buzzards Bay. At sea all species of jaeger will come to a boat to look it over and will work over an oil slick; appearance of large numbers depends on proper "bait" in the water to attract and hold the terns on which the jaegers depend.

HISTORY: Old accounts of 1880–1890 suggest numbers approximately equal to present counts, i.e., no significant change can be proven. Flight years follow no set pattern; 1937, 1941, 1953, and 1954 have been notable flight years.

*   *

LONG-TAILED JAEGER
Stercorarius longicaudus Vieillot

STATUS: Represented in BMS collection.
SPRING: Very rare migrant.
Average migration period: May 27–30; single birds only.
FALL: Rare transient, often overlooked or misidentified.
Earliest transient date: July 12, 1953, off Chatham (Griscom).
Average migration period: August 10–September 15; usually 1–2 birds, maximum 6 on September 21, 1941, at Monomoy (Griscom).
Latest transient date: September 25, 1955, at Nauset (Griscom).
DISTRIBUTION: Much the most pelagic of the jaegers, rarest in inshore waters, but apparently more common far offshore. Records are exclusively from Provincetown south to Monomoy with greatest numbers between Nauset and Monomoy.
HISTORY: No data.

*   *

SKUA
Catharacta skua Brünnich

STATUS: Represented in BMS and Kansas State collections.
Rare but probably regular far offshore, a vagrant only in inshore waters. Reported thus far only in fall.
SPECIMENS: Two on August 11, 1957 (Kleber, in BMS), and one on September 10, 1884 (Goss, in Kansas, see *Auk*, *1*, 395, 1884), all off Chatham.
SIGHT RECORDS: August 2, 1958, at Stellwagon Bank (Bailey);

September 17–18, 1960, at Orleans (Mazzeo); October 24, 1949, at Nauset (Hill). Far offshore recorded at all seasons, most common in fall (Collins, *Auk*, *1*, 236, 1884) and more recently from July 10, 1955 (Grayce), to December 10, 1955 (Morgan).

SUBSPECIES: Specimen collected September 10, 1884, tentatively referred to *C. s. antarctica*, see Griscom & Snyder, 1955; other specimens are *C. s. skua*.

*   *

GLAUCOUS GULL
Larus hyperboreus Gunnerus

STATUS: Represented in MCZ collection.

WINTER: Rare and often irregular visitant.
Earliest arrival date: October 12, 1934, at Provincetown (Low).
Average period: November 18–April 19.
Counts: Usually single birds, maximum 5 on December 26, 1916, at Provincetown (Peters, Hagar, Brainerd, Kittridge).

SUMMER: Irregular stragglers through June and July, latest August 3, 1945, at Chatham (Griscom), apparently never persisting throughout the entire season.

DISTRIBUTION: Most often where fishing vessels unload, particularly Provincetown and Chatham, less frequently elsewhere; appears with gatherings of other species of gulls. Much less frequent than north of Boston.

HISTORY: Formerly not uncommon, particularly at Provincetown, but steadily declining as fishing industry declined.

*   *

ICELAND GULL
Larus glaucoides Meyer

STATUS: Represented in MCZ collection.

WINTER: Rare and often irregular visitant.
Earliest arrival date: December 1, 1946, at Monomoy (Griscom).

Average period: December 15–April 19; almost invariably single birds.

SUMMER: Irregular straggler, may remain entire season.

DISTRIBUTION: As with Glaucous Gull, this species concentrates in harbors where fishing fleets come in, but scattered individuals have occurred more widely than is the case with that species.

HISTORY: Formerly fewer than Glaucous Gull as elsewhere in Massachusetts, but on the Cape it has not increased as the larger bird decreased, having in fact decreased also. Less frequent than north of Boston.

SUBSPECIES: Kumlien's Gull (*L. g. kumlieni*) has been recorded in very small numbers, mostly December to February, but occasionally throughout the year.

* *

GREAT BLACK-BACKED GULL
Larus marinus Linnaeus

STATUS: Represented in MCZ, BMS, Chicago, and British Museum collections.

SPRING: Fairly common migrant.

Average migration period: March 20–May 1, poorly defined.

Counts: Average 300–600 birds.

SUMMER: Breeding in small groups mostly on islands since about 1955 and increasingly common in non-breeding flocks; see below for counts.

FALL: Common migrant.

Average migration period: August 5–November 20.

Peak: September 1–30; 800+ migrating at rate of 120/hour on September 6, 1958, at Sagamore, mostly crossing Cape at Canal (Hill), and 1000 on September 30, 1950, at Nauset (Griscom, Baird, Bailey, Emery).

WINTER: Common resident, see below for counts and distribution.

DISTRIBUTION: Chiefly on beaches and around harbors with fishing industry, but also on ponds; found over entire Cape at all seasons. Generally maintains proportion of 1 to 8 with Herring Gull, but in winter this species may concentrate around Provincetown and occasionally outnumber that species 4 to 1.

HISTORY: Original numbers unknown; vague references suggest rapid diminution shortly after settlement. Shot frequently for food until about 1860. Protection became effective about 1915. Forbush (1925) reported this species as "locally common in winter" and a "few individuals" in summer with up to 100 in migration. Summer increase on Cape may be summarized as follows: none in 1929, 15 in 1932, 100 in 1938, 250 in 1944, 700 in 1947, and averaging 1000–2000 from 1951 to 1960 with maximum of 5000 on August 8, 1950, at Provincetown (Elkins). Early-winter counts also increased, e.g., maxima in Christmas Counts of 230 in 1930's, 1550 in 1940's, and same in 1950's; counts drop later in the winter.

* *

HERRING GULL

Larus argentatus Pontoppidan

STATUS: Represented in MCZ, BMS, Chicago, and British Museum collections.

SPRING: Abundant migrant.

Average migration period: March 25–May 25, poorly defined.

Counts: Average 1000–3000, maximum 10,000 migrating April 10, 1949, at Chatham and Orleans (Griscom, Parker, Crain).

SUMMER: Breeding in small groups all over Cape seriously disrupting and displacing tern and Laughing Gull colonies; also very common in non-breeding flocks; see below for counts.

FALL: Abundant migrant.

Earliest transient date: Uncertain, probably as early as July 10.

Average migration period: Adults from August 1 and immatures from August 10, both to December 1.

Counts: Average 2000–7000, maximum 15,000 migrating on August 3, 1952, at Monomoy (Griscom, Drury, Bailey).

WINTER: Abundant resident; see below for counts.

DISTRIBUTION: Ubiquitous, from following trawlers at sea to dumps in pine woods and roosting on roofs and chimneys; highest counts along beaches and larger bays and estuaries.

HISTORY: Original status not known in detail, clearly abundant but rapidly reduced. Used for food until about 1860 and began increasing thereafter. Mackay in 1892 (*Auk*, 9, 221, 1892) reported they appeared in early September, occasionally in late August, and departed in early April with a few lingering to June 1 and a few summering in lower Buzzards Bay where nesting began on Weepecket Island in 1888. Forbush (1925) reported further increase. Nesting began at multiple locations 1925–1930. Recent summer increase may be summarized as follows: 100 in 1938, 645 in 1944, 1800 in 1947, 10,000 in 1950, 15,000 in 1956. Winter counts have shown less change, e.g., range in Christmas Counts 1000–10,000 in 1930's and 2000–10,000 in 1950's, maximum 21,487 in 1960.

SUBSPECIES: One specimen approaching *L. a. thayeri* found on February 25, 1940, at Barnstable (Eaton); also several sight records which are not confirmable.

* *

RING-BILLED GULL
Larus delawarensis Ord

STATUS: Represented in MCZ and BMS collections.

SPRING: Uncommon migrant.

Average migration period: March 28–April 25.

Peak: April 3–10; average 30–60 birds, maximum 400 on April 7, 1950 (Griscom, Barry, DeWindt).

Latest transient date: Uncertain, probably about May 30.

SUMMER: Rare non-breeding straggler.

FALL: Common migrant.

Earliest transient date: Uncertain, probably about July 6.

Average migration period: July 18–December 1.

Peak: Variable from year to year, often August 5–September 5 and another September 30–November 1; see below for counts.

Latest transient date: Uncertain, probably about January 5.

WINTER: Uncommon resident; see below for counts.

DISTRIBUTION: Concentrates in bays, estuaries, and protected beaches. Found over entire Cape, increases eastward in winter.

HISTORY: No data on early status as apparently confused with Herring Gull. Increasing steadily since 1935. Fall averages have risen from 10–100 in 1930's to 50–250 in 1950's, maximum 380 on September 3, 1949, at Eastham-Orleans (Griscom). First began wintering about 1900, and averages have risen from 1–5 in 1930's to 20–40 in 1950's.

* *

MEW GULL
Larus canus Linnaeus

STATUS: Represented in MCZ collection.

Accidental vagrant, probably from Old World.

SPECIMEN: February 8, 1908, at Chatham (Eldredge, in MCZ, see Peters, *Auk*, *54*, 205, 1937), this being the Old World subspecies.

SIGHT RECORDS: September 2, 1945, at Nauset (Griscom, Cottrell) and probably the same bird September 4, 1945, at Monomoy (Griscom, Maclay). At least one other record less well observed.

* *

BLACK-HEADED GULL
Larus ridibundus Linnaeus

STATUS: Hypothetical.

Rare and irregular vagrant from Old World.

Sight records only, chiefly in November, but also December, March, and possibly in summer. Some probably correct, but conditions of most observations not completely satisfactory.

* *

LAUGHING GULL
Larus atricilla Linnaeus

STATUS: Represented in MCZ and BMS collections.

SPRING: Common migrant.

Earliest arrival date: March 22, 1958, at Brewster (Gardler).

Average migration period: April 12–June 4.

Peak: May 20–30; average 75–200 birds, maximum 300 on May 25, 1941, at Chatham (Griscom, Scott, Eliot, Cottrell).

SUMMER: Small number of non-breeding residents plus wandering birds from nearby colonies. No known breeding colonies on Cape at present, but has occasionally nested at Monomoy in past.

FALL: Common migrant.

Earliest transient date: Uncertain, probably about July 10.

Average migration period: July 20–October 12.

Peak: July 25–August 15 for adult birds, first young August 8–20; average 100–300 birds, maximum 700 on July 29, 1939, at Monomoy (Griscom, Curtis).

Latest departure date: Uncertain, probably about January 1.

WINTER: Very rare straggler, persisted to February 13, 1955, at Chatham (Mosher) but never proven to have survived the entire season.

DISTRIBUTION: On protected beaches, inlets, etc., occasionally off-shore; inland catching seventeen-year cicadas when a brood hatches.

HISTORY: Local during early historical period increasing greatly after 1900 and extending dates of occurrence, e.g., formerly only May 1 to October 1. Now decreasing again due to competition from Herring Gull.

* *

FRANKLIN'S GULL
Larus pipixcan Wagler

STATUS: Hypothetical.
Accidental vagrant from the West.
Reported September 7–9, 1941, at Monomoy (Griscom, Eliot, Kraus, Clement) and September 7 to November 5, 1942, at Nauset (Griscom, Drury, Emerson, Curtis, Mason), both well seen under satisfactory conditions. Several other probable records in 1947, 1948, 1950, 1951, and 1958, but no specimen yet obtained.

* *

BONAPARTE'S GULL
Larus philadelphia (Ord)

STATUS: Represented in MCZ, BMS, and Chicago collections.
SPRING: Rare and somewhat irregular migrant.
Average migration period: April 22–June 1; average 5–15 birds, maximum 26 on May 26, 1940, at Monomoy (Hill, Davis, Drury, Nash).
SUMMER: Not uncommon non-breeding straggler.
FALL: Uncommon migrant, rarely common.
Earliest transient date: Uncertain, probably about August 1.
Average migration period: September 1–January 1.
Peak: November 25–December 25; see below for counts.
WINTER: Rather rare and irregular.
DISTRIBUTION: In fall more regular and in higher numbers west of Barnstable, e.g., average 30–150 birds in Falmouth-Woods Hole area vs. 4–40 on outer Cape; occasional flights to latter, however, as 1000 on December 21, 1939, at Chatham (Griscom, Bagg, Bishop, Robbins). The same distribution applies to wintering birds. Main spring flight does not strike Cape at all. Summering stragglers may appear anywhere.
HISTORY: No evidence of change in numbers.

* *

LITTLE GULL
Larus minutus Pallas

STATUS: Hypothetical.
Accidental vagrant from Old World.
Sight record of an immature at North Beach, Chatham, from September 3 to December 30, 1951 (Griscom, Rich, Fox, Morgan). Also reported in summers of 1959 and 1960 and in November 1960.

* *

IVORY GULL
Pagophila eburnea (Phipps)

STATUS: Specimen obtained but not preserved.
Accidental vagrant from the North.
SPECIMEN: Shot on December 1, 1886, at Monomoy (unknown coastguardman, see Cahoon, *O & O, 12*, 206, 1887).
SIGHT RECORD: March 1931 at Nauset (Hamilton, Rotch).

* *

BLACK-LEGGED KITTIWAKE
Rissa tridactyla (Linnaeus)

STATUS: Represented in MCZ, BMS, Chicago, and British Museum collections.
FALL: Usually rare migrant, occasionally abundant.
Earliest arrival date: August 25, 1891, at Provincetown (Miller, in British Museum).
Average migration period: November 1–December 31; average 1–3 birds, great flights being dependent on severe easterly gales as 15,000 on November 30, 1957, at Nauset (Smart).
WINTER: Regular offshore, rare inshore.
SPRING: Very rare migrant, no pattern of occurrence.

SUMMER: Probably very rare non-breeding straggler, chiefly at sea.

DISTRIBUTION: Highly pelagic, entering inshore waters along sand beaches only when storm-blown. Recorded chiefly from Provincetown to Monomoy, but occasionally penetrates both Cape Cod Bay and the sounds; specimens from both areas.

HISTORY: No data available except that it is now less frequently found around Provincetown with the decline of the fishing industry.

*   *

SABINE'S GULL

Xema sabini (Sabine)

STATUS: Represented in MCZ, BMS, and British Museum collections.

SPRING: Probably very rare vagrant; no completely satisfactory proof of occurrence, but reported from May 20 to June 2.

FALL: Very rare migrant.

Earliest transient date: July 27, 1941, at Monomoy and for five weeks thereafter (see Mason, *Auk*, 68, 236, 1951).

Average migration period: August 13–September 15; all single birds.

Latest departure date: September 29, 1888, off Chatham (Gould, in MCZ).

DISTRIBUTION: Pelagic migrant, so chiefly recorded offshore where bird will come to a "slick." Inshore records largely Eastham to Monomoy. Has entered Cape Cod Bay casually, collected on August 21, 1889, three miles west of Truro (Miller, in British Museum, *Auk*, 7, 226, 1890) and seen August 4, 1953, off Sagamore (Hill).

HISTORY: No data.

*   *

Pitch Pine (Pinus rigida)

GULL-BILLED TERN
Gelochelidon nilotica (Gmelin)

STATUS: Presumptive.

SUMMER: Rare and irregular visitant from South, often after late-summer hurricanes.

Earliest arrival date: July 18, 1949, at Nauset (Griscom).

Average period: August 15–September 5; always single birds.

Latest departure date: September 19, 1954, at Monomoy (Griscom, Beattie, Emery).

DISTRIBUTION: Records are mainly from Monomoy and Nauset, probably reflecting only the concentration of observers; one record at Sagamore.

HISTORY: Early history unknown, appears to have increased slightly since 1940; see Griscom, *Auk*, 56, 186, 1939.

ADDENDUM: Hybrid tern, Gull-billed x Forster's, collected September 6, 1941, at Nauset (Griscom, in MCZ).

*   *

FORSTER'S TERN
Sterna forsteri Nuttall

STATUS: Represented in MCZ and BMS collections.

FALL: Rare but regular wandering migrant; no satisfactory spring records.

Earliest arrival date: July 29, 1959, at Nauset (Bailey); earlier dates not satisfactorily confirmed.

Average period: August 12–October 15.

Peak: September 8–28; average 1–3 birds, maximum 24 on September 23, 1945, at Eastham (Griscom, Cottrell).

Latest departure date: November 22, 1953, at Nauset (Griscom, Beattie, Emery).

DISTRIBUTION: Largely over salt ponds and marshes, roosting on beaches and occasionally migrating offshore. Recorded over entire Cape. Frequently reported after hurricanes.

HISTORY: Overlooked until 1871, then reported or collected yearly to 1889 (Brewster, *Bull. N.O.C.*, 4, 14, 1879); again overlooked to 1924 (Bent, see Allen, *Auk*, 46, 100, 1929), and reported yearly since 1936; increase in reports is due to increase in observers, not birds.

* *

COMMON TERN

Sterna hirundo Linnaeus

STATUS: Represented in MCZ, BMS, Chicago, and British Museum collections.

SPRING: Arrival of residents, abundant as transient.

Earliest arrival date: April 20, 1932, off Chatham (local fisherman, *fide* Austin), appears offshore first.

Average resident arrival period: May 5–15; usually second tern to arrive.

Average transient period: May 12–June 1.

Peak: May 14–25; average 2000–5000 birds, maximum 10,000 on May 14, 1952, at Chatham (Hill).

SUMMER: Locally abundant breeding resident. Austin (many papers in *Bird-Banding*) has shown that within the Atlantic coast population the Cape Cod terns form a distinct self-sustaining group free of association with others, even the nearby Vineyard group, in the breeding season; the extra-limital colony at Plymouth Beach is clearly part of the Cape group, but the colonies on islands in Buzzards Bay have a less constant relation to it. Tern Island, Chatham, is the pivotal colony, with larger or smaller colonies appearing and disappearing according to ecological conditions at Provincetown, Truro, Wellfleet, Nauset, North Beach, Cotuit, Monomoy, Poponesset, Falmouth, Cataumet, Sagamore, Barnstable, etc., on the Cape as well as Plymouth Beach and Ram and Bird islands. Number breeding at each location highly variable from year to year. Birds move freely among these colonies; if driven out at one, will renest elsewhere.

FALL: Abundant migrant, local and transient birds not fully separable.

Earliest transient date: Uncertain, probably about July 12.

Average migration period: July 20–October 25.

Peak: Somewhat variable, July 28–August 10; average 1000–5000 birds, maximum 18,000 on July 30, 1938, at Monomoy (Griscom, Hagar, Garrison, Curtis) and occasionally a second peak September 10–October 3; average 500–2000 birds, maximum 12,000 on September 30, 1950, at North Beach (Griscom, Emery).

Latest transient date: Uncertain, probably about November 27.

WINTER: Casual straggler, recorded to February 20, 1891, at Woods Hole (Edwards, see Mackay, *Auk*, *12*, 36, 1895); never surviving entire season.

DISTRIBUTION: Breeds on islands and isolated barrier beaches; see above for breeding distribution. Found widely from offshore to protected salt water and often feeding over inland fresh-water ponds. Spring arrivals appear first on outer Cape, e.g., massed arrival of 8000 coming in high from south at sunset on May 13, 1952, at Chatham, so 10,000 there and only 10 at Sagamore the next day (Hill); seen migrating past both at Sagamore, having crossed Cape along Canal, and from Chatham to Provincetown. Post-breeding gatherings in midsummer mainly at Monomoy and Nauset and are dependent on both a successful nesting season and adequate feed in inshore waters. Fall transient adults make up part of these flocks and more adults, accompanied by young, stream south after mid-August, e.g., up to 200/hour about September 1 at Sagamore, crossing Cape along Canal to Buzzards Bay. Transient birds form a larger proportion of the late-September gatherings. In fall three separate routes are apparent: 1) offshore past Provincetown and southward; 2) inshore entering Cape Cod Bay and part crossing along Canal and part moving east to outer Cape; and 3) from overland passing high over Sagamore from northwest and disappearing toward outer Cape.

HISTORY: Early status unknown. Reduced during persecution for plumes about 1880–1900, but never critically so on Cape; recovered rapidly with protection. Austin in 1946 (*Bird-Banding*, *17*, 10, 1946) estimated the aggregate to be 30,000 breeding birds yearly for the previous fifteen years, but by 1956 he estimated (*Bird-Banding*, 27, 55, 1956) the total to have decreased to 15,000–20,000, presumably due to gradual loss of breeding areas. On the other hand, counts of transients have shown a moderate increase since 1952.

*   *

ARCTIC TERN
Sterna paradisaea Pontoppidan

STATUS: Represented in MCZ, BMS, and Chicago collections.

SPRING: Arrival of residents only, no evidence of transients.
Earliest arrival date: May 13, 1885, at Monomoy (Cahoon, collected).
Average arrival period: May 20–25; usually last tern to appear.

SUMMER: Rather uncommon and very local breeding species. Estimated total "a few hundred" (Austin, *Bird-Banding*, 27, 55, 1956); average 10–20 pairs each at Monomoy, North Beach, Tern Island, Orleans, Nauset, Provincetown, etc. Number in each location variable, maximum 100 pairs at North Beach in 1946 (Griscom & Parker).

FALL: Poorly known as sight identification at this season is unreliable and has been repeatedly proven wrong on collection. Only a few specimens taken after early August, and general departure believed to occur then, thus the earliest tern to depart.

Latest departure date: October 24, 1886, at "Cape Cod" (Carpenter, in MCZ).

DISTRIBUTION: Outer beaches and offshore waters where flocks presumed to be this species are seen on migration. Notably limited to easternmost areas of Cape; the few records westward are not adequately confirmed.

HISTORY: Parallel to Common Tern, this species was reduced but not eliminated by 1890 (collected repeatedly by Cahoon 1885–1888). Increasing slowly thereafter with marked increase after 1942, now apparently stabilized in numbers.

* *

ROSEATE TERN
Sterna dougallii Montagu

STATUS: Represented in MCZ, BMS, Chicago, and British Museum collections.

SPRING: Arrival of residents, common as transient.
Earliest arrival date: May 10, 1953, at Sagamore (Hill).
Average resident arrival period: May 15–26; usually third tern to appear.
Average transient period: May 20–June 1.
Counts: Average 100–500 birds, maximum 2000 on several occasions.

SUMMER: Locally fairly common breeding resident. Within the Cape Cod tern group, this species estimated at 4000 birds (Austin, *Bird-Banding*, 27, 55, 1956); fluctuating counts at any given location: Monomoy, North Beach, Tern Island, Wellfleet, Cotuit, Barnstable, etc., and extra-limitally at Plymouth Beach and on islands in Buzzards Bay.

FALL: Common to abundant migrant.
Earliest transient date: Uncertain, probably about July 8.
Average migration period: July 20–September 15.
Peak: Somewhat variable, July 28–August 10; average 800–

1500 birds, maximum 3000 on August 4, 1940, at Monomoy (Griscom) and often a second peak August 20–September 4; average 1000–2500 birds, maximum 7000 on August 22, 1954, at Monomoy (Griscom, Parker, Bowen, Morgan, Kleber).

Latest departure date: October 29, 1910, at Barnstable (Redfield, in BMS); later dates unconfirmed.

DISTRIBUTION: On outer beaches, often migrating offshore. See above for breeding distribution. Migrants over entire Cape; greatest counts on outer Cape, but migrates in numbers past Sagamore and along Canal in fall, maximum about August 20, thus earlier than Common Tern maximum there.

HISTORY: Original status unknown, but seriously reduced and probably temporarily eliminated by plume trade. Recovered slowly, but now increasing steadily as a transient and probably as a breeding species.

*   *

SOOTY TERN

Sterna fuscata Linnaeus

STATUS: Found dead, not preserved (Evans, *fide* Kelly).

Rare vagrant from tropical Atlantic, usually after hurricanes.

Total of at least nine records, July 2 to September 11, mostly adults; usually single birds and pairs, maximum 9 on August 29, 1958, off Sagamore after hurricane "Daisy" (Hill). Most other reports from outer Cape from Provincetown south to Monomoy.

*   *

BRIDLED TERN

Sterna anaethetus Scopoli

STATUS: Represented in MAS collection.

Accidental vagrant from tropical Atlantic, usually after southern storms.

SPECIMEN: Immature on September 14, 1960, at Monomoy (Bailey, in MAS).

SIGHT RECORDS: Total of six, August 30–September 25, from Monomoy, Nauset, and Harwichport.

* *

LEAST TERN
Sterna albifrons Pallas

STATUS: Represented in MCZ, BMS, and Chicago collections.

SPRING: Arrival of residents, uncommon as transient.

Earliest arrival date: May 7, 1876, at Monomoy (Brewster).

Average resident arrival period: May 10–15; usually the earliest tern to appear.

Average transient period: May 20–30.

Counts: Average 30–60 birds, maximum 100 on May 28, 1949, at Chatham (Eliot).

SUMMER: Locally fairly common breeding resident. Estimated total of 500+ pairs with numbers fluctuating from year to year in any given location; found on suitable beaches over entire Cape from Falmouth and Sagamore east to Chatham and north to Provincetown.

FALL: Uncommon migrant.

Earliest transient date: Uncertain, probably about July 15.

Average migration period: July 20–September 10.

Peak: July 25–August 5; average 30–100 birds, maximum 200 on several occasions.

Latest departure date: September 27, 1947, at Nauset (Griscom, Mazzeo).

DISTRIBUTION: Outer beaches almost exclusively, chiefly on drier white sand. See above for breeding distribution. Transients mostly along outer Cape.

HISTORY: Formerly common to abundant, markedly reduced by both egging and plume hunting, but survived on most of Cape (Forbush, 1925). Increased slowly to about 1945, but then decreased due to "beach buggy" traffic through nesting areas. Transients reappeared after 1946 and have increased coincident with re-establishment of colonies northward.

* *

ROYAL TERN

Thalasseus maximus (Boddaert)

STATUS: Collected, specimen now lost (Cahoon).

SUMMER: Rare but recently regular visitant from the South, most frequently after hurricanes; no known breeding record.

Earliest arrival date: June 25, 1960, at Nauset (Bailey).

Average period: August 1–September 15; mostly single birds, rarely a pair, and occasionally more after a hurricane.

Latest departure date: November 22, 1953, at Nauset (Earle).

DISTRIBUTION: Recorded over entire Cape, but concentration of reports eastward.

HISTORY: No data of original status when suspected of breeding on Nantucket. Increasing since 1940 and now recorded every year.

* *

SANDWICH TERN

Thalasseus sandvicensis (Latham)

STATUS: Collected, specimen now lost (J. A. Allen).

SUMMER: Very rare vagrant from South, mostly after hurricanes.

Specimen: August 1865 at Chatham (Allen).

Sight records: July 10, 1918, at Sandwich (Higgins, see Forbush, 1925); August 13, 1961, at Nauset (Bailey); September 1, 1954, at Nauset (Hill, Mason); July and August 1964, at North Beach and Nauset (many observers); possibly a few others.

* *

CASPIAN TERN
Hydroprogne caspia (Pallas)

STATUS: Represented in MCZ and BMS collections.
SPRING: Rare and rapid migrant.
Earliest arrival date: April 19, 1955, at Sagamore (Hill).
Average migration period: April 28–May 20; recently only single birds.
SUMMER: Very rare non-breeding straggler, recorded from Barnstable westward.
FALL: Rare and rapid migrant, more numerous after hurricanes.
Earliest transient date: Uncertain, probably mid-July.
Average migration period: August 25–September 25; usually single birds, maximum 6 on September 24, 1932, at Monomoy (Griscom).
Latest transient date: October 12, 1953, at Sagamore (Hill).
DISTRIBUTION: Occurs over entire Cape, but appears somewhat more frequently westward, particularly in spring.
HISTORY: Formerly regular and more numerous, seen in "flocks" in May 1876 at Monomoy and Chatham (Brewster). Then decreased and became quite irregular; appearing somewhat more frequently since 1950.

* *

BLACK TERN
Chlidonias niger (Linnaeus)

STATUS: Represented in MCZ, BMS, Chicago, and British Museum collections.
SPRING: Rather uncommon migrant.
Earliest arrival date: May 14, 1952, at Orleans (Hill).
Average migration period: May 22–June 5; average 1–3 birds, maximum 5 on several occasions (the report of 175 in Griscom & Snyder, 1955, is an error due to a *lapsus calami*).

SUMMER: Casual non-breeding straggler, collected twice in mid-June (in BMS) and seen in additional years.

FALL: Uncommon to fairly common migrant.

Earliest transient date: Uncertain, probably about July 5.

Average migration period: July 25–September 20.

Peak: August 27–September 10; average 3–30 birds, occasional marked flights with maximum 500 on September 3, 1948, at Monomoy (Maclay).

Latest departure date: October 10, 1944, at Nauset (Griscom).

DISTRIBUTION: Chiefly estuaries and marshes and over brackish ponds, occasionally offshore. Occurs over entire Cape with concentration along south shore and maxima at Monomoy and Woods Hole. Frequently seen at Sagamore migrating past but not staying, arriving both overland from northwest and alongshore from north, disappearing eastward along bay shore.

HISTORY: Formerly very rare in spring, increasing since 1945 with eastward extension of the breeding range. Fall flight pattern in past, i.e., 1885–1888 (Cahoon), similar to that at present; fall flight shows general increase in numbers since 1947.

*   *

WHITE-WINGED BLACK TERN
Chlidonias leucopterus (Temminck)

STATUS: Hypothetical.

Reported July 18, 1960, at Nauset and August 4, 1960, at Monomoy (Bailey).

*   *

BLACK SKIMMER
Rynchops nigra Linnaeus

STATUS: Represented in MCZ and BMS collections.

SPRING: No data on arrival of nesting pairs.

SUMMER: Recently has nested casually in 1956 and 1960 at Cotuit

(Higgins, Morgan); rare scattered non-breeding birds otherwise.

FALL: Variably rare to common, wandering birds from South, most often after hurricanes.

Earliest arrival date: Uncertain, probably about July 1.

Average period: July 25–September 20; average 1–5 birds; see below for record of invasions.

Latest departure date: October 18, 1954, at Chatham (Mosher).

DISTRIBUTION: Outer beaches adjacent to marshes and protected estuaries over entire Cape. Maximum reports are from Monomoy and Nauset, reflecting both location of satisfactory feeding areas and concentration of observers.

HISTORY: Breeding at Nauset in 1605 (Champlain, see Purdie, *Bull. N.O.C.*, 7, 125, 1882), rapidly eliminated in colonial times and became very rare vagrant except for invasions after hurricanes: 1879 when collected August 19 at Sandwich and Woods Hole (see Deane and Brewer, *Bull. N.O.C.*, 4, 243, 1879); 1924 when collected August 27 at Monomoy and flocks present for several weeks (Bent, Earle); 1944 when seen from September 17 on at Nauset and Chatham, flocks to 386 (see Hill, *Auk*, 62, 410, 1945); 1954 when seen from September 1 on at Nauset, Monomoy, and elsewhere, flocks to 250 (many observers). Wandering birds from South regular since 1936, even in absence of storms, coincident with increase in colonies southward, usually 1–5 birds and widely scattered over entire Cape in favorable areas (see Griscom, *Auk*, 54, 206, 1937).

*   *

GREAT AUK

Pinguinus impennis (Linnaeus)

EXTINCT: Reported by Gosnold as taken off south shore of Cape Cod in summer of 1602, either at Monomoy or Point Gammon or between these points. Freeman (*Coll. Mass. Hist. Soc.*, 3, 1st series, 199, 1794) at Truro reported them "plenty on the shore and in the bay," and bones have been found in Indian shell heaps. The suggestion by Forbush (1912) that they bred on Mashnee and/or other islands in upper Buzzards Bay is rejected; summering stragglers may well have occurred there, but the habitat is utterly different from all known breeding stations.

*   *

RAZORBILL
Alca torda Linnaeus

STATUS: Represented in MCZ, BMS, and Chicago collections.

WINTER: Rare to uncommon visitant, numbers irregular.

Earliest arrival date: November 10, 1946, off Monomoy (Griscom, Elkins, Parker).

Average period: November 28–May 1; average 1–2 birds, maximum 400 in storm on November 16, 1959, at Wellfleet (Bailey).

SUMMER: Scattered oiled or crippled birds, rarely surviving to September.

DISTRIBUTION: Pelagic but entering larger bays, occurs over both sandy and rocky sea bottom; oiled birds occasionally found inland. Largest numbers offshore from Provincetown to Monomoy, but regular throughout Cape Cod Bay and westward through the sounds to lower Buzzards Bay.

HISTORY: Variably uncommon to common in early historical period, i.e., great flights periodically as in 1886 when it was common in Provincetown Harbor and offshore (Cahoon, see Brewster, *Auk*, 4, 158, 1887). Then quite uncommon until 1947 when a slow increase became apparent, and now again subject to flights as in 1959.

*   *

COMMON MURRE
Uria aalge (Pontoppidan)

STATUS: Represented in BMS collection.
WINTER: Very rare and irregular visitant.
   Specimens: Total of at least five, not all preserved, dating from
      December 10, 1960, in Cape Cod Bay (Higginbotham) to
      April 3, 1930, at Chatham (Eldredge).
   Sight record: One in breeding plumage on May 20, 1934, at
      Monomoy (Griscom, Peterson).
SUMMER: Casual straggler, collected off Woods Hole on June 26,
   1913 (Cobb, in BMS).

*   *

THICK-BILLED MURRE
Uria lomvia (Linnaeus)

STATUS: Represented in MCZ and BMS collections.
WINTER: Rather rare visitant.
   Earliest arrival date: October 11, 1953, at Eastham (Griscom,
      Beattie, Bailey).
   Average period: November 15–April 1; exclusively single birds
      recently except for 190 in storm on November 16, 1959, at
      Wellfleet (Bailey).
   Latest departure date: May 20, 1934, at Monomoy (Griscom,
      Peterson).
DISTRIBUTION: Open ocean and larger bays, once in Eastham Great
   Pond. Occurs chiefly offshore from Provincetown to Monomoy,
   also in Cape Cod Bay and through the sounds to lower Buzzards
   Bay.
HISTORY: Formerly fairly common, occasionally abundant as in
   1883–1884. Then decreased steadily, more slowly than Razor-
   bill, but not showing as much recent increase.

*   *

DOVEKIE
Plautus alle (Linnaeus)

STATUS: Represented in MCZ, BMS, Chicago, and British Museum collections.

WINTER: Uncommon visitant, occasionally abundant.

Earliest arrival date: October 25, 1949, at Nauset (Hill).

Average period: November 5–April 10.

Peak: November 12–December 1; counts extremely variable, usually a few present, maxima 2000 in storm on November 16, 1959, at Wellfleet (Bailey) and 400/hour on November 12, 1949, past Nauset (Griscom, Emery, Parker, Snyder). No evidence of northward flight in spring.

Latest departure date: April 19, 1938, at Monomoy (Griscom, Bishop, Tousey).

SUMMER: Casual straggler, June 16, 1940, at Monomoy (Griscom).

DISTRIBUTION: Largely pelagic, reported as common off Cape (Nichols, *Auk*, *30*, 505, 1913) but with scattered birds regularly near shore and occasionally greater flights, usually dependent on severe easterly gales; flights may be quite localized as on November 25–26, 1885, when Provincetown Harbor was "alive with them" but "no flight at other points" (Bangs, *in litt.* to Brewster). Occasionally found inland on ponds or even on bare ground. See also Murphy and Voigt, *Auk*, *50*, 325, 1933. Recorded fairly regularly in Cape Cod Bay, e.g., 1000 on November 16, 1959, at Sandwich (Clark).

HISTORY: No evidence of any change in numbers.

*   *

BLACK GUILLEMOT
Cepphus grylle (Linnaeus)

STATUS: Represented in MCZ collection.

WINTER: Very rare and irregular visitant; total of six satisfactory records at most.

Earliest arrival date: December 10, 1939, at Monomoy (Griscom, Bucheister, Robbins, Parker, Bishop).

Latest departure date: February 22, 1942, at Monomoy (Griscom, Hill, Street, Cottrell).

DISTRIBUTION: Occurs off rocky shores, so absence on Cape is due to habitat factor. Most records on outer Cape, rare at Woods Hole.

HISTORY: No data.

* *

CRESTED AUKLET

Aethia cristatella (Pallas)

STATUS: Hypothetical.

Bird allegedly answering description of this species killed in winter of 1884–1885 at Chatham (Baker, see Allen, *Auk*, 2, 388, 1885).

* *

COMMON PUFFIN

Fratercula arctica (Linnaeus)

STATUS: Represented in MCZ collection.

WINTER: Casual visitant from pelagic wintering areas.

Specimens: Total of seven with five extant; dates from December 18, 1886, at Provincetown (Cahoon, in MCZ) to June 5, 1924, at Sandwich (Harrison, see Forbush, 1925). Five from outer Cape from Provincetown to Chatham and two in Cape Cod Bay.

Sight records: Total of 4–5 which are satisfactory and which do not significantly change above dates.

* *

MOURNING DOVE
Zenaidura macroura (Linnaeus)

STATUS: Represented in MCZ, BMS, and Chicago collections.

Three populations involved: 1) breeding; 2) wintering; and 3) transient. Individuals not identifiable as to population and some birds of some population present at all times. These distinct populations proven for this species (Austin, *Bird-Banding*, *21*, 149, 1951) whereas largely surmised for other species.

1) BREEDING.

Average arrival period: March 25–April 5, but still migrating to mid-May.

Counts: Uncommon but widespread, estimated density 2 pairs/100 acres in satisfactory territory.

Average departure period: Flocking by mid-August, 5–20 birds, and leave from late August through September, latest October 31.

2) WINTERING.

Average arrival period: September 25–early December.

Counts: Uncommon and wide-ranging resident; only fair survival in average winters; see below for counts.

Average departure period: Late February and through March, latest April 3.

3) TRANSIENT.

Spring: Arrive with breeding population, but the excess numbers disappear after mid-May, route not known.

Fall: Occasional transients in August, more often in September and fill hiatus between departure of breeding population and arrival of winter population; remain relatively short time; flocks average 5–20 birds, maximum 155 on September 8–10, 1950 (M.A.S.).

DISTRIBUTION: Abandoned pastures and open woods. Widespread over entire Cape; a little more numerous than on mainland as breeder and considerably more numerous as winterer; now comes to feeding stations in winter.

HISTORY: Confused with next species much of time prior to 1900. Marked decrease after 1850, however, and slow increase with protection after 1908 (Forbush, 1912), leveling out about 1920 for breeding population. Winter flocks have been favored by cycle of mild winters; e.g., Christmas Count range of 0–24 and missed three times in 1930's vs. 3–60 and never missed in 1950's.

*   *

PASSENGER PIGEON
Ectopistes migratorius (Linnaeus)

STATUS: Represented in MCZ collection.

EXTINCT: Data prior to deforestation of Cape Cod incomplete but probably not uncommon as "multitudes" occurred as close as Plymouth in 1643 and 1648 (Forbush, 1912). Obviously rare during historical period, the only dates suggest occurrence of an early fall flight; immature male on September 4, 1883, at East Orleans (Lamb, in MCZ); August 23–24, 1890, at East Falmouth (Plummer, *in litt.* to Brewster); and a female on August 28, 1892, at Orleans (Brewster collection, in MCZ).

*   *

YELLOW-BILLED CUCKOO
Coccyzus americanus (Linnaeus)

STATUS: Represented in MCZ and BMS collections.

SUMMER: Rare, local, and often irregular resident.

Earliest arrival date: May 6, 1962, at Sagamore (Hill).

Average period: June 1–September 30.

Counts: Singles and pairs in summer; very few transients in fall except for 1954 (see below).

Latest departure date: November 7, 1910 (Bangs, in BMS) [not 1890 and not now in MCZ].

DISTRIBUTION: Very widely scattered pairs, more numerous westward but occasionally north to Wellfleet. Occupies moister areas and richer woods than Black-billed Cuckoo and thus less common than that species though more on Cape than on adjacent mainland.

HISTORY: Always irregular with influxes during caterpillar infestations as in 1944 in Hyannis-Centerville area (Snyder). Great influx of storm-blown waifs after 1954 hurricanes with 200 birds reported from September 16 to November 1 and maximum of 31 on October 12, 1954, in Brewster-Eastham-Chatham area (Hill, Petty); see Griscom, *Bull. Mass. Audubon Soc.*, *39*, 151, 1955.

* *

BLACK-BILLED CUCKOO
Coccyzus erythropthalmus (Wilson)

STATUS: Represented in MCZ and British Museum collections.

SUMMER: Rather uncommon and local resident.

Earliest arrival date: April 16, 1961, at Orleans (Fox), after southern storm.

Average period: May 25–October 1.

Counts: Singles and pairs in spring and summer; some increase due to transients about August 22 to September 22, maximum 13 on August 24, 1958 (Parker, Bowen, Hill).

Latest departure date: October 24, 1939, at Monomoy (Griscom, Garrison).

DISTRIBUTION: Widely scattered pairs in wide variety of habitats from sand-dune thickets to brushy upland pastures; occurs over whole Cape, but slightly more numerous westward.

HISTORY: No evidence of basic change at least since 1890, but subject to fluctuation in number of breeding pairs from year to year, maximum 23 birds in the Brewster-Orleans-Eastham area in 1940 (Griscom).

*   *

BARN OWL
Tyto alba (Scopoli)

STATUS: Specimens obtained, present location unknown (*fide* May).

Very rare and irregular resident; no evidence of migration. Nested successfully in 1952 at North Chatham (Rich) and in 1961 at Chatham (Copland). Recorded in January, March, June, July, August, and December; east to Monomoy and north to Truro.

*   *

SCREECH OWL
Otus asio (Linnaeus)

STATUS: Represented in MCZ and British Museum collections.
Uncommon and local permanent resident.

DISTRIBUTION: Scattered in open woods from Sagamore and Falmouth, decreasing eastward to Chatham and Orleans and fewer north at least to Wellfleet. Slightly increased numbers in fall and early winter, probably represent locally raised young plus a few wanderers from mainland.

HISTORY: No data on early historical period; no evidence of change 1930–1955, but appears sharply decreased since then.

*   *

GREAT HORNED OWL
Bubo virginianus (Gmelin)

STATUS: Represented in MCZ and BMS collections.
Fairly common permanent resident.

DISTRIBUTION: Widespread in mixed woods from Sagamore and

Falmouth east to Chatham and Eastham, decreasing northward but present to Provincetown. Nesting recorded in every township and in multiple locations in some. By far the commonest owl on Cape except possibly north of Wellfleet, and considerably commoner than on mainland. Irregularly a small influx in fall or winter from off Cape.

HISTORY: Increasing steadily since 1935 as woods grow and spread; best shown in Christmas Count reports: range of 0–4 and missed six years in 1930's vs. 1–12 and never missed in 1950's.

* *

SNOWY OWL

Nyctea scandiaca (Linnaeus)

STATUS: Represented in MCZ, BMS, and Sandwich Historical Society collections.

WINTER: Usually absent, occasionally rare to uncommon visitor. Earliest arrival date: October 20, 1941, at Monomoy (Eldredge).

Average period: November 10 in flight years but December 15 otherwise, to January 15. Usually single birds; see below for flights.

Latest departure date: March 19, 1938, at Monomoy (Smith).

DISTRIBUTION: Largely along dunes of outer beaches and adjacent marshes, recorded over entire Cape, but may concentrate around Falmouth as in 1926–1927 or at Monomoy as in 1949–1950. Much less regular, less numerous, and leaving much earlier than north of Boston; reaches Cape only in flight years and even then in fewer numbers than on mainland.

HISTORY: Always erratic. Great flights recorded include: 1905–1906 with about twenty from Cape (Deane, *Auk*, *23*, 100 and 283, 1906); 1926–1927 with about fifty from Cape (Gross, *Auk*, *44*, 479, 1927); 1930–1931 with about six from Cape

(Gross, *Auk*, 48, 501, 1931); 1949–1950 with four or five from Cape; 1960–1961 with three or four from Cape. Flights of 1941–1942 and of 1945–1946 barely reached Cape, only one bird each, and thus no more than in non-flight years.

*   *

HAWK-OWL
Surnia ulula (Linnaeus)

STATUS: Collected but specimens now lost.
Very rare and irregular vagrant from North.
SPECIMENS: Winter of 1883–1884 at Chatham (Baker, see Allen, *Auk*, 2, 383, 1885); March 25, 1890, at Sandwich (Frazer, *Forest & Stream*, 34, 268); and February 1941 at Dennis (Finley, specimen seen following summer by Hill). Several unconfirmed sight records.

*   *

BARRED OWL
Strix varia Barton

STATUS: Presumptive.
Very rare and irregular straggler. One record each in January, March, July, August, and December and two each in September and October; consistent with wandering birds from mainland.
DISTRIBUTION: Usually deep woods, so absence on Cape is essentially due to lack of preferred habitat. Recorded from Sandwich, Cotuit, Chatham, Brewster, and Wellfleet.
HISTORY: No data as to whether bird was more numerous on Cape prior to deforestation.

*   *

LONG-EARED OWL
Asio otus (Linnaeus)

STATUS: Represented in MCZ and British Museum collections.
Rather rare and local permanent resident, a few migrants in fall.
DISTRIBUTION: Widely scattered in coniferous woods from Sagamore and Cotuit to Chatham and Brewster, less regular northward. Nesting recorded in 1921 (Hersey, nestling in MCZ) at
Chatham and suspected elsewhere. Occasional birds in fall from
mainland, this being more marked around Canal than eastward.
HISTORY: No information on early status; no evidence of change
1935–1960.

* *

SHORT-EARED OWL
Asio flammeus (Pontoppidan)

STATUS: Represented in MCZ and BMS collections.
Rather rare and local permanent resident, a few migrants in fall.
DISTRIBUTION: Marshes, dunes, and open uplands. Probably nests
only at Monomoy and East Orleans at present, though formerly
at South Chatham, Falmouth (Forbush, 1927), and Barnstable.
Recorded over entire Cape chiefly as an influx in fall, variable in
numbers, has been seen arriving from due north over the ocean
(Hill).
HISTORY: Formerly much more common, particularly in fall; migrants now much decreased and local breeding stations reduced
by human intrusion.

* *

BOREAL OWL
Aegolius funereus (Linnaeus)

STATUS: Specimen obtained, location now unknown.
Only record is of one bird caught in trap in January 1923 at
Sandwich (Torrey).

* *

SAW-WHET OWL
Aegolius acadicus (Gmelin)

STATUS: Represented in MCZ collection.
Uncommon permanent resident, much overlooked.
DISTRIBUTION: Widespread breeding in low open coniferous growth. Possibly commonest owl from Wellfleet north, but second to Great Horned Owl elsewhere. Definite increase in fall about mid-October probably both locally raised birds plus an influx from the mainland.
HISTORY: No data on original status. Increased as reforestation began, but now gradual reduction as woods mature and Great Horned Owl moves in; this has not yet occurred north of Wellfleet.

* *

CHUCK-WILL'S-WIDOW
Caprimulgus carolinensis Gmelin

STATUS: Hypothetical
One bird heard singing on June 21, 1964 at South Wellfleet (Bailey).

* *

WHIP-POOR-WILL
Caprimulgus vociferus Wilson

STATUS: Represented in BMS collection.
SUMMER: Common breeding resident.
Earliest arrival date: April 19, 1959, at Falmouth (Sargent); no evidence of transients in spring.
Average period: May 5–September 28.
Counts: See below for breeding birds. Migrants in fall only, average 1–4 birds, August 24–September 28.

Latest departure date: October 16, 1954, at Chatham (Griscom).

DISTRIBUTION: Nests throughout the pine barrens. Greatest counts from Bourne south to Cotuit and North Falmouth and east to Brewster; 32 singing along ten miles of road with 3–6 within hearing distance at once in Bourne and Sandwich (Hill), 15 along ten miles in Brewster (Griscom) and further decrease south to Chatham and east to Orleans, considerably fewer north to Wellfleet and Truro. More common on the Cape than on the mainland except for the immediately adjacent pine barrens of southern Plymouth County.

HISTORY: No data on original status when Cape was heavily wooded or after deforestation. Present boom coincident with rise in pitch pines; high concentrations shift and decline as pines are invaded by oaks; this has resulted in a small decrease generally in the past twenty years.

* *

COMMON NIGHTHAWK
Chordeiles minor (Forster)

STATUS: Represented in MCZ and British Museum collections.

SPRING: Formerly arrival of breeding populations but dates unknown, now a very rare and irregular migrant.
Average period: May 15–30.

SUMMER: Formerly bred commonly on the ground through the pine barrens, particularly from Bourne to Cotuit and Mashpee prior to 1903 (Cobb) and probably very locally to 1942, as recorded regularly through June and July at Sagamore from 1936 to 1942 but not since (Hill). Not now nesting on Cape Cod.

FALL: Rather uncommon migrant westward and rare eastward.
Earliest transient date: August 16, 1941, at Nauset (Eaton).
Average migration period: August 25–September 20.

Counts: Formerly fairly common westward but decreasing steadily, e.g., at Sagamore 50 birds on September 14–15, 1941, and similar numbers in earlier years but much rarer since 1950, usually 1–2 and maximum 4 (Hill). Always much rarer eastward, usually single birds, occasionally two, and not recorded every year.

Latest departure date: October 17, 1954, at Monomoy (Griscom).

DISTRIBUTION: See above. Migrating often along beaches and hawking over marshes; once seen migrating south with terns over ocean September 17, 1949, at Monomoy (Griscom).

HISTORY: See above.

* *

CHIMNEY SWIFT
Chaetura pelagica (Linnaeus)

STATUS: Represented in MCZ, BMS, and British Museum collections.

SPRING: Arrival of breeding residents, fairly common as transient; populations usually separable by behavior.

Earliest arrival date: May 1, 1938, at Sagamore (Hill).

Average resident arrival period: May 5–10.

Average transient period: May 15–30.

SUMMER: Common to locally abundant breeding resident, occurring in all villages but probably more common westward on the Cape and generally less common than on mainland.

FALL: Common transient.

Average migration period: August 20–September 15.

Counts: Average 10–30 on outer Cape and 50–150 near Canal, maximum 200 on August 27, 1953, at Woods Hole (Freeland).

Latest departure date: Seen on October 23, 1954, at Chatham (Griscom), after hurricanes, presumed to be this species of swift.

DISTRIBUTION: See above for breeding distribution. Nests in all villages, ranges widely over the land but seldom over marshes or dunes; seen migrating several times in late May ten or fifteen miles at sea.

HISTORY: No information regarding this species in original forest; no evidence of recent change in numbers.

* *

RUBY-THROATED HUMMINGBIRD
Archilochus colubris (Linnaeus)

STATUS: Represented in MCZ collection.

SUMMER: Uncommon and local breeding species; no evidence of spring transients.

Earliest arrival date: April 26, 1961, at Woods Hole (Wigley).

Average arrival period: May 3–10.

FALL: Uncommon migrant.

Earliest transient date: Uncertain, probably about July 5.

Average migration period: July 25–September 18; average 1–4 birds, maximum 10 on September 7–9, 1951 (M.A.S.).

Latest departure date: November 14, 1958, at Chatham (Norman).

DISTRIBUTION: Breeds chiefly in villages, 1–3 pairs each, occasionally in wilder areas. Found over entire Cape and probably slightly more numerous than on mainland. In fall has been seen five to ten miles offshore both in Cape Cod Bay and off Chatham.

HISTORY: No evidence of any change in numbers.

* *

BELTED KINGFISHER
Megaceryle alcyon (Linnaeus)

STATUS: Represented in MCZ and British Museum collections.

SPRING: Arrival of residents, irregular as transient.

Average migration period: March 22–May 26.

Peak: April 19–30; average 2–4 birds, maximum 12 on April 28, 1941 (Griscom, Mason, Bergstrom).

SUMMER: Rather rare and local breeding species, probably 10–12 pairs on Cape.

FALL: Uncommon migrant.

Average migration period: August 15–November 20.

Peak: September 5–25, average 3–6, maximum 16 on September 9–10, 1949 (M.A.S.).

WINTER: Rather uncommon resident, probably a different population from summer; average 2–6, maximum 16 on January 3, 1954 (C.C.), usually surviving the season.

DISTRIBUTION: Waterways, either salt or fresh, with clay or gravel banks for breeding; found over entire Cape. Migrants and winter birds along any water margin, the latter concentrating eastward.

HISTORY: No evidence of any significant change in numbers.

* *

YELLOW-SHAFTED FLICKER
Colaptes auratus (Linnaeus)

STATUS: Represented in MCZ, BMS, Chicago, and British Museum collections.

SPRING: Individuals and loose flocks from winter, uncommon as both terminal and transient migrant.

Average migration period: March 25–April 25; average 10–25, maximum 75 on April 12, 1955 (Hill, Petty).

SUMMER: Common and widespread breeding species occupying a wide variety of habitat including fence posts and telephone poles in absence of trees.

FALL: Abundant migrant.

Average migration period: September 15–November 25.

Peak: September 22–October 10; average 25–60 birds, maximum 100 on several occasions, though flight may fail entirely as in 1945.

WINTER: Common resident; average 40–90, maximum 152 on January 3, 1954 (C.C.), at beginning of season, but with considerable mortality according to severity of the season.

DISTRIBUTION: Open wooded areas. Equally common as breeding species over entire Cape; fall transients concentrate to southeast. Numbers about the same as on adjacent mainland but greater than inland or northward on the mainland.

HISTORY: No data from period when Cape was wooded or after deforestation. Recent counts have shown a modest increase since 1940.

*   *

RED-BELLIED WOODPECKER
Centurus carolinus (Linnaeus)

STATUS: Presumptive.
Very rare vagrant from South.
SIGHT RECORDS: October 2–3, 1930, at North Eastham (Low) and during November and December 1960 in Eastham-Orleans area, presumably one individual (many observers).

*   *

RED-HEADED WOODPECKER
Melanerpes erythrocephalus (Linnaeus)

STATUS: Represented in Chicago and British Museum collections.
FALL: Very irregular wandering visitant at present.
Earliest arrival date: August 27, 1944, at Eastham (Hill).
Average period: September 1–30; half of all records occur in this single month, always single birds.
WINTER: Occasionally lingers into winter and rarely into spring, e.g., April 23, 1950, at Harwich (Howes) and June 24, 1933, at North Eastham (Austin).

DISTRIBUTION: Reported over entire Cape.

HISTORY: Bred at North Truro in 1889 (Miller, female and two young in British Museum); Forbush (1927) also reported a nesting record at Wellfleet, details now lost. Otherwise the data available indicate that the bird was never more than an irregular wanderer on the Cape, less numerous than on the mainland, and furthermore that there has been no change in its seasonal occurrence.

*   *

YELLOW-BELLIED SAPSUCKER
Sphyrapicus varius (Linnaeus)

STATUS: Represented in BMS and British Museum collections.

FALL: Uncommon migrant.

Earliest arrival date: September 9, 1951, at Orleans (Baird).

Average migration period: September 20–October 12; average 1–3 birds, occasionally to 8.

WINTER: Casually attempts to winter, Harwich in 1950 (Howes), Orleans in 1955 (Lund), but never known to have survived.

SPRING: Rare but regular migrant.

Earliest arrival date: April 2, 1943, at Chatham (Griscom).

Average migration period: April 19–May 1; always single birds.

Latest departure date: May 11, 1937, at Chatham (Smith, in BMS).

DISTRIBUTION: Open mixed woods on migration, usually around feeder in winter. Recorded from entire Cape, more common westward in spring. Counts essentially same as on mainland coastal areas south of Boston but less than inland or north of Boston.

HISTORY: No data.

*   *

HAIRY WOODPECKER

Dendrocopos villosus (Linnaeus)

STATUS: Represented in MCZ collection.

SPRING AND SUMMER: No migrants. Rare and local breeding species, estimated 8–10 pairs for entire Cape, chiefly in deeper woods of higher land of the Falmouth-Sandwich moraine, occasionally along south shore; very rare or lacking from Eastham northward.

FALL: Rare and irregular as migrant from mainland augmenting local population; usually 1–2 birds, occasionally a small flight as in 1954, but never in great numbers.

WINTER: Rare and local resident; average 1–3 birds, maximum 10 in 1949 and 1958 (C.C.), usually surviving season.

DISTRIBUTION: See above for breeding distribution. Fall migrants more widespread over entire Cape, including to Monomoy Point.

HISTORY: No evidence of change in status recently. No data on early period.

* *

DOWNY WOODPECKER

Dendrocopos pubescens (Linnaeus)

STATUS: Banded at Austin Station.

SPRING AND SUMMER: No migrants. Fairly common breeding species, more tolerant than Hairy of smaller and more open woodlands, and hence more common and widespread over entire Cape; no estimate on number of pairs.

FALL: Local population rarely and irregularly augmented by migrants from mainland.

WINTER: Fairly common resident; average 5–10 birds, maximum 36 on January 1, 1950 (C.C.), largely successful in survival.

DISTRIBUTION: Widespread over entire Cape in woods and uplands.

HISTORY: No data from early periods, no change since 1935.

* *

BLACK-BACKED THREE-TOED WOODPECKER
Picoides arcticus (Swainson)

STATUS: Represented in BMS collection.
Very rare vagrant from North.
SPECIMENS: December 5, 1903, at Wellfleet (Nichols, in BMS, *Auk*, *21*, 81, 1904) and found dead on October 17, 1958, at Pocasset (Gifford).
SIGHT RECORDS: February 2–April 7, 1958, at Falmouth (Evans), October 19, 1958, at Brewster (Pierce), and October 21–25, 1962, at Wellfleet and Nauset (Bailey).
HISTORY: No data from past and particularly from the great flight years.

* *

EASTERN KINGBIRD
Tyrannus tyrannus (Linnaeus)

STATUS: Represented in MCZ, Chicago, and British Museum collections.
SPRING: Arrival of residents, no evidence of transients.
Earliest arrival date: April 19, 1929, at Sandwich (Burbank) and April 19, 1935, at Chatham (Eldredge), after southern storms.
Average arrival period: May 12–18.
SUMMER: Fairly common breeding resident.
FALL: Very common migrant, occasionally abundant.
Earliest transient date: Uncertain, probably late July.
Average migration period: August 15–September 20.
Peak: August 21–September 14; average 12–35 birds, maximum 50 on September 3, 1944, at Chatham (Griscom).
Latest departure date: October 12 on two occasions.
DISTRIBUTION: Breeding in hedgerows, open woods, etc., over en-

tire Cape, including the Provincelands. Migrants also widespread, including along outer beaches.

HISTORY: No evidence of any change in status.

* *

WESTERN KINGBIRD

Tyrannus verticalis Say

STATUS: Represented in MCZ, BMS, and Chicago collections.

FALL: Rare but regular migrant.

Earliest arrival date: August 25, 1963, at Monomoy (Parker,
Bowen, Kleber, Hill, Bailey, Dana).

Average migration period: September 5–November 15.

Counts: Nearly half of all records have occurred in September,
then in approximately equal numbers for October and November, so the October hiatus reported in the rest of the state
(Griscom & Snyder, 1955) is not apparent on the Cape. Usually single birds, maximum 4 on November 2–10, 1940, at
Eastham (many observers).

Latest departure date: December 26, 1949, at Orleans (Cum-
mings).

DISTRIBUTION: Reported over entire Cape, greatest number in
Orleans-Eastham area.

HISTORY: First specimen taken October 3, 1887, at Great Island,
Hyannis (in Cory collection, Chicago); reported erratically prior
to 1930 and nearly every year since then, but counts have shown
no significant rise, so this increase in frequency is believed due
to increase in observers, i.e., I doubt any real change in status,
contrary to opinion expressed by Griscom & Snyder (l.c.). Average 2–6 birds yearly during this period but subject to occasional flights as in 1940 and 1955 with ten and eleven birds
respectively.

* *

CASSIN'S KINGBIRD
Tyrannus vociferans Swainson

STATUS: Represented in MAS collection.
Accidental vagrant from West. Collected on October 22, 1962, at Eastham (Bailey).

* *

SCISSOR-TAILED FLYCATCHER
Muscivora forficata (Gmelin)

STATUS: Photographed, on file at Wellfleet Bay Sanctuary.
Accidental vagrant from the Southwest. One record, June 25, 1960, at Wellfleet (Bailey).

* *

GREAT CRESTED FLYCATCHER
Myiarchus crinitus (Linnaeus)

STATUS: Presumptive.
SPRING: Arrival of residents, no evidence of transients.
   Earliest arrival date: May 5, 1944, at Sandwich (Burbank).
   Average arrival period: May 15–20.
SUMMER: Rare and rather local breeding resident, scattered pairs only and most numerous in woods of Falmouth-Sandwich moraine and south to sound shores from Woods Hole to Osterville, decreasing east to Brewster, rare to Orleans, and casual north to Truro.
FALL: Very rare as transient, mostly wandering local birds.
   Average departure period: September 10–15.
   Latest departure date: November 25, 1956, at Eastham (Smart), reported as this species of *Myiarchus* but not collected.
DISTRIBUTION: Open mixed woods, feeding at middle height. See above for distribution on Cape, fewer than on mainland.

HISTORY: No data on original status. Increasing in numbers and extending eastward since 1940 as woods mature and oaks increase, e.g., 1–2 in 1940–1945, and 5–6 in 1959–1960 at Brewster.

* *

EASTERN PHOEBE
Sayornis phoebe (Latham)

STATUS: Represented in MCZ and British Museum collections.

SPRING: Arrival of residents, very rare as transient.
Earliest arrival date: March 17, 1945, at Sandwich (Burbank).
Average arrival period: April 5–10.

SUMMER: Very rare and local breeding resident, probably not more than 6–8 pairs total, but widely distributed from Canal to Wellfleet.

FALL: Rare and irregular as transient, also wandering local birds.
Earliest transient date: Uncertain, probably about August 18.
Average migration period: August 28–September 30; average 1–3 birds, maximum 6 on September 11, 1948, at Chatham (M.A.S.).

WINTER: Casually attempts to winter, recorded erratically to December and January, possibly surviving in very mild years.

DISTRIBUTION: Breeds at bridges, hunting shacks, etc., near fresh water. Recorded over entire Cape, but much less common than on mainland. More migrants westward on Cape.

HISTORY: No data on original status. Appears to be decreasing near Canal but holding its own eastward since 1940.

* *

SAY'S PHOEBE
Sayornis saya (Bonaparte)

STATUS: Represented in British Museum collection.
Accidental vagrant from West.

Collected September 30, 1889, at North Truro (Miller, in British Museum, *Auk*, 7, 228, 1890). Several sight records since.

* *

YELLOW-BELLIED FLYCATCHER

Empidonax flaviventris (Baird & Baird)

STATUS: Represented in BMS and British Museum collections.

SPRING: Very rare and irregular migrant, dependent on favorable winds.

Average migration period: May 28–31; usually single birds, once a pair.

FALL: Rare migrant, probably occurring yearly; sight and even banding identification of fall *Empidonaces* is speculative at best.

Earliest transient date: August 8, 1956, at Chatham (Griscom).

Average migration period: August 18–September 15; appearance dependent on northwest wind; usually single birds, maximum 4, including 1 collected on August 22, 1954, at Monomoy (Griscom, Morgan, Kleber).

Latest departure date: September 28, 1940, at Monomoy (Griscom, in BMS).

DISTRIBUTION: May appear anywhere over Cape in brushy thickets, swamps, and woods but mostly in shore-line traps.

HISTORY: Data prior to 1930 unsatisfactory, no evidence of change since that date.

* *

ACADIAN FLYCATCHER

Empidonax virescens (Vieillot)

STATUS: Hypothetical.

The scattering of banding and sight records are not satisfactory.

* *

TRAILL'S FLYCATCHER
Empidonax traillii (Audubon)

STATUS: Collected (Griscom), location of specimen unknown.

SUMMER: Very local resident; Forbush (1927) gives a summer, not specifically breeding, record for Wellfleet, details now lost; singing male with mate there in 1961 and 1962, but nest could not be found (Hill). Dates of spring arrival not known.

FALL: Rare though probably regular migrant, a very few birds apparently accompanying other species of *Empidonax* in the larger flights.

Specimens: August 22–September 3.

Sight records: August 17–September 18.

DISTRIBUTION: Summer occurrence in Wellfleet in alder thickets along Herring River. Migrants widely scattered over entire Cape, most often in shore-line traps.

HISTORY: No data; most records are since 1941 and reflect only the increase in observers.

* *

LEAST FLYCATCHER
Empidonax minimus (Baird & Baird)

STATUS: Represented in MCZ and British Museum collections.

SPRING: Arrival of residents, very rare as transient.

Earliest arrival date: May 5, 1923, at Orleans (Earle).

Average arrival period: May 18–25.

SUMMER: Very rare, local, and irregular breeding resident, largely at Falmouth, Cotuit, and Sandwich east to Barnstable and perhaps casually to Orleans. Probably maximum of 3–5 pairs on Cape and hence much rarer than on mainland.

FALL: Uncommon migrant, occasionally common, presumed to be the most numerous *Empidonax* in fall flights.

Earliest transient date: August 10, 1942, at Monomoy (Griscom).

Average migration period: August 20–September 20.

Counts: Average 1–6 birds, maximum 50 on August 22, 1954, at Monomoy (Griscom, Bowen, Parker, Baird). Flights dependent on northwest wind at height of migration.

Latest departure date: October 24, 1956, banded at North Eastham (Austin Station), later dates not confirmed.

DISTRIBUTION: Breeding in elms of village streets, rarely in deciduous second growth. Confined to richer soil of Falmouth moraine. On migration occurs in essentially equal numbers over entire Cape with concentration in shore-line traps.

HISTORY: No evidence of change in either breeding or migrant status.

* *

EASTERN WOOD PEWEE
Contopus virens (Linnaeus)

STATUS: Represented in MCZ and British Museum collections.

SPRING: Arrival of residents, no evidence of transients.

Earliest arrival date: May 13, 1936, at Chatham (Bishop).

Average arrival period: May 26–30.

SUMMER: Very common breeding resident found in numbers over entire Cape, particularly in the pitch pine woods and hence fewer north of Wellfleet. Estimated density 16 pairs/100 acres at Brewster (Hill), 14 pairs/100 acres at Sagamore (Hill), 11 pairs at Woods Hole (Freeland), 3 pairs at Provincetown (Smith), etc., more numerous than on mainland except for the immediately adjacent Plymouth pine barrens.

FALL: Common migrant.

Average migration period: August 10–October 1.

Peak: September 5–15; average 3–10 birds, maximum 35 on September 11, 1948, at Chatham (Griscom).

Latest departure date: October 22, 1937, banded at North Eastham (Austin Station).

DISTRIBUTION: Widespread over entire Cape in woodlands, appearing in shore-line traps in migration.

HISTORY: No data from early periods when ecological conditions
were different; no evidence of change since 1935.

* *

OLIVE-SIDED FLYCATCHER
Nuttallornis borealis (Swainson)

STATUS: Represented in MCZ collection.

SPRING: Formerly arrival of breeding population but dates unknown; no recent records.

SUMMER: Formerly not uncommon breeding resident from Bourne
south to Falmouth, Mashpee, and Cotuit (Brewster, Bangs),
with nests found during month of June. Forbush (1927) gave
in addition two summer, not specifically breeding, records from
Wellfleet and Harwich, details now lost. Forbush (l.c.) knew
of no confirmed breeding after about 1900 but suspected persistence of a few pairs to at least 1917.

FALL: Former status unknown; at present a rare and irregular
migrant dependent on northwest winds.

Earliest arrival date: August 16, 1952, at Chatham (Mosher).

Average migration period: August 25–September 16; always
single birds.

Latest departure date: September 20, 1954, at Yarmouthport
(Sargent); one November record seen but not collected.

DISTRIBUTION: See above for former breeding areas, occurred in
pine barrens and not particularly associated with swamps and
water. Migrants occur widely and most often found in shore-line
traps.

HISTORY: See above. No evidence of change in numbers of migrants since 1935.

* *

VERMILION FLYCATCHER
Pyrocephalus rubinus (Boddaert)

STATUS: Hypothetical.
One sight record in fall of 1961.

* *

HORNED LARK
Eremophila alpestris (Linnaeus)

STATUS: Represented in MCZ, BMS, Chicago, and British Museum collections. At least two populations involved: 1) breeding, *E. a. praticola*; 2) wintering, *E. a. alpestris*; and possibly 3) an irregular transient population, subspecies unknown.

1) BREEDING, Prairie Horned Lark, *E. a. praticola*.

SPRING: Arrival of residents, no transients.

Earliest arrival date: February 21, 1937, at Chatham (Griscom).

Average arrival period: February 26–March 20.

SUMMER: Locally common on outer beaches, airports, golf courses, and barren fields; see below for counts.

FALL: Gradual disappearance of residents, probably a few transients from the mainland in flocks of other races.

Average departure period: October 5–20.

Latest departure date: December 15, 1888, at Great Island, Hyannis (Brewster, in BMS, *Auk*, 6, 71, 1889).

DISTRIBUTION: Breeding widely over Cape, greatest number at Monomoy (10–12 pairs), also Provincetown (5–6 pairs), Nauset (2–3 pairs), Sandy Neck (5–7 pairs), Hyannis Airport (4–5 pairs), Sagamore (3–4 pairs), etc. In migration equally over entire Cape and mixing with flocks of other races.

HISTORY: Spreading rapidly eastward. Miller failed to collect this subspecies at North Truro about 1890, but early-winter transients known from 1888 (see above); Forbush (1927) recorded breeding only at Sandwich; see above for present breeding distribution. Steady increase in numbers of breeding pairs since 1935 with midsummer gatherings up to 60 birds. No satisfactory winter records.

2) WINTERING, Northern Horned Lark, *E. a. alpestris.*

FALL: Common to abundant migrant.

Earliest arrival date: September 20, 1942, at Monomoy (Scott, Curtis).

Average migration period: October 15–January 5.

Peak: November 20–January 1; average 50–150 birds, maximum 352 on December 28, 1952 (C.C.).

WINTER: Usually fairly common resident, flocks of ten to sixty.

SPRING: Uncommon migrant.

Average migration period: February 20–April 1.

Peak: February 25–March 10; average 20–30 birds, maximum 35 on several occasions.

Latest departure date: April 19, 1938, at Monomoy (Griscom, Tousey).

DISTRIBUTION: Widespread in open country, uplands, pastures, and dunes along outer beaches over entire Cape. Fall migrants observed to reach Cape across water from both north and northeast.

HISTORY: No evidence of change in status.

3) POSSIBLE IRREGULAR TRANSIENT POPULATION: "White-browed" birds in winter or in flocks other than in summer may represent some additional race such as *E. a. hoyti,* but the only specimens collected have not been typical and field identification is not convincing.

* *

TREE SWALLOW
Iridoprocne bicolor (Vieillot)

STATUS: Represented in MCZ and British Museum collections.

SPRING: Arrival of residents, uncommon as transient.

Earliest arrival date: March 15, 1955, at Monomoy (Hill, Bryan).

Average resident arrival period: April 1–19.

Average transient period: April 1–May 3; seldom over 100 birds.

SUMMER: Fairly common but local breeding resident, almost exclusively in specially placed nesting boxes and often around cranberry bogs.

FALL: Abundant migrant.

Earliest transient date: Uncertain, probably about July 18.

Average migration period: August 15–October 10.

Peak: Not well marked, late August and most of September; see below for counts.

Latest transient date: Uncertain, probably about December 1.

WINTER: Casually attempts to winter in very small numbers; known to have survived entire season of 1943–1944 at Harwich (Cahoon) and possibly in 1924 at Sandwich (Carleton, Earle).

DISTRIBUTION: Breeding pairs fairly evenly spread over entire Cape. Migrants concentrate along shore lines and feed over marshes. A major flight line crosses southwest along Canal, e.g., 1000–15,000 daily August 15–31 with a total of 56,000 for month in 1952 at Sagamore (Hill); smaller numbers along Cape side of Buzzards Bay, e.g., 18,500 for August 1953 at Woods Hole (Freeland). Outer Cape peaks later, usually mid-September, and are dependent on northwest wind, so counts are irregular from year to year, 500 to 10,000.

HISTORY: Entire population subject to fluctuation according to wintering conditions in South and to local nesting success, e.g., large losses in June 1959. Rapid recovery from losses, however, and no evidence of long-term trend.

* *

BANK SWALLOW

Riparia riparia (Linnaeus)

STATUS: Represented in MCZ, BMS, and British Museum collections.

SPRING: Arrival of residents, a few transients near Canal.

Earliest arrival date: April 30, 1958, at Falmouth (Athearn).
Average arrival period: May 10–30.

SUMMER: Uncommon and very local breeding resident. Colonies present over entire Cape and run through cycles according to condition of banking: At Highland Light, Truro, 200 pairs in 1850–1855 (Thoreau), 100 pairs in 1891 (Brewster), 25 pairs in 1924 (Earle), 100 pairs in 1961 (Hill); at Nauset 115 pairs in 1924, only 2 pairs in 1925, and no real recovery thereafter (Earle); present at Great Island, Hyannis, in 1895 (Brewster), none now; at Falmouth 15 pairs in 1953 (Benjamin) to 8 pairs in 1961 (Hill); etc.

FALL: Rare and inconspicuous migrant, often confused with other species.

Average migration period: July 28–August 25.

Latest departure date: September 7, 1952, at Eastham (Mason).

DISTRIBUTION: See above for breeding colonies. Migrants probably more common westward as often seen moving southwest along Canal in fall; no large numbers.

HISTORY: No evidence of long-term change; see above for local changes.

* *

ROUGH-WINGED SWALLOW
Stelgidopteryx ruficollis (Vieillot)

STATUS: Banded at Austin Station.

SPRING: Arrival of residents, no transients.

Earliest arrival date: April 18, 1948, at South Orleans (Earle).
Average arrival period: April 25–May 5.

SUMMER: Isolated pairs in suitable banks, recorded from Sagamore, Falmouth, Hyannis, Brewster, South Harwich, Chatham, and Orleans, but not northward; probably no more than ten pairs on Cape.

FALL: Wandering local birds, possibly a very few transients from mainland.

Average departure period: July 10–August 15.

Latest departure date: Uncertain due to confusion with other species.

DISTRIBUTION: See above.

HISTORY: May (*Bird-Banding*, *1*, 29, 1930) reported only two migrational records for Cape, both west of Barnstable, up to 1930. First breeding records in 1937 at South Harwich (Bishop), in 1941 at Brewster (Griscom), in 1942 at South Orleans (Earle), in 1945 at Chatham (Griscom); increasing at Chatham and Brewster during the 1950's.

* *

BARN SWALLOW
Hirundo rustica Linnaeus

STATUS: Represented in MCZ, BMS, and British Museum collections.

SPRING: Arrival of residents, regular as transient but more common westward.

Earliest arrival date: April 7, 1940, at Orleans (Drury, Nash, Davis, Hill).

Average resident arrival period: May 1–7.

Average transient migration period: May 10–30.

SUMMER: Rather uncommon breeding resident, much fewer than on mainland, but widespread over entire Cape.

FALL: Fairly common migrant.

Average migration period: July 20–September 20; average 30–300 birds, occasionally to 500.

Latest departure date: Frequently southern storms bring a group of late records, latest November 28, 1953, at Eastham (Earle).

DISTRIBUTION: Breeding over entire Cape wherever suitable open buildings are available; migrants widely and evenly distributed.

HISTORY: Evidence inconclusive for Cape but probably consistent with decrease parallel to that elsewhere in Massachusetts (see Griscom & Snyder, 1955).

* *

CLIFF SWALLOW
Petrochelidon pyrrhonota (Vieillot)

STATUS: Represented in British Museum collection.
SPRING: Very few records, not establishing any pattern, May 19 on.
SUMMER: Formerly breeding locally, 25–30 pairs in 1891 at North Truro (Brewster) and 3–6 pairs until 1937 at Barnstable (Griscom), but none since. Wandering birds scattered throughout the summer.
FALL: Rare and irregular migrant.
  Average migration period: July 20–September 20; single birds and small flocks to 33.
  Latest departure date: October 31, 1937, at Monomoy (Taber, Stackpole).
DISTRIBUTION: See above for former breeding stations. Migrants recorded more widely over entire Cape.
HISTORY: Steady decrease throughout historical period for both breeding birds and migrants.

* *

PURPLE MARTIN
Progne subis (Linnaeus)

STATUS: Represented in MCZ and British Museum collections.
SPRING: Arrival of residents, no transients.
  Earliest arrival date: April 2, 1960, at Sandwich (Pratt).
  Average arrival period: April 20–30.
SUMMER: Rare and very local breeding resident. At present fairly persistent colonies at Falmouth (8–10 pairs) and Woods Hole (4–6 pairs) with shifting colonies at Chatham, Dennis, and

Beach Grass (Ammophila breviligulata)
Seaside Goldenrod (Solidago sempervirens)

elsewhere in Falmouth. Eggs imported in 1960 to Wellfleet, hatched successfully under other swallows, returned but did not nest in 1961.

FALL: Very rare and irregular migrant probably including some transients from mainland.

Average migration period: July 2–September 10; usually single birds.

Latest departure date: September 24, 1951, at Chatham (Griscom).

DISTRIBUTION: Breeding as above. Migrants and summer wanderers may appear anywhere over entire Cape.

HISTORY: Known to have bred at Woods Hole (Bryant) and Falmouth (Brewster) prior to 1903; no known survival of colony thereafter. Re-establishment of nesting began in 1947 at two sites in Falmouth and occurred east to Chatham after 1952.

* *

GRAY JAY
Perisoreus canadensis (Linnaeus)

STATUS: Hypothetical.
One unconfirmed sight record.

* *

BLUE JAY
Cyanocitta cristata (Linnaeus)

STATUS: Represented in MCZ and British Museum collections.

SPRING: Dispersal of wintering groups, usually only a few transients.

Average migration period: May 15–June 13; seldom more than 50.

SUMMER: Fairly common breeding resident widespread over entire Cape from Canal to Orleans, more local north to Wellfleet and absent northward.

FALL: Abundant migrant.

Average migration period: September 10–January 1.

Peak: September 28–October 28; average 30–70 birds, maximum 285 on October 2, 1954, at Chatham (Griscom, Morgan, Snyder); occasionally an additional late flight in December after severe weather on mainland, maximum 324 on December 28, 1958 (C.C.).

WINTER: Irregular in numbers from nearly absent to fairly common, greatest number linger after later fall flights.

DISTRIBUTION: Breeding distribution given above. Of migrating fall flocks at Sagamore 85 per cent turn southwest along Canal, remainder cross and move eastward. Late fall and winter birds concentrate on outer Cape, and late spring migrants have been seen moving north at Eastham (Donohue); nothing known about crossings over water at either season.

HISTORY: No evidence of any change in status.

* *

BLACK-BILLED MAGPIE

Pica pica (Linnaeus)

STATUS: Hypothetical.

Seen October 19, 1952, at Eastham (Higgins) and April 9, 1953, at Monomoy (Smith); species had been released in New Jersey and Vermont previously.

* *

COMMON RAVEN

Corvus corax Linnaeus

EXTIRPATED: no specimens preserved. Presumed to have been present in early colonial times but rapidly eliminated as "vermin," date of disappearance unknown. One unconfirmed recent sight record.

* *

COMMON CROW

Corvus brachyrhynchos Brehm

STATUS: Represented in MCZ, Chicago, and British Museum collections. Probably two populations which are separable only by banding: 1) breeding, some of which remain all winter and some of which depart southward; and 2) northern, some of which remain on Cape all winter and some of which are only transients (modified from Low, *Bird-Banding*, 5, 192, 1934).

SPRING: Fairly common migrant.

Average migration period: February 17–April 12; occasionally over 200.

SUMMER: Uncommon but widespread breeding resident; wide ranging, so probably fewer pairs than might appear.

FALL: Fairly common migrant.

Average migration period: October 15–December 20; seldom over 100 birds migrating, but builds up to 200–350 by late December (C.C.).

WINTER: Counts average 40–100 with mortality according to season; no great roosts ever reported on Cape.

DISTRIBUTION: Breeds in heavier woods over entire Cape and found over all types of terrain, including dunes and outer beaches.

HISTORY: No evidence of any change in status.

* *

FISH CROW

Corvus ossifragus Wilson

STATUS: Presumptive.

Rare and irregular around Buzzards Bay estuary; recorded August 3, 1959, at Pocasset (Robbins) and a pair on May 25, 1960, there, nest not found (Hill). Collected July 16, 1884, at Wareham, only three or four miles away but not on Cape Cod

(Bangs, in BMS, see Brewster, *Auk*, 4, 162, 1887) and up to
17 seen there in 1905 (Forbush, 1927). Scattered sight records
at Sagamore, Barnstable, Osterville, and Truro.

* *

BLACK-CAPPED CHICKADEE
Parus atricapillus Linnaeus

STATUS: Represented in MCZ and British Museum collections.

SPRING: Dispersal of wintering flocks, no evidence of transients.

SUMMER: Common and widespread breeding resident, more numerous than on mainland.

FALL: Common migrant, sometimes abundant.
Average migration period: September 20–November 10.
Peak: October 15–30; average 15–60, maximum 100+ on
several occasions.

WINTER: Common and widespread resident, greatest number after
heavy fall flights, e.g., 1230 on December 30, 1961 (C.C.),
decreasing according to severity of season.

DISTRIBUTION: Breeds in pitch pine and mixed woods over entire
Cape. Fall migrants at Sagamore follow edge of uplands with
only 25 per cent crossing Canal and remainder going westward
along north bank. On outer Cape migrants collect southeastward
even to sand-dune thickets on outer beaches.

HISTORY: No old data and no evidence of recent change.

* *

BOREAL CHICKADEE
Parus hudsonicus Forster

STATUS: Presumptive.

Very rare and irregular visitant from North. Penetrates to Cape
only in the more marked mainland flights: November 2, 1913,
at Sagamore (Robbins, see Wright, *Auk*, *31*, 236, 1914); De-

cember 21, 1941, at Chatham (Hill); twice in 1954, November 24 at Orleans (Wilson) and December 12 at Sandwich (Romaine); two present October 20, 1961, to February 10, 1962, at North Eastham (Bailey).

* *

TUFTED TITMOUSE
Parus bicolor Linnaeus

STATUS: Presumptive.

Rare vagrant from South. Appears chiefly at feeding stations from late fall on and remains into March. First reported in 1954 at Orleans (Lund) and since 1957 at Falmouth, Woods Hole, Osterville, Chatham, and Orleans. Has never been recorded in late spring or summer and hence no suspicion of breeding.

* *

WHITE-BREASTED NUTHATCH
Sitta carolinensis Latham

STATUS: Collected but not preserved (Hill).

FALL: Uncommon migrant westward, rare and sometimes absent eastward.

Earliest transient date: August 9, 1941, at Monomoy (Griscom, Peterson, Garrison, Hickey).

Average migration period: October 1–December 1; usually singles, occasional flights as in 1961 with 27 (C.C.).

WINTER: Rather rare and irregular, often at feeding stations.

SPRING: Dispersal of wintering birds, rare migrant near Canal, but very rare or even absent eastward.

Average migration period: April 2–May 20; usually single birds, maximum 3 on April 23, 1961, at Sagamore (Hill).

Latest departure date: May 26, 1940, at North Eastham (Nash, Drury, Hill).

DISTRIBUTION: Thinly but widely scattered in heavier mixed woods and shade trees; definitely more common westward on Cape and much fewer than on mainland. Migrants more widely found and may even appear in sand-dune thickets.

HISTORY: No evidence of change in status.

* *

RED-BREASTED NUTHATCH
Sitta canadensis Linnaeus

STATUS: Represented in BMS and British Museum collections.

FALL: Irregular migrant, erratic in time of arrival.

Earliest arrival date: Uncertain, probably about mid-August.

Average migration period: August 25–October 25.

Peak: September 8–25; extremely variable in numbers, probably never absent and up to 20 per day in flight year, maximum 35 on September 19, 1943, at Monomoy (Griscom).

WINTER: Irregular, absent to fairly common; presence not dependent on heavy fall flight; maximum 202 on December 29, 1963, but absent on eight of thirty years (C.C.).

SPRING: Dispersal of wintering birds, otherwise a rare and irregular migrant at Canal and very rare eastward.

Average migration period: April 15–May 15; average 1–2 birds, rarely to 5.

SUMMER: Casual throughout season, probably nesting sporadically.

DISTRIBUTION: Normally in pitch pine woods, but in flights may appear anywhere, including sand-dune thickets and on boats ten to twenty miles offshore.

HISTORY: No evidence of change; flights of same size recorded throughout historical period as at present, e.g., 30 on November 21, 1886, at Great Island, Hyannis (Brewster). Flights appear about every second or third year but follow no clear-cut pattern.

* *

BROWN CREEPER
Certhia familiaris Linnaeus

STATUS: Represented in British Museum collection.

FALL: Rather uncommon migrant.

Earliest arrival date: September 1, 1960, at Sagamore (Hill).

Average migration period: September 15–January 1; average 1–3 birds, maximum 6 on September 28, 1952, at Monomoy (Griscom, Halberg).

WINTER: Rather rare and irregular; average 1–3 birds but may be absent.

SPRING: Rarely recorded unless individuals have wintered, occasionally a very small transient flight.

Average migration period: April 1–May 1.

SUMMER: Recorded sporadically in Centerville, Wianno, Cotuit, and Marstons Mills; nesting suspected but never proven.

DISTRIBUTION: Mixed woods over entire Cape, migrants even to sand-dune thickets.

HISTORY: Probably decreasing in numbers during historical period, but this is not well documented for Cape Cod; apparently always less numerous than on mainland as is still the case. No evidence of change since 1935.

*   *

HOUSE WREN
Troglodytes aedon Vieillot

STATUS: Represented in British Museum collection.

SPRING: Arrival of residents, no evidence of transients.

Arrival dates: Not known.

SUMMER: Rare and local breeding resident, regular at Falmouth (2 pairs), Mashpee (1 pair), and Sandwich (2 pairs); irregularly to Centerville, North Chatham, Orleans, and Wellfleet.

FALL: Rare migrant.

Earliest transient date: September 9, 1951, at Chatham (Griscom).

Average migration period: September 15–October 15; always single birds.

Latest departure date: January 1, 1954, at Woods Hole (Kelly).

DISTRIBUTION: Dooryards and brushland, usually in areas of richer soil. Breeding distribution above; migrants may appear anywhere but are probably more numerous westward.

HISTORY: Original status unknown, but apparently absent in early historical period. Now moving eastward on Cape, in 1947 to Centerville (Snyder), in 1957 to Orleans (Earle), in 1961 to Chatham (Mosher) and Wellfleet (Hill); the more easterly stations are still irregularly occupied.

* *

WINTER WREN
Troglodytes troglodytes (Linnaeus)

STATUS: Represented in BMS and British Museum collections.

FALL: Rare migrant.

Earliest arrival date: September 17, 1887, at Monomoy (Cahoon).

Average migration period: September 25–December 1; always single birds.

WINTER: Very rare and irregular resident, sometimes surviving.

SPRING: Casual, successful wintering birds only, no transients.

Latest departure date: April 16, 1958, at Bass River (O'Regan).

DISTRIBUTION: Migrants may appear in any habitat over entire Cape. Wintering birds in dense thickets in deeper woods. Recorded on boat sixteen miles east of Truro (Rankin, *Bird-Banding, 32,* 58, 1961).

HISTORY: No data from early period, no evidence of change since 1930.

* *

CAROLINA WREN
Thryothorus ludovicianus (Latham)

STATUS: Banded at Austin Station.
Permanent resident in very irregular numbers.
DISTRIBUTION: Chiefly thick swamps with some wandering, especially to feeding stations, when not breeding. Records rather evenly distributed over Cape from Woods Hole and Sagamore to Eastham with a concentration in Orleans and Chatham probably representing only increased observation; less common north to Wellfleet and no known records northward. Breeding actually proven only in Orleans (Earle) and Eastham (Clark).
HISTORY: Traditionally increasing during cycles of mild seasons only to be eliminated by cold and snowy winters. Data on early fluctuations incomplete. From 1935 to 1949, zero to five birds reported annually; then 3 in 1952, 15 in 1955, to maximum of 33 in 1958; very cold and snowy winter of 1960–1961 reduced this to one in December 1961 (C.C.).

*   *

LONG-BILLED MARSH WREN
Telmatodytes palustris (Wilson)

STATUS: Represented in MCZ collection.
SPRING: Arrival of residents, very rare as transient in late May. Arrival dates: Not known.
SUMMER: Very local breeding resident, known at present only at Mashpee, 6–8 pairs and nest found (Hill), and West Harwich, 25 pairs (Fox, Hill); casual wanderers elsewhere.
FALL: Rather rare but fairly regular migrant.
Earliest transient date: August 22, 1953, at Monomoy (Bailey).
Average migration period: September 12–November 20; average 1–3 birds, maximum 7 on November 11, 1952, at Monomoy (Griscom, Emery).

WINTER: Regularly attempts to winter in small numbers, 1–5 birds, no known survival beyond early February.

DISTRIBUTION: Breeding colonies noted above, both in cattails growing in brackish water. Migrants largely in salt marshes over entire Cape; winter birds chiefly southeastward.

HISTORY: There is only negative evidence that the colonies did not exist prior to 1955, though such was probably the case; the West Harwich colony has increased since it was first found. No evidence of change in status of migrants since 1930.

* *

SHORT-BILLED MARSH WREN
Cistothorus platensis (Latham)

STATUS: Hypothetical.

Sight records on September 21 and 26, 1937, at Morris Island and Monomoy (Griscom, Garrison).

* *

MOCKINGBIRD
Mimus polyglottos (Linnaeus)

STATUS: Represented in BMS, Chicago, and British Museum collections.

Permanent resident in variable numbers. Nests sporadically, perhaps every year; spotted young collected August 30, 1891, at Hyannis (Cory, *Auk*, 8, 395, 1891), immature seen September 15, 1937, at Chatham (Fuller), nested in 1959 at Wellfleet (Bailey). Single birds reported throughout entire year, maxima 3 on September 11, 1890, at North Truro (Miller, *Auk*, 8, 117, 1891) and 3 on October 10, 1959, at Wellfleet (Bailey).

DISTRIBUTION: Reported over entire Cape; may remain in small area for several months and often at feeding station.

HISTORY: No evidence of change in numbers during historical period.

* *

CATBIRD
Dumetella carolinensis (Linnaeus)

STATUS: Represented in MCZ and British Museum collections.

SPRING: Arrival of residents, probably a few transients.

Earliest arrival date: April 17, 1961, at Chatham (Copeland), after a southern storm.

Average arrival period: May 2–12 with full numbers by May 20–25.

SUMMER: Abundant breeding resident, more common than elsewhere in state. Estimated 50 pairs/100 acres at Woods Hole (Hill), 35 pairs/100 acres at Sagamore (Hill), 40 pairs/100 acres at Brewster (Griscom), 40–60 pairs at Provincetown (Kelly), etc.

FALL: Mostly departure of residents, some transients.

Average migration period: September 20–October 10; occasionally to 70 birds per day.

WINTER: Regularly attempts to winter, has probably survived occasionally, especially at feeding stations.

DISTRIBUTION: Edges, brushy fields, thickets, ornamental shrubbery, etc. Found over entire Cape.

HISTORY: No evidence of change in status except for increase in late-fall and early-winter records with occasional successful survival since 1948.

* *

BROWN THRASHER
Toxostoma rufum (Linnaeus)

STATUS: Represented in MCZ and British Museum collections.

SPRING: Arrival of residents, a few transients regularly.

Earliest arrival date: April 29, 1933, at North Eastham (Low).

Average migration period: May 1–20; average 1–3 birds, maximum 8 on May 17, 1959, at Wellfleet (Bailey).

SUMMER: Rather rare and local breeding resident over entire Cape in fluctuating numbers.

FALL: Uncommon migrant.

Average migration period: September 10–October 20; average 1–3 birds, maximum 6 on September 30, 1951, at Chatham (Griscom, Emery, Beattie).

WINTER: Regularly attempts to winter, has probably survived occasionally since 1954, especially at feeding stations.

DISTRIBUTION: Nests in thickets and edge habitats, mostly in uplands but occasionally in sand-dune thickets on Monomoy and in the Provincelands.

HISTORY: Inexplicably erratic, mortality in southern winters cannot account for all variation, though it certainly explains much. Reported as common in Falmouth and Hyannis in 1891 but with great decrease by 1895 (Brewster, Bangs); common at Cotuit in 1917 but none in 1918 (Cobb); common at Harwich in 1936 but none in 1937 (Bishop). At present rather rare generally but probably increasing.

* *

ROBIN

Turdus migratorius Linnaeus

STATUS: Represented in MCZ and British Museum collections.

SPRING: Arrival of residents, common as transient.

Average resident arrival period: March 24–April 10.

Average transient migration period: March 28–April 19; average 100–200, maximum 345 on April 3–4, 1942 (Hill, Briggs).

SUMMER: Common and widespread breeding resident, though fewer than on mainland. Maximum numbers in villages; less common though still present in woodlands, but rare in brushy uplands and none in sand-dune thickets.

FALL: Very common migrant.

Average migration period: September 12–November 25.

Peak: Somewhat irregular and sometimes lacking, chiefly October 1–31, average 50–200 birds, maximum 500 on October 2, 1960, at Sagamore (Hill).

WINTER: Regular but extremely variable in numbers, early-winter counts range from one to 423 (C.C.); a few birds sedentary in cedar swamps, but main flocks quite mobile, often appearing after heavy snow on mainland.

DISTRIBUTION: See above for breeding distribution. Migrants more widely distributed in all types of habitat, including sand-dune thickets.

HISTORY: No evidence of change throughout historical period until about 1955, when a slow decline appeared.

SUBSPECIES: A few specimens of *T. m. nigrideus* have been taken and a few sight records reported, mostly in fall migration. Otherwise, all records pertain to *T. m. migratorius*.

* *

VARIED THRUSH
Ixoreus naevius (Gmelin)

STATUS: Hypothetical.

Sight record of adult male on October 13, 1963, at South Harwich (Mayo).

* *

WOOD THRUSH
Hylocichla mustelina (Gmelin)

STATUS: Represented in MCZ collection.

SPRING: Arrival of residents, casual as transient.

Earliest arrival date: May 2, 1932, at North Eastham (Brown).

Average arrival period: May 10–20.

SUMMER: Local breeding resident, chiefly westward; 2 pairs at

Falmouth, 2 pairs at Mashpee, 1 pair at East Sandwich. Mostly wandering birds eastward at present, though possibly a pair sporadically at Orleans.

FALL: Rare migrant.

Earliest transient date: August 29, 1955, at Orleans (Griscom, Rich).

Average migration period: September 1–15; always single birds.

Latest transient date: October 18, 1945, banded at North Eastham (Austin Station).

DISTRIBUTION: Breeding pairs occupy small moist areas with richer vegetation within the heavier woods in the outwash plains on the western part of the Falmouth-Sandwich moraine. Migrants more tolerant and more widely distributed, though not yet recorded north of Wellfleet.

HISTORY: No data on original status. Recorded in present breeding area by 1928, but date of first nesting not known. Slowly increasing and spreading eastward.

*   *

HERMIT THRUSH

Hylocichla guttata (Pallas)

STATUS: Represented in MCZ, BMS, and British Museum collections.

SPRING: Arrival of residents, perhaps a few transients.

Earliest arrival date: April 2, 1943, at Monomoy (Griscom).

Average arrival period: April 16–May 5.

SUMMER: Uncommon breeding resident, exclusively in the pine barrens.

FALL: Fairly common migrant.

Average migration period: September 5–December 5.

Peak: October 20–November 15; average 3–6 birds, maximum 15 on November 9, 1952, at Monomoy (Griscom, Bailey, Emery).

WINTER: Regular in small numbers, 1–5 birds early in season with mortality proportional to severity of season with some usually surviving.

DISTRIBUTION: Breeds in dry pine barrens; migrants more widespread, including along outer beaches. Recorded over entire Cape but concentrates eastward in winter.

HISTORY: No data on original status when Cape was wooded or after deforestation. Reported as fairly common during early historical period and to about 1941. Since then it has decreased westward, apparently as pine barrens have been invaded and partially replaced by oak; still in good numbers from Eastham to Wellfleet.

* *

SWAINSON'S THRUSH
Hylocichla ustulata (Nuttall)

STATUS: Represented in MCZ and British Museum collections.

SPRING: Very rare and irregular migrant.

Earliest transient date: May 17, 1956, at Orleans (Earle); April dates not confirmed but may be valid and accounted for by southern storms.

Average migration period: May 20–25.

Latest transient date: May 31, 1891, at North Truro (Brewster).

FALL: Uncommon to rare migrant.

Earliest transient date: September 6, 1942, at Monomoy (Griscom).

Average migration period: September 15–October 15; average 1–2 birds, occasionally a great flight as 50+ mostly this species on September 22, 1955, at Monomoy (Goodale). This species invariably outnumbers the Gray-cheeked Thrush, the proportion varying between 4 to 1 and 10 to 1 in banded birds (Austin Station).

Latest transient date: October 29, 1942, at Monomoy (Griscom, Kellogg).

DISTRIBUTION: May appear over entire Cape, but records concentrate eastward, probably representing both a "land's end" gathering and increased observation.

HISTORY: No data.

*   *

GRAY-CHEEKED THRUSH
Hylocichla minima (Lafresnaye)

STATUS: Banded at Austin Station.

SPRING: Casual migrant. Four records only, including three banded. Dates from May 21, 1933, at North Eastham (Austin Station) to May 30, 1941, at Monomoy (Griscom, Curtis, Garrison, Bergstrom, Parker).

FALL: Rather rare but apparently regular migrant.

Earliest transient date: September 7, 1939, banded at North Eastham (Austin Station).

Average migration period: September 23–October 12; usually single birds, maximum 4 on September 30, 1951, at Monomoy (Griscom, Beattie).

Latest transient date: October 22, 1947, banded at North Eastham (Austin Station).

DISTRIBUTION: Recorded only on outer Cape from Wellfleet to Monomoy, probably reflects only the distribution of observers.

HISTORY: No data.

SUBSPECIES: Both *H. m. minima* and *H. m. aliciae* have been reported but no specimens preserved.

*   *

VEERY
Hylocichla fuscescens (Stephens)

STATUS: Banded at Austin Station.

SPRING: Casual migrant at Sagamore and Sandwich in late May, none reported eastward.

Allen H. Morgan

Great Outer Beach, Wellfleet

Oak forest replacing pine

Old pasture, Orleans

SUMMER: Casual wandering birds occasionally reported, including three singing in June 1918 at Mashpee (Cobb), none there in 1959 and 1960. No breeding proven, this in marked contrast to mainland.

FALL: Very rare migrant.

Earliest transient date: August 23, 1958, at Chatham (Drury).

Average migration period: September 1–25; almost invariably single birds and not recorded every year.

Latest transient date: October 10, 1953, at Chatham (Emery).

DISTRIBUTION: The casual summer birds appeared in cedar swamps and wooded streamsides, mostly along sound shores from Woods Hole eastward. Migrants more widely distributed, including to sand-dune thickets.

HISTORY: No data.

*   *

EASTERN BLUEBIRD

Sialia sialis (Linnaeus)

STATUS: Represented in MCZ and British Museum collections.

SPRING: Arrival of residents, probably no transients.

Average migration period: March 15–April 20; average 10–20 birds, maximum 30 on April 9, 1949, at Chatham and Brewster (Griscom, Crain).

SUMMER: Regular breeding resident; numbers erratic, see below.

FALL: Fairly common migrant.

Average migration period: September 12–November 30; average 25–75 birds, maximum 100+ on several occasions, rarely a late flight as 200 on November 11–12, 1950 (Snyder).

WINTER: Uncommon resident, often with considerable mortality.

DISTRIBUTION: Nesting birds and migrants over entire Cape occupying orchards and edge habitats; wintering birds concentrate eastward. More numerous than on mainland.

HISTORY: No data on early periods. Always subject to unexplained fluctuation, e.g., 31 nests in 1932 vs. 55 in 1933 at Austin Station (Low, *Bird-Banding*, 5, 39, 1934). Superimposed on these variations, the species is subject to very marked decrease following severe winters in the South, e.g., rare or lacking on Cape in 1895 (Brewster); reduced after 1940 to one-third (Austin); nearly complete eradication after 1958 (many observers), in particular only 2 pairs at Wellfleet Bay Sanctuary (the former Austin Station) in 1960–1962. There has as yet been essentially no recovery from this latest decrease.

*   *

WHEATEAR
Oenanthe oenanthe (Linnaeus)

STATUS: Hypothetical.
One bird seen repeatedly on September 25–26, 1954, at Chatham (Rich, *Bull. Mass. Audubon Soc.*, 38, 357, 1954), not in October as previously recorded.

*   *

BLUE-GRAY GNATCATCHER
Polioptila caerulea (Linnaeus)

STATUS: Represented in BMS and British Museum collections.
SPRING: Very rare and irregular migrant.
   Earliest transient date: April 28, 1959, at Orleans (Bigelow).
   Average migration period: May 1–5; always single birds.
   Latest transient date: May 10, 1955, at North Chatham (Mosher).
SUMMER: Casual, one record only.
FALL: Uncommon to rare migrant.
   Earliest transient date: August 17, 1941, at Monomoy (Griscom, Bowen, Clement).
   Average migration period: August 25–September 30; average

1–2 birds, maximum 10 reported, but probably some repetition, on September 14, 1958, at Morris Island, Chatham (M.A.S.).

Latest transient date: December 18, 1877, collected at Falmouth (Swift, see Brewer, *Bull. N.O.C.*, *3*, 146, 1878).

DISTRIBUTION: Recorded over entire Cape from Sagamore and Falmouth to Chatham and Provincetown. Found in swamps and brushy habitats, including sand-dune thickets.

HISTORY: Recorded in small numbers in fall throughout historical period. No convincing evidence of over-all change or even of much fluctuation in numbers.

* *

GOLDEN-CROWNED KINGLET

Regulus satrapa Lichtenstein

STATUS: Represented in British Museum collection.

SPRING: Rather rare migrant.

Average migration period: April 5–May 5; average 2–5 birds.

SUMMER: Casual; also one unconfirmed breeding record.

FALL: Fairly common migrant.

Earliest transient date: September 11, 1949, at Chatham (M.A.S.).

Average migration period: September 20–November 20.

Peak: September 25–October 10; average 5–15 birds, maximum 100 on October 8, 1960, at Monomoy (Bailey).

WINTER: Uncommon to rare resident, usually surviving but occasionally departing or succumbing by late February.

DISTRIBUTION: Recorded over entire Cape. Occurs largely in pitch pine woods with migrants to sand-dune thickets.

HISTORY: Data incomplete for past; no evidence of change since 1930.

* *

RUBY-CROWNED KINGLET
Regulus calendula (Linnaeus)

STATUS: Represented in British Museum collection.
SPRING: Rare migrant.
   Earliest transient date: April 15, 1960, at Wellfleet (Bailey).
   Average migration period: April 25–May 15; almost always
      single birds.
   Latest transient date: May 31, 1954, at Monomoy (Griscom,
      Ross, Beattie).
FALL: Uncommon migrant.
   Earliest transient date: September 10, 1938, at Monomoy (Gris-
      com).
   Average migration period: September 20–November 15; aver-
      age 1–4 birds.
WINTER: Occasionally persists into early winter in mild seasons,
   but survival even at feeding stations not proven.
DISTRIBUTION: Recorded over entire Cape, occurs largely in mixed
   woods.
HISTORY: No evidence of change in status except for the survival
   into January in recent mild seasons; first so recorded in 1949
   and thereafter in seven of twelve years (C.C.).

* *

WATER PIPIT
Anthus spinoletta (Linnaeus)

STATUS: Represented in BMS and British Museum collections.
SPRING: Casual; only two reports, 60 seen on March 22, 1958, at
   Eastham (Gardler) and one collected on May 30, 1958, at
   Nauset (Morgan).
FALL: Fairly common migrant.
   Earliest transient date: August 29, 1888, collected at Monomoy
      (Cahoon), earlier dates unconfirmed.
   Average migration period: September 15–November 30.

Peak: October 10–20; average 15–100 birds, maximum 400 on
October 12, 1947, at Nauset (Fessenden).

Latest departure date: January 2, 1939, at Monomoy (Peabody,
Walcott).

DISTRIBUTION: Recorded over entire Cape in uplands, grassy fields,
and sand dunes, occasionally on margins of marshes.

HISTORY: No evidence of any change in status.

* *

BOHEMIAN WAXWING
Bombycilla cedrorum Vieillot

STATUS: Hypothetical.
One unconfirmed sight record.

* *

CEDAR WAXWING
Bombycilla cedrorum (Vieillot)

STATUS: Represented in British Museum collection. Tentatively
separated into three populations: 1) breeding; 2) transient; and
3) wintering.

1) BREEDING. Rather rare and local, more common westward on
Cape, but less than on mainland.

Average arrival period: Late May and early June.

Average departure period: Uncertain due to merging with next
population.

2) TRANSIENT.

Spring: Probably none.

Fall: Common migrant, occasionally abundant.

Average migration period: August 20–November 15.

Peak: September 10–25; average 30–75 birds, maximum 200
on September 9–11, 1949 (M.A.S.).

Latest transient date: Uncertain, probably in late December.

3) WINTERING. Very erratic and wandering, may be lacking or
may appear at any time from January into February in small

groups and occasionally flocks to 200, may disappear as abruptly as it arrived.

DISTRIBUTION: Recorded over entire Cape as a migrant and in winter; see above regarding breeding birds.

HISTORY: No evidence of any change in status.

* *

NORTHERN SHRIKE
Lanius excubitor Linnaeus

STATUS: Represented in British Museum collection.

FALL: Irregular migrant, mostly terminal, but possibly a few transients.

Earliest arrival date: October 19, 1941, at West Barnstable (Eaton).

Average arrival period: November 1–10; always single birds.

WINTER: Rare resident, probably never absent, average 1–2 birds, maximum 6 on February 23, 1930, at Chatham (Griscom).

SPRING: Departure of wintering birds, probably no transients.

Average departure period: March 15–30.

Latest departure date: April 9, 1950, at North Eastham (Austin Station).

DISTRIBUTION: Mostly in open brushland, dunes, etc., seldom in woods. Recorded over entire Cape but in greater numbers eastward.

HISTORY: Always in small and irregular numbers, more in some years, but no well-marked flights recorded on Cape Cod.

* *

LOGGERHEAD SHRIKE
Lanius ludovicianus Linnaeus

STATUS: Represented in British Museum collection.

FALL: Rare but regular migrant.

Earliest transient date: August 12, 1904, at South Yarmouth (Milliston, *in litt.* to Brewster).

Average migration period: August 22–November 10.

Peak: September 1–15; usually single birds, maximum 4 on September 12, 1954 (M.A.S.).

WINTER: Lingers irregularly into early winter and very rarely persists throughout the season.

SPRING: Very rare and irregular, probably surviving winter birds rather than migrants; reported in March and April in five of last twenty-five years, latest date April 30, 1955, at Chatham (Freeland).

DISTRIBUTION: In open country, marshes, etc., over entire Cape. May appear at identical spot on nearly same date for several consecutive years.

HISTORY: Early status unknown. Has occurred every year without significant change in numbers since adequate records have been kept.

*   *

STARLING

Sturnus vulgaris Linnaeus

STATUS: Represented in MCZ collection.

Permanent resident; common to abundant at all seasons with largest flocks November 15 to January 1, probably due to influx from mainland; average 200–800, maximum 9140 on December 28, 1958 (C.C.).

DISTRIBUTION: Found over entire Cape in all types of habitat but fewer than on mainland.

HISTORY: Appeared on Cape Cod later than on mainland. First recorded in December 1916 at Provincetown (Peters) and breeding in 1918 at Barnstable (Penard); had increased to 400 by December 1923 at Orleans (Earle). Population built up to about 1932, then stabilized; dropped after hurricane in 1944, but rising steadily again since about 1954.

*   *

WHITE-EYED VIREO
Vireo griseus (Boddaert)

STATUS: Banded at Austin Station.

SUMMER: Breeds locally and probably regularly along the Buzzards Bay shore of Falmouth, probably only 2–3 pairs; pair found feeding young July 6, 1890 (Brewster, Faxon), and reported regularly to present time. Arrival date May 17, 1951 (Wellman). Said to have bred sporadically to Truro (Forbush, 1929), but no recent records.

FALL: Rare and irregular migrant.

Earliest transient date: September 15, 1941, banded at North Eastham (Austin Station).

Average migration period: September 18–October 1; always single birds.

Latest transient date: November 1, 1945, banded at North Eastham (Austin Station).

DISTRIBUTION: See above for breeding distribution. Migrants reported only on outer Cape from Wellfleet south to Monomoy.

HISTORY: No data.

* *

YELLOW-THROATED VIREO
Vireo flavifrons Vieillot

STATUS: Represented in BMS collection.

FALL: Very rare and irregular migrant.

Earliest transient date: August 10, 1948, at Sagamore (Hill).

Average migration period: August 25–September 25; always single birds.

Latest transient date: October 13, 1936, banded at North Eastham (Austin Station).

DISTRIBUTION: Very thinly spread over entire Cape, mostly in woods and thickets, less often in shore-line traps.

HISTORY: No Cape Cod data available for when bird was common elsewhere in eastern Massachusetts; probably never bred on Cape, but possibly more numerous as migrant. No evidence of recent change in status.

* *

SOLITARY VIREO
Vireo solitarius (Wilson)

STATUS: Banded at Austin Station.

SPRING: Very rare and irregular migrant; May 8, 1934, at North Eastham (Brown) to May 19, 1935, at Sandwich (Burbank).

FALL: Rare migrant, probably regular.

Earliest transient date: August 30, 1953, at Chatham (Griscom, Rich, Parker).

Average migration period: September 10–October 15; usually single birds, rarely to three.

Latest transient date: November 1, 1949, banded at North Eastham (Austin Station).

DISTRIBUTION: Recorded over entire Cape, mostly in woodlands, a little more regular westward on Cape.

HISTORY: No evidence of any change in status.

* *

RED-EYED VIREO
Vireo olivaceus (Linnaeus)

STATUS: Represented in MCZ, Chicago, and British Museum collections.

SPRING: Arrival of residents, rare as transient.

Earliest arrival date: May 5, 1940, at Osterville (Eaton).

Average arrival period: May 20–31; arrives later than on mainland.

SUMMER: Common breeding resident but less numerous than on

mainland. Occupies deciduous woods and avoids pitch pines, found throughout Cape, but decreased from Wellfleet north due to diminished available habitat. Estimated density: 10–12 pairs/ 100 acres at Brewster (Hill), 6–8 pairs/100 acres at Sagamore (Hill), 5 pairs at Provincetown, 12–15 pairs/100 acres at Woods Hole (Hill), etc.

FALL: Common migrant.

Earliest transient date: Uncertain, probably about August 15.

Average migration period: August 28–October 10.

Peak: September 10–30; average 3–10 birds, maximum 20 on September 25, 1957, at Sandy Neck, Barnstable (Hill).

Latest transient date: November 13, 1954, at Chatham (Snyder).

DISTRIBUTION: Breeding distribution given above. Migrants widespread, including in shore-line traps.

HISTORY: No evidence of any change in status.

* *

PHILADELPHIA VIREO
Vireo philadelphicus (Cassin)

STATUS: Represented in BMS collection.

SPRING: Casual migrant; banded on May 24, 1933, at North Eastham (Austin Station) and seen on May 31, 1959, at Wellfleet (Bailey).

FALL: Rare migrant.

Earliest transient date: August 16, 1948, banded at North Eastham (Austin Station).

Average migration period: September 1–30.

Peak: September 10–20; usually single birds, up to three on two occasions.

Latest transient date: October 31, 1943, banded at North Eastham (Austin Station).

DISTRIBUTION: Recorded over entire Cape but with concentration of records from Wellfleet to Monomoy. More regular and numerous on Cape than on mainland in fall.

HISTORY: Unreported until 1933, probably due to lack of observation rather than to a true change in status. No change in numbers since then.

*   *

WARBLING VIREO
Vireo gilvus (Vieillot)

STATUS: Banded at South Wellfleet (Baird).
One unconfirmed breeding record. Probably a casual fall migrant with reports from August 15 to September 13.

*   *

BLACK-AND-WHITE WARBLER
Mniotilta varia (Linnaeus)

STATUS: Represented in MCZ and BMS collections.
SPRING: Arrival of residents, uncommon as transient.
Earliest arrival date: April 21, 1954, at South Orleans (Earle).
Average arrival period: April 28–May 25.
SUMMER: Rather uncommon breeding resident, scattered pairs only.
FALL: Uncommon migrant.
Earliest transient date: July 27, 1941, banded at North Eastham (Austin Station).
Average migration period: August 20–September 25.
Peak: August 25–September 10; average 2–5 birds, maximum 10 on several occasions.
Latest transient date: November 1, 1955, at Chatham (Mosher).
DISTRIBUTION: Breeding almost exclusively in low deciduous woods and found from Woods Hole and Sagamore to Orleans, a few south to Chatham and north to Truro. Less numerous than

on mainland. Transients found more widely and in shore-line traps.

HISTORY: Local breeding groups increase as deciduous trees invade and replace pines but then decrease as trees mature. No evidence of any over-all change in status.

* *

PROTHONOTARY WARBLER
Protonotaria citrea (Boddaert)

STATUS: Found dead, not preserved (Maclay).
Very rare vagrant from South.
SPRING: May 4–11, 1958, at Osterville (Cross) and April 10–20, 1960, at Eastham (Bailey).
FALL: At least nine birds after Hurricane "Edna" in 1954, September 12 to October 12, at South Harwich, Chatham, Monomoy, and Orleans (many observers). Also October 28–29, 1953, at Osterville (Johnson), October 3, 1944, at Sandwich (Burbank), September 2, 1956, at Chatham (Maclay), and September 14, 1962, at Chatham (Earle).

* *

WORM-EATING WARBLER
Helmitheros vermivorus (Gmelin)

STATUS: Banded at Austin Station.
Casual vagrant from South.
SPRING: April 16, 1932, banded at North Eastham and present to May 15 (Brown, *Bird-Banding*, 3, 176, 1932); sight records on April 19, 1946, at Sandwich (Burbank) and May 12, 1944, at Orleans (Earle).
FALL: August 23, 1960, banded at Wellfleet (Jenkins); sight records on September 15, 1953, at Monomoy (Goodell) and October 13, 1962, at Chatham (Earle).

* *

GOLDEN-WINGED WARBLER
Vermivora chrysoptera (Linnaeus)

STATUS: Banded at Austin Station.

SPRING: Casual straggler; May 9, 1931, banded at North Eastham (Austin Station) to May 25, 1960, at Woods Hole (Hill).

FALL: Also casual straggler; August 21, 1949, at Eastham (Mason) and August 18, 1963, at Morris Island (Snyder).

* *

BLUE-WINGED WARBLER
Vermivora pinus (Linnaeus)

STATUS: Found dead and preserved, location of specimen unknown (Austin Station).

SPRING: Casual straggler; seen May 9, 1943, at Osterville (Eaton), three on May 13, 1962, at Falmouth (Garry), and found dead May 16, 1931, at North Eastham (Austin Station).

FALL: Very rare and irregular migrant.

Earliest transient date: August 11, 1941, banded at North Eastham (Austin Station).

Average migration period: September 5–20; always single birds.

Latest departure date: October 12, 1943, banded at North Eastham (Austin Station).

DISTRIBUTION: Most records thus far from outer Cape, reflecting concentration of observers.

HISTORY: No data.

HYBRIDS: Sight record of Lawrence's Warbler well seen under satisfactory conditions June 22, 1958, and for a few days thereafter at Woods Hole (Edwards, *in litt.* to Fox).

* *

TENNESSEE WARBLER
Vermivora peregrina (Wilson)

STATUS: Banded at Austin Station.
SPRING: Casual migrant; three records including one banded, May 15–31.
SUMMER: Once recorded, July 4, 1962, at South Orleans (Earle).
FALL: Uncommon migrant.
> Earliest transient date: August 14, 1948, at Sagamore (Hill).
> Average migration period: August 25–September 30; average 1–3 birds, maximum 7 on September 3, 1944, at Chatham (Griscom).
> Latest transient date: October 17, 1948, banded at North Eastham (Austin Station).

DISTRIBUTION: Recorded over entire Cape.
HISTORY: No evidence of any change in status.

* *

ORANGE-CROWNED WARBLER
Vermivora celata (Say)

STATUS: Banded at Austin Station.
FALL: Rare but regular migrant.
> Earliest transient date: August 29, 1954, at Monomoy (Griscom, Jaques).
> Average migration period: September 15–November 15; average 1–2 birds.

WINTER: Rare resident, often collecting near feeding stations as 5 on January 1, 1949, at Chatham (Griscom); usually not surviving the season, but has been recorded to March 24, 1949, at Orleans (de Windt).
DISTRIBUTION: Recorded over entire Cape but in greater numbers eastward, particularly late in season.

HISTORY: Slight increase probably since 1948; no change apparent prior to that date.

* *

NASHVILLE WARBLER
Vermivora ruficapilla (Wilson)

STATUS: Represented in MCZ and British Museum collections.
SPRING: Rare migrant.
  Earliest transient date: May 6, 1959, at Wellfleet (Bailey).
  Average migration period: May 14–30; always single birds.
  Latest transient date: May 31 on several occasions.
SUMMER: Casual reports during June and July, mostly in the Harwich-Brewster-Orleans area; no known breeding.
FALL: Uncommon migrant.
  Earliest transient date: August 16, 1941, at Monomoy (Griscom).
  Average migration period: September 1–October 10.
  Peak: September 8–18; numbers erratic, average 1–2 birds, rarely 3.
  Latest transient date: October 27, 1940, banded at North Eastham (Austin Station).
DISTRIBUTION: Recorded over entire Cape and appearing in a wide variety of habitats.
HISTORY: No evidence of any change in status.

* *

PARULA WARBLER
Parula americana (Linnaeus)

STATUS: Represented in MCZ and BMS collections.
SPRING: Arrival of residents, very few transients.
  Earliest arrival date: May 2 on several occasions.
  Average arrival period: May 5–20.

SUMMER: Fairly common but very local breeding resident. Occurs widely in swamps and along streams but only where *Usnea* moss is present, largely along sound shore and inland around ponds. At present 2–3 pairs at Woods Hole, 8+ pairs at Mashpee, 10 pairs at Brewster, 3–4 pairs at Morris Island, Chatham, 2–3 pairs at Orleans, and much rarer or lacking northward.

FALL: Fairly common migrant.

Earliest transient date: Probably July 29, 1937, banded at North Eastham (Austin Station).

Average migration period: September 1–October 15.

Peak: September 12–28; average 2–4 birds, maximum 18 on September 14, 1953, at Orleans (Freeland).

Latest transient date: November 7, 1953, at Woods Hole (Kelly).

DISTRIBUTION: See above for breeding distribution. Migrants occur widely over Cape, usually in thickets and swamps.

HISTORY: Steady reduction throughout historical period due at first to loss of habitat from conversion of swamps to cranberry bogs, cf. Woodcock; more recently an unexplained reduction of *Usnea* has decreased the population about 50 per cent.

*   *

YELLOW WARBLER
Dendroica petechia (Linnaeus)

STATUS: Represented in MCZ, BMS, and British Museum collections.

SPRING: Arrival of residents, few or no transients.

Earliest arrival date: May 2 on several occasions.

Average arrival period: May 7–15.

SUMMER: Rather uncommon and local breeding resident occurring mostly in maple swamps.

FALL: Fairly common migrant.

Earliest transient date: Uncertain, probably about July 15.

Average migration period: July 28–September 15; no peak period, average 1–5 birds.

Latest transient date: October 5, 1952, at Monomoy (Griscom, Bailey, Beattie).

DISTRIBUTION: Breeding in maple swamps over entire Cape. Migrants more widespread including into shore-line traps.

HISTORY: No evidence of any significant change in status.

SUBSPECIES: Specimens tentatively assigned to *D. p. amnicola* and *D. p. rubiginosa* have been taken on a number of occasions, mostly late in the fall migration, see Griscom & Snyder, 1955. Breeding birds are *D. p. aestiva*.

*   *

MAGNOLIA WARBLER
Dendroica magnolia (Wilson)

STATUS: Banded at Austin Station.

SPRING: Rare migrant.

Earliest transient date: May 13, 1959, at Wellfleet (Bailey).

Average migration period: May 18–28; always single birds.

Latest transient date: June 1, 1891, at North Truro (Brewster, Miller).

FALL: Uncommon migrant.

Earliest transient date: August 4, 1937, banded at North Eastham (Austin Station).

Average migration period: August 25–October 3.

Peak: September 8–15; average 1–4 birds, maximum 15 on September 10, 1938, at Monomoy (Griscom).

Latest transient date: October 25, 1927, at Sandwich (Burbank).

DISTRIBUTION: Recorded over entire Cape with concentration in shore-line traps.

HISTORY: No evidence of any significant change in status.

*   *

CAPE MAY WARBLER
Dendroica tigrina (Gmelin)

STATUS: Represented in BMS collection.

SPRING: Casual migrant; dates from May 10, 1931, seen at Eastham (Low), to May 25, 1937, banded at North Eastham (Austin Station).

FALL: Uncommon migrant, occasionally common.

Earliest transient date: August 13, 1958, at Chatham (Mosher).

Average migration period: August 20–October 10.

Peak: September 1–20; average 2–8 birds, maximum 30 on August 23, 1962, at Monomoy (Harrington).

Latest transient date: October 31, 1954, at Orleans (Griscom, Earle, Mason).

DISTRIBUTION: Reported over entire Cape with concentration in shore-line traps. Known to reach Cape over water in fall, taken or seen several times on boats both in Cape Cod Bay and ten miles off Chatham.

HISTORY: Low numbers recorded 1930–1940, then steady increase to 1950 and remaining essentially stable since, an apparent increase of 500 per cent!

* *

BLACK-THROATED BLUE WARBLER
Dendroica caerulescens (Gmelin)

STATUS: Represented in British Museum collection.

SPRING: Very rare migrant.

Earliest transient date: May 17, 1936, banded at North Eastham (Austin Station).

Average migration period: May 20–25, always single birds.

Latest transient date: May 27, 1951, at Brewster (Parker, Smart).

FALL: Uncommon migrant.

Earliest transient date: August 9, 1953, at Provincetown (Gammell).

Average migration period: September 5–October 12; average 1–3 birds but counts very irregular.

Latest transient date: November 10, 1953, at Chatham (Mixner, Day).

DISTRIBUTION: Recorded over entire Cape, seems to go into shoreline traps less than other warblers.

HISTORY: No evidence of any significant change in status.

* *

MYRTLE WARBLER

Dendroica coronata (Linnaeus)

STATUS: Represented in MCZ, BMS, and British Museum collections. Probably two populations: 1) terminal wintering; and 2) transients of which few individuals reach the Cape.

FALL: Common to abundant migrant, largely terminal.

Earliest arrival date: August 16, 1952, at Monomoy (Griscom, Hill).

Average migration period: September 20–December 1.

Peak: For transients October 5–30, counts variable, average 100–400, maximum 1000 on October 17, 1954, at Chatham and Monomoy (Griscom); see below for winter population.

WINTER: Common to abundant resident. This population arrives in late October and early November, building up to peak in late December, maximum 3280 on December 31, 1950 (C.C.), but often with marked mortality in severe seasons, particularly when heavy snow buries the bayberries.

SPRING: Departure of wintering birds, a few transients.

Average migration period: April 1–May 10; counts depend on success of wintering birds, maximum 250 on April 9, 1949 (Griscom); most transients April 20–May 10, average 30–50 birds.

Latest departure date: May 26, 1931, banded at North Eastham (Austin Station).

DISTRIBUTION: Recorded from entire Cape, but concentrates southeastward both as migrant and as winter resident.

HISTORY: Numbers fluctuate moderately from year to year, migrants according to prevailing winds and winter residents according to success of previous winter season. No evidence of significant long-term change in numbers.

* *

BLACK-THROATED GRAY WARBLER
Dendroica nigrescens (Townsend)

STATUS: Represented in MAS collection.

Accidental vagrant from West. Collected on September 26, 1962, at Chatham (Bailey).

* *

BLACK-THROATED GREEN WARBLER
Dendroica virens (Gmelin)

STATUS: Represented in MCZ and British Museum collections.

SPRING: Arrival of residents, uncommon as transient.

Earliest arrival date: May 5, 1923, at Orleans (Earle).

Average migration period: May 12–30; mostly single birds.

SUMMER: Very rare and local breeding resident; see below for distribution.

FALL: Uncommon migrant.

Earliest transient date: August 2, 1958, at Sagamore (Hill).

Average migration period: August 20–October 10.

Peak: September 8–25; average 2–4 birds, maximum 13 on September 10, 1938, at Monomoy (Griscom).

Latest transient date: October 28, 1945, at Orleans (Bailey).

DISTRIBUTION: Breeding now known only at Brewster, 2 pairs lo-

cated in 1961. Migrants over entire Cape, including into shore-
line traps; more transients both spring and fall nearer Canal
than eastward.

HISTORY: Formerly uncommon but widespread as breeding resident in pitch pines, e.g., 5 pairs in 1918 in Mashpee-Cotuit area
(Cobb); 6–8 pairs in 1924 at Orleans (Earle); present in July
1881 at Sandwich (Bangs, in MCZ) and in 1927–1929 there
(Burbank); in 1890 at Falmouth (Brewster); 2–3 pairs until 1938 at Morris Island, Chatham (Griscom); 10–12 pairs
in 1924 at Brewster (Earle). Reason for decrease not certain,
possibly replacement of pitch pine by oak. No evidence of
change in status of migrant birds.

* *

CERULEAN WARBLER
Dendroica cerulea (Wilson)

STATUS: Banded at Austin Station.
Accidental vagrant, banded May 17, 1931, at North Eastham
(Brown, *Bird-Banding*, 3, 177, 1932) and seen August 12,
1961, at Monomoy (Bailey).

* *

BLACKBURNIAN WARBLER
Dendroica fusca (Müller)

STATUS: Represented in British Museum collection.
SPRING: Rare and irregular migrant.
   Earliest transient date: May 8, 1959, at Wellfleet (Bailey).
   Average migration period: May 12–24; usually single birds,
      maximum 4 on May 13, 1959, at Wellfleet (Bailey).
   Latest transient date: May 30 on several occasions.
FALL: Rare migrant, but more regular than in spring.
   Earliest transient date: August 17, 1941, at Monomoy (Gris-
      com, Bowen, Clement).

Average migration period: August 25–September 25; no peak dates and only single birds.

Latest departure date: October 5, 1954, at Chatham (Mosher).

DISTRIBUTION: Recorded over entire Cape with concentration in shore-line traps.

HISTORY: No evidence of any significant change in status.

* *

YELLOW-THROATED WARBLER

Dendroica dominica (Linnaeus)

STATUS: Represented in MCZ collection.

Accidental vagrant from South. Specimen found dead on September 3, 1962, at Morris Island, Chatham (Gardler, in MCZ); sight records in 1954 after Hurricane "Edna," 4 on September 12 at Chatham (Emery) and 1 on September 15 at Monomoy (Goodell).

* *

CHESTNUT-SIDED WARBLER

Dendroica pennsylvanica (Linnaeus)

STATUS: Represented in British Museum collection.

SPRING: Arrival of residents, rare as transient.

Earliest arrival date: May 1, 1949, at Chatham (A. Griscom).

Average migration period: May 10–27; usually single birds.

SUMMER: Very rare and local breeding resident; see below for distribution.

FALL: Rare migrant.

Earliest transient date: August 2, 1958, at Sagamore (Hill).

Average migration period: August 20–September 20; average 1–3 birds.

Latest transient date: October 11, 1944, banded at North Eastham (Austin Station).

DISTRIBUTION: Breeding known at present only at Cliff Pond, Brewster, and Long Pond, Harwich, each 1–2 pairs (Hill). Migrants recorded over entire Cape with more nearer Canal than eastward, some concentration in shore-line traps.

HISTORY: Formerly more breeding stations than at present, but never as many as for Black-throated Green Warbler; 4 pairs in 1890 at Falmouth (Brewster), 2 pairs in 1904 at Forestdale (Cobb), 1–2 pairs in 1918 in Mashpee-Cotuit area (Cobb), and 4–6 pairs in 1924 at Cliff Pond (Earle).

* *

BAY-BREASTED WARBLER

Dendroica castanea (Wilson)

STATUS: Collected (Griscom), location of specimen unknown.

SPRING: Casual; one record, May 29, 1945, at Sandwich (Burbank).

FALL: Rather rare migrant.

Earliest transient date: August 9, 1955, at Chatham (Smart).

Average migration period: August 20–September 25; no peak, average 1–2 birds, maximum 11 on September 13, 1958, at Chatham (Gardler), subject to sporadic flights.

Latest transient date: October 20, 1954, at Sandwich (Romaine).

DISTRIBUTION: Recorded over entire Cape with some but not marked concentration in shore-line traps.

HISTORY: No evidence of any change in status.

* *

BLACKPOLL WARBLER

Dendroica striata (Forster)

STATUS: Represented in BMS and British Museum collections.

SPRING: Rather uncommon migrant, occasionally common.

Earliest transient date: May 13 on several occasions.

Average migration period: May 18–30; average 1–3 birds, maximum 12 on May 30, 1946, at Chatham (Griscom, Cottrell, Parker).

Latest transient date: June 2, 1951, at Eastham (Emery).

FALL: Uncommon migrant, occasionally common.

Earliest transient date: September 6 on several occasions.

Average migration period: September 10–October 20.

Peak: September 15–30; average 3–10 birds, maximum 25 on September 28, 1952, at Monomoy (Griscom, Elkins, Snyder, Halberg).

Latest transient date: December 3, 1945, at Centerville (Anderson).

DISTRIBUTION: Recorded over entire Cape; concentrates in shoreline traps in fall.

HISTORY: No evidence of any change in status.

* *

PINE WARBLER
Dendroica pinus (Wilson)

STATUS: Represented in MCZ, BMS, and British Museum collections.

SPRING: Arrival of residents, probably no transients.

Earliest arrival date: March 24, 1962, at Sagamore (Hill).

Average arrival period: April 5–18.

SUMMER: Common to abundant breeding resident throughout pitch pine barrens over entire Cape; no satisfactory estimate of density.

FALL: Common to abundant migrant.

Average migration period: August 1–October 5.

Peak: September 10–25; average 10–75 birds, maximum 150 on several occasions.

WINTER: Casually attempts to winter, counts depend on weather and are reduced rapidly by severe weather. Survives rarely except at feeding stations.

DISTRIBUTION: Widespread in all pitch pine stands of entire Cape, including isolated groves in sand dunes as in Provincelands. Migrant flocks widespread in brush and along hedgerows often associated with other small birds.

HISTORY: No data on occurrence in original forest or after deforestation. Presumed to have enjoyed a "boom" with growth of pitch pine forests but specific data lacking. Decreasing slowly at present proportional to replacement of pines by oaks.

*   *

PRAIRIE WARBLER

Dendroica discolor (Vieillot)

STATUS: Represented in MCZ, BMS, and British Museum collections.

SPRING: Arrival of residents, no evidence of transients.

Earliest arrival date: May 1, 1949, at Chatham (A. Griscom).
Average arrival period: May 4–12.

SUMMER: Common but local breeding resident in scrub-oak barrens, quite sensitive to ecological changes and so disappear as oaks mature and clearings fill in.

FALL: Common migrant.

Average migration period: August 15–October 1.
Peak: September 5–15; average 5–20 birds, maximum 75 on September 11, 1948, at Chatham (Griscom).
Latest departure date: Probably November 24, 1947, at Eastham (Griscom).

WINTER: Accidental straggler, never known to have survived, collected January 2, 1909 [not 1910], at South Yarmouth (McKechnie, *Auk*, 26, 195, 1909) .

DISTRIBUTION: Widespread in breeding season over entire Cape according to habitat; migrants concentrate eastward in fall and are probably largely locally raised birds.

HISTORY: No data on early status. Species has clearly increased as open land grew to brush, maximum numbers 1920–1930; now decreasing due to maturation of forests.

*   *

PALM WARBLER
Dendroica palmarum (Gmelin)

STATUS: Represented in BMS, Chicago, and British Museum collections, both subspecies. Subspecies separable in field: 1) *D. p. palmarum*, Western Palm; and 2) *D. p. hypochrysea*, Yellow Palm.

1) *D. p. palmarum*, Western Palm.

    FALL: Fairly common migrant.

        Earliest arrival date: August 6, 1945, banded at North Eastham (Austin Station).

        Average migration period: September 4–November 20.

        Peak: September 12–October 1; average 5–20 birds, maximum 69 on September 29, 1951, at Monomoy (Griscom, Emery, Barry, Beattie).

    WINTER: Regular early in season in some numbers, maximum 19 on December 23, 1938 (C.C.), but rapidly reduced by severe weather; probably survives but rarely.

    SPRING: Two late-February sight records and one banded April 22, 1932, at North Eastham (Brown, *Bird-Banding*, 3, 177, 1932) are probably surviving winterers rather than transients.

    DISTRIBUTION: Recorded over entire Cape, but concentrated eastward and in shore-line traps.

    HISTORY: No evidence of change since 1930.

2) *D. p. hypochrysea*, Yellow Palm.

    SPRING: Rare and probably irregular migrant.

        Earliest transient date: April 13, 1924, at South Orleans (Earle).

        Average migration period: April 29–May 5; usually single birds, rarely a small flock.

Latest departure date: May 13, 1940, banded at North Eastham (Austin Station).

FALL: Rather uncommon migrant.

Earliest transient date: September 13, 1940, banded at North Eastham (Austin Station).

Average migration period: September 25–November 5.

Peak: October 8–18; average 1–2 birds, maximum 10 on October 10, 1953, at Monomoy (Griscom, Bailey, Snyder).

Latest transient date: January 1, 1942, at Eastham (Eliot, Kraus).

DISTRIBUTION: Recorded over entire Cape in spring but more numerous nearer the Canal than eastward. Fall records predominantly eastward.

HISTORY: No evidence of change in status since 1930.

* *

OVENBIRD

Seiurus aurocapillus (Linnaeus)

STATUS: Banded at Austin Station.

SPRING: Arrival of residents, few or no transients.

Earliest arrival date: May 3, 1938, at Brewster (Bishop).

Average arrival period: May 8–15.

SUMMER: Fairly common but somewhat local breeding resident; see below for distribution.

FALL: Uncommon migrant westward and rare eastward.

Earliest transient date: Probably July 28, 1941, banded at North Eastham (Austin Station).

Average migration period: August 20–September 28; mostly single birds.

Latest departure date: October 22, 1943, banded at North Eastham (Austin Station).

DISTRIBUTION: Breeding birds largely in deciduous woods but overflowing into pitch pine, seldom in scrub oak. Fairly common in suitable habitat from Sagamore and Falmouth east to Barnstable and along the Sandwich moraine to Brewster, diminishing east to Orleans and becoming rare and local north to Wellfleet. Migrants more widespread.

HISTORY: Data incomplete but probably diminishing since 1920.

* *

NORTHERN WATERTHRUSH

Seiurus noveboracensis (Gmelin)

STATUS: Represented in MCZ and British Museum collections.

SPRING: Rare migrant.

Earliest transient date: May 14, 1932, banded at North Eastham (Austin Station).

Average migration period: May 16–26; single birds daily to average total of five per year (Austin Station).

Latest transient date: May 31, 1891, at North Truro (Brewster).

FALL: Fairly common migrant.

Earliest transient date: July 26, 1936, banded at North Eastham (Austin Station).

Average migration period: August 12–October 1.

Peak: No marked peak, moving in considerable numbers through late August and whole of September; average 1–3 daily, maximum 8 on September 27, 1958, at Chatham (Rich).

Latest transient date: October 27, 1949, banded at North Eastham (Austin Station).

DISTRIBUTION: Found over entire Cape in wide variety of habitats, including upland hedgerows and sand-dune thickets as well as fresh-water swamps.

HISTORY: No evidence of any change in status.

SUBSPECIES: "White-browed" birds reported as *S. n. notabilis* have been seen but none collected; some probably account for late-summer reports of the Louisiana Waterthrush.

* *

Cord Grass (Spartina alterniflora) with *Eel Grass* (Zostera marina) caught around base of stems.

LOUISIANA WATERTHRUSH
Seiurus motacilla (Vieillot)

STATUS: Banded at Austin Station.
The only satisfactory record is May 1–11, 1933, banded at North
Eastham (Low).

* *

KENTUCKY WARBLER
Oporornis formosus (Wilson)

STATUS: Banded at Austin Station.
Accidental straggler from South. Recorded only after the 1954
hurricanes: male on September 8 banded at North Eastham
(Austin Station) and male (? same) seen and heard singing
September 18 at Chatham (Griscom, Halberg).

* *

CONNECTICUT WARBLER
Oporornis agilis (Wilson)

STATUS: Represented in British Museum collection.
FALL: Rare migrant.
Earliest transient date: August 30, 1953, at Woods Hole (Free-
land).
Average migration period: September 5–October 10.
Peak: September 20–October 1; average 1–2 birds, maximum 8
on September 30, 1951, at Monomoy (Griscom, Emery,
Barry, Bailey, Beattie).
Latest transient date: November 9, 1952, at Monomoy (Gris-
com, Barry).
DISTRIBUTION: Recorded over entire Cape, some concentration in
shore-line traps.
HISTORY: No evidence of change in status since 1935.

* *

MOURNING WARBLER
Oporornis philadelphia (Wilson)

STATUS: Represented in British Museum collection.
FALL: Rare migrant.
   Earliest transient date: August 6, 1951, at Chatham (Griscom).
   Average migration period: August 15–September 20; usually
      single birds, maximum 4 on August 22, 1954, at Monomoy
      (Griscom).
   Latest transient date: October 11, 1888, at North Truro (Miller,
      in British Museum).
DISTRIBUTION: Recorded only on outer Cape and mostly in shore-
   line traps.
HISTORY: No evidence of any change in status.

* *

YELLOWTHROAT
Geothlypis trichas (Linnaeus)

STATUS: Represented in MCZ and British Museum collections.
SPRING: Arrival of residents, uncommon to rare as transient.
   Earliest arrival date: April 28, 1960, at Monomoy (Bailey).
   Average arrival period: May 5–12.
SUMMER: Common to abundant breeding resident over entire
   Cape; 10 pairs at Woods Hole, 20 pairs at Sagamore, 25–30
   pairs at Brewster, 50 pairs at Provincetown, 40 pairs at Well-
   fleet, 15 pairs at Truro, 20 pairs at Chatham, etc., but no ac-
   curate density statistics.
FALL: Common as transient, residents present to September 15.
   Average migration period: August 15–October 20.
   Peak: August 25–September 25; average 5–10 birds, maximum
      25 on August 30, 1953, at Monomoy (Griscom).
   Latest transient date: Uncertain, regularly recorded into No-
      vember.
WINTER: Lingering into early winter after mild falls, rarely sur-

Pitch pine forest, Wellfleet

Allen H. Morgan

Norman P

Grass moorland, Eastham

An inland pond, Harwich

Norman P.

viving to January, but once to February 20, 1954, at Chatham
(Griscom).

DISTRIBUTION: Edge habitats and brushy thickets chiefly near water
over entire Cape.

HISTORY: No evidence of any change in status.

*   *

YELLOW-BREASTED CHAT
Icteria virens (Linnaeus)

STATUS: Represented in British Museum collection.

SPRING: Very rare and erratic, stray birds may appear at any date.

SUMMER: Also very rare and erratic, may nest casually, but no
satisfactory proof as yet.

FALL: Recently rare though regular; 1–4 birds may appear at any
date, but maximum number of records fall in September.

WINTER: Recently fairly regular in early winter, concentrating at
feeding stations, very rarely surviving the season even with such
assistance.

DISTRIBUTION: Recorded over entire Cape, also on boat sixteen
miles east of Truro (Rankin, *Bird-Banding, 32,* 58, 1961).

HISTORY: Never as regular on Cape as on mainland, but said to
have nested at Hyannis and Harwichport (Forbush, 1929), details now lost. Scattered reports thereafter until 1940 with steady
increase since, at first in September, but since 1950 recorded in
every month of the year with greater proportional increase in
late fall and early winter.

*   *

HOODED WARBLER
Wilsonia citrina (Boddaert)

STATUS: Represented in BMS collection.

SPRING: Casual after southern storms as April 15, 1960, at Chatham (Mosher), April 16, 1961, at Woods Hole (Wickersham,

fide Garry), and banded May 26, 1933, at North Eastham (Austin Station).

SUMMER: Casual, collected June 25, 1888, at Provincetown (Whorf, in BMS).

FALL: Rare but recently regular migrant.

Earliest transient date: August 5, 1953, at Woods Hole (Freeland).

Average migration period: August 20–September 25; usually single birds, maximum at least 15 on September 12–15, 1954, at Chatham and Monomoy after Hurricane "Edna" (many observers).

Latest transient date: November 2, 1954, at Orleans (Elliott).

DISTRIBUTION: Recorded over entire Cape without marked concentration.

HISTORY: Steadily increasing as fall migrant. One record each in 1888, 1932, and 1933, then in four years of the 1940's, every year since 1950 with 3–5 birds yearly since 1955, the 1954 hurricane-borne birds being a "bonus."

* *

WILSON'S WARBLER
Wilsonia pusilla (Wilson)

STATUS: Banded at Austin Station.

SPRING: Rare and irregular migrant.

Earliest transient date: May 13, 1959, at Wellfleet (Bailey).

Average migration period: May 18–28; usually single birds.

Latest transient date: May 30 on several occasions.

FALL: Rare migrant.

Earliest transient date: August 9, 1951, banded at North Eastham (Austin Station).

Average migration period: September 1–30; counts quite erratic, average 1–2 birds, maximum 12 on September 10, 1938, at Monomoy (Griscom, Maclay).

Latest transient date: December 6, 1953, at Woods Hole (Kelly).

DISTRIBUTION: Recorded mostly from Wellfleet to Monomoy with concentration in shore-line traps, very rarely elsewhere on Cape.

HISTORY: No evidence of any change in status.

* *

CANADA WARBLER
Wilsonia canadensis (Linnaeus)

STATUS: Banded at Austin Station.

SPRING: Very rare and irregular migrant; dates from May 20 to 30; always single birds.

FALL: Rare migrant.

Earliest transient date: August 17, 1941, at Monomoy (Griscom, Clement, Bowen).

Average migration period: August 23–September 20; usually single birds, once to three.

Latest transient date: October 14, 1940, banded at North Eastham (Austin Station).

DISTRIBUTION: Thinly distributed over entire Cape, concentrating in shore-line traps.

HISTORY: No evidence of any change in status.

* *

AMERICAN REDSTART
Setophaga ruticilla (Linnaeus)

STATUS: Banded at Austin Station.

SPRING: Arrival of residents, a few transients late in May.

Earliest arrival date: May 3, 1938, at Brewster (Bishop).

Average arrival period: May 8–15, but full numbers not until May 25–28.

SUMMER: Common but somewhat local breeding resident over entire Cape. Recent counts of 10 pairs at Sagamore, 5 pairs at

Woods Hole, 3 pairs at Mashpee, 30+ pairs at Brewster, 25 pairs at Wellfleet, 15–20 pairs in Provincelands, 8–10 pairs at Chatham, etc., but no accurate density statistics.

FALL: Fairly common migrant.

Earliest transient date: Uncertain, probably late July.

Average migration period: August 20–October 8.

Peak: September 1–20, not well marked; average 3–8 birds, maximum 20 on September 12, 1954, at Chatham (M.A.S.).

Latest transient date: December 6, 1953, at Woods Hole (Kelly).

DISTRIBUTION: Breeds in taller deciduous woods over entire Cape. Migrants widespread in wide variety of habitats, including sand-dune thickets.

HISTORY: Always present as a breeding species during historical period; numbers low until oak woods began to mature and re-place pine, e.g., only 2–3 pairs at Brewster in 1923 (Earle), increase apparent by 1936 and steadily thereafter; formerly out-numbered by Black-throated Green Warbler and about equal to Chestnut-sided, now exceeded only by Pine, Prairie, and Yellowthroat. No evidence of change in status of migrants.

* *

HOUSE SPARROW

Passer domesticus (Linnaeus)

STATUS: Represented in Chicago and British Museum collections. Uncommon and quite local permanent resident. Wandering va-grants at all seasons, even occasionally to Monomoy Point, but no evidence of migration.

DISTRIBUTION: Largely confined to villages, congregates at feeding stations in winter.

HISTORY: Date of first appearance on Cape not recorded. Abundant in 1895 at Falmouth (Brewster) with flocks up to 200 in the fields. Steady decline after 1915, but stable since 1930.

* *

BOBOLINK
Dolichonyx oryzivorus (Linnaeus)

STATUS: Represented in BMS collection.

SPRING: Very rare and probably irregular migrant, May 11 to June 1; one or two birds only, more often recorded near Canal than eastward.

SUMMER: By implication (Thoreau, 1857) and by tradition a common breeding resident in first half of nineteenth century, but no specific data; none recorded in historical period.

FALL: Uncommon to rare migrant.

Earliest transient date: August 17, 1941, at Monomoy (Griscom, Bowen, Clement).

Average migration period: August 22–September 25.

Peak: August 28–September 12; present every year but in irregular numbers, average 1–6, but occasionally to 45, maximum 110 on September 11, 1948, at Chatham (Griscom).

Latest transient date: October 14, 1942, banded at North Eastham (Austin Station).

DISTRIBUTION: No data on former breeding distribution but traditionally widespread and presumed to have occupied the moorland. Migrants recorded over entire Cape with concentration in shore-line traps in fall.

HISTORY: Maximum numbers presumed to have coincided with maximum deforestation but with rapid disappearance with regrowth of trees; no breeding for at least a century. Decreasing numbers of migrants throughout most of historical period, but apparently stabilized since 1935.

* *

EASTERN MEADOWLARK
Sturnella magna (Linnaeus)

STATUS: Represented in MCZ, BMS, and British Museum collections.

SPRING: Dispersal of wintering flocks, a few terminal migrants.

Average migration period: March 15–April 15.

SUMMER: Formerly abundant, now uncommon to rare and local. Estimated 20 pairs in Eastham-Orleans-Chatham area (Griscom), 20 pairs at Barnstable, much smaller numbers elsewhere.

FALL: Uncommon, mostly local birds with a few transients from the mainland.

Average migration period: October 15–November 30; counts irregular, average 2–10, maximum 81 on November 9, 1941 (Griscom, Hill).

WINTER: Regular; average 50–100 (C.C.) at beginning of season with mortality according to severity of season, but always surviving in small numbers.

DISTRIBUTION: Breeding in drier parts of salt meadows and in lower open uplands, formerly more widespread in grassy pastures. Found over entire Cape in proportion to extent of suitable habitat.

HISTORY: Clearly a species which had benefited from deforestation of Cape and which maintained numbers longer than Bobolink, described as "very abundant" 1870–1890 (Brewster) but also shy due to hunting pressure. Drastically reduced by series of severe winters, notably 1892–1893 (Brewster, 1906, page 245). Restriction of breeding area by regrowth of trees prevented recovery of population which was further reduced in 1899, 1917–1918, 1933–1934, 1940, 1948, and 1960–1961, so population now at lowest point ever recorded.

*   *

WESTERN MEADOWLARK
Sturnella neglecta Audubon

STATUS: Hypothetical.

One bird seen and heard singing on June 8, 1964 at South Wellfleet (Bailey).

*   *

YELLOW-HEADED BLACKBIRD

Xanthocephalus xanthocephalus (Bonaparte)

STATUS: Represented in BMS and Chicago collections.

SPRING: Accidental; two on June 29, 1960, at Orleans (Lund, Bailey).

FALL: Very rare and irregular vagrant from the West.

Earliest arrival date: August 16, 1957, at Falmouth (Garry).

Average migration period: August 30–September 15; total of four specimens with two extant and five sight records.

Latest departure date: November 14, 1954, at Eastham (Nickerson, Brooks).

DISTRIBUTION: Recorded from Falmouth to Chatham and north to Eastham.

HISTORY: Recorded sporadically throughout historical period.

* *

REDWINGED BLACKBIRD

Agelaius phoeniceus (Linnaeus)

STATUS: Represented in MCZ, BMS, and British Museum collections.

SPRING: Arrival of residents, a few transients.

Earliest arrival date: February 17, 1960, three males flying in from southwest at Barnstable (Hill).

Average resident arrival period: For males, March 15–May 20 with peak April 10–20; for females, April 15–May 30 with peak May 10–20 (Packard, *Bird-Banding*, 8, 139, 1937); average flocks 20–150 birds. Usually first blackbird to arrive.

Average transient period: April 1–May 5; irregular numbers of transients, occasionally to several hundred.

SUMMER: Common breeding resident in all suitable habitats.

FALL: Dispersal of summer birds, a few migrants from mainland.

Average resident departure period: For males, July 25–August

5 and for females and young by August 15; usually leave Cape (Packard, *Bird-Banding*, 7, 28, 1936), but a few may remain in small roosts mostly along sound shores, up to one hundred birds.

Average transient period: September 8–October 28; counts irregular and seldom over 30; banding has shown that they come from the mainland and northward (Packard, l.c.).

WINTER: Rare and irregular straggler in early winter, rapidly eliminated by severe weather, though a few individuals may occasionally survive.

DISTRIBUTION: Breeds in cattails in fresh and brackish water, occasional in brushy swamps. Widespread over entire Cape, but fewer than on mainland. Late-summer roosts may occur in cedar swamps.

HISTORY: No evidence of any significant change in status.

*   *

ORCHARD ORIOLE

Icterus spurius (Linnaeus)

STATUS: Presumptive.

SPRING: Casual straggler, often associated with southern storms as April 19, 1952, at Chatham (Griscom); also several May records.

SUMMER: Said to have bred at Harwichport (Forbush, 1929), but details now lost. Pairs reported in 1950 at Sagamore (Hill) and 1953 at Eastham (Floyd), but breeding not proven. Wandering single birds reported widely but rarely.

FALL: Casual straggler in September, latest on September 12, 1948, at Chatham (M.A.S.).

DISTRIBUTION: Recorded over entire Cape.

HISTORY: No evidence that this species was ever more common on Cape, even when more widespread on mainland.

*   *

BALTIMORE ORIOLE
Icterus galbula (Linnaeus)

STATUS: Represented in MCZ and BMS collections.

SPRING: Arrival of residents, rare as transient.

Earliest arrival date: April 5, year unrecorded, at Osterville (Lovell, see Forbush, 1929); thus occasional after southern storms.

Average arrival period: May 5–16; regularly appear first near mainland and slowly work eastward and then north, often a week later at Wellfleet than at Sagamore.

SUMMER: Fairly common but rather local breeding resident, 1–4 pairs in most villages.

FALL: Fairly common migrant.

Earliest transient date: Uncertain, probably mid-July.

Average migration period: August 20–September 30.

Peak: September 1–15, average 3–6 birds, maximum 23 on September 9–11, 1949 (M.A.S.).

Latest transient date: Uncertain, probably mid-November.

WINTER: Formerly very irregular straggler but markedly increased since 1950 with cycle of mild falls and increased feeding stations. Very rarely survives entire season.

DISTRIBUTION: Breeding birds distributed over entire Cape, largely in villages, but occasionally in oak or even pine woods. Migrants also widespread and occur in shore-line traps. Associated with feeding stations in winter. In general less numerous than on mainland except in winter.

HISTORY: Except for increase in winter records noted above, there is no evidence of any change in status.

* *

BULLOCK'S ORIOLE
Icterus bullockii (Swainson)

STATUS: Photographed, on file at M.A.S.
Very rare vagrant from the West.
Male and probable female from December 2, 1952, to April 24, 1953, at feeder at Falmouth (Collins), photographed. Male on April 24, 1954, at Osterville (Johnson), banded and photographed. Several other reports less well substantiated, see Mason, *Bull. Mass. Audubon Soc.*, 37, 231, 1953.

* *

RUSTY BLACKBIRD
Euphagus carolinus (Müller)

STATUS: Represented in MCZ collection.
SPRING: Rare and probably irregular migrant.
    Earliest transient date: March 5, 1942, at Osterville (Eaton).
    Average migration period: Split migration as on mainland, March 8–20 and April 12–23; average 1–2 birds.
    Latest transient date: May 3, 1959, at Sagamore (Hill).
FALL: Rare migrant.
    Earliest transient date: September 15, 1954, at Monomoy (Goodell).
    Average migration period: September 25–October 31; average 1–2 birds, maximum 5 on October 3, 1950, at Nauset (Griscom, Hill).
    Latest transient date: January 3, 1960, at Brewster (Baird, Hill).
WINTER: Casual straggler, recorded into February at least twice, but not known to have survived the entire season.
DISTRIBUTION: Recorded over entire Cape, apparently a little more regular nearer the Canal than eastward. Much fewer than on mainland.

HISTORY: Satisfactory data available only since 1930; no evidence of change in status since then.

* *

COMMON GRACKLE
Quiscalus quiscula (Linnaeus)

STATUS: Represented in MCZ, BMS, and British Museum collections.

SPRING: Arrival of residents, fairly common as transient.

Earliest arrival date: February 27, 1957, at Bourne (Hill).

Average resident arrival period: March 20–April 15; usually third blackbird to arrive.

Average transient period: April 1–15; flocks of 50–200, separate from residents.

SUMMER: Common breeding resident in small colonies.

FALL: Uncommon migrant except near Canal where common.

Average migration period: August 28–November 10; no peak period, average 50–100 birds near Canal with maximum 400+ on September 10, 1961, at Bourne (Hill) vs. average 8–35 on outer Cape with maximum 45 on October 14, 1951, at Eastham and Orleans (Griscom).

WINTER: Rare and irregular straggler early in season, may occasionally survive in mild years.

DISTRIBUTION: Breeding birds over entire Cape in wide variety of habitats including sand-dune thickets at Monomoy Point, more commonly in thicker deciduous or cedar swamps, but even in cattails as at North Truro (Brewster). Migrants over entire Cape, in greater numbers westward particularly in fall; much fewer than on mainland.

HISTORY: No evidence of any change in status.

SUBSPECIES: Most specimens are referred to *Q. q. versicolor*, but some individuals of the southern race variously reported as both *stonei and "ridgwayi"* have been taken in Chatham.

* *

BROWN-HEADED COWBIRD
Molothrus ater (Boddaert)

STATUS: Represented in MCZ and British Museum collections.

SPRING: Arrival of residents, uncommon as transient.
Earliest arrival date: February 21, 1954, at Brewster (Griscom).
Average resident arrival period: March 20–April 15; usually second blackbird to arrive.
Average transient period: April 1–15; flocks of 25–125, separate from residents.

SUMMER: Common and widespread resident. On Cape Cod, eggs reported in nests of Red-eyed Vireo, Yellowthroat, Redstart, Yellow Warbler, Savannah, Song, Chipping, and Grasshopper Sparrows.

FALL: Common migrant.
Average migration period: August 25–October 15; no peak period, average 8–40 birds but more numerous westward as maximum of 500 in August 1953 at Woods Hole (Freeland) vs. maximum of 200 on October 6, 1946, at Chatham and Eastham (Griscom).

WINTER: Formerly uncommon but regular, recently in flocks to 275 in early winter; only occasionally survives the season.

DISTRIBUTION: Occurs over entire Cape in breeding season, migrants more common westward.

HISTORY: No data from early periods. Breeding population appears about doubled since 1940 over entire Cape. Early-winter flocks increased since 1950 because of mild falls.

* *

WESTERN TANAGER
Piranga ludoviciana (Wilson)

STATUS: Photographed, on file at M.A.S.
Very rare vagrant from West, chiefly in fall.

Sight records from September 13 on, several records at feeders in winter, including January to March 1953 photographed at Cotuit (Higgins); sight records in spring to May 5 and believed to be surviving winter birds.

* *

SCARLET TANAGER
Piranga olivacea (Gmelin)

STATUS: Represented in MCZ and British Museum collections.

SPRING: Arrival of residents, otherwise rare and irregular after southern storms in April.

Earliest date: April 8, 1958, at Chatham (Mosher).

Average transient period: April 15–24, often picked up dead or exhausted, mostly in southern or eastern areas. No transients in May.

Average resident arrival period: May 12–25.

SUMMER: Rare and local breeding resident.

FALL: Uncommon migrant.

Earliest transient date: August 24, 1952, at Monomoy (Hill).

Average migration period: September 1–October 1; average 1–2 birds, maximum 4 on several occasions.

Latest transient date: October 22, 1932, banded at North Eastham (Austin Station); later dates not confirmed.

DISTRIBUTION: Breeds in deeper woods of Falmouth-Sandwich moraine where oaks are replacing pines, scattered pairs throughout; much fewer east of Brewster but regular to Orleans, though no further. Much less numerous than on mainland. Migrants widespread in woodlands and into shore-line traps.

HISTORY: Breeding pairs slowly increasing and moving eastward as forests grow and spread. No change in migrant status.

* *

SUMMER TANAGER
Piranga rubra (Linnaeus)

STATUS: Found dead, apparently not preserved; also banded at Austin Station.

SPRING: Rare vagrant from South after coastal storms.

Earliest date: Late March 1958 at Osterville (Bearse).

Average period: April 15–25, see May, *Auk*, *46*, 393, 1929, and Brown, *Bird-Banding*, *3*, 176, 1932; mostly single birds, often dead or exhausted, and mostly in southern or eastern areas.

Latest date: May 31, 1954, at Monomoy (Hill).

FALL: Rare wandering vagrant.

Earliest date: September 8, 1946, at Eastham (Griscom, Eliot).

Average period: September 12–20.

Latest date: October 24, 1959, at Chatham (Mosher).

DISTRIBUTION: Wandering birds both spring and fall almost entirely from Centerville to Chatham and north to Nauset; this probably represents both actual landfall of migrants and concentration of observers.

HISTORY: Subject to April flights dependent on southern storms; recent flights recorded on Cape include 1929, 1932, 1954, 1958, and 1961, see Bagg, *Bull. Mass. Audubon Soc.*, *39*, 106 & 159, 1955. Fall birds apparently always wandering vagrants and not dependent on any specific weather pattern.

＊   ＊

CARDINAL
Richmondena cardinalis (Linnaeus)

STATUS: Presumptive.

Formerly rare straggler from South appearing erratically at very long intervals at any date, often at feeding stations. At present increasing parallel to but much slower than on southeastern mainland of state. More recorded nearer Canal than eastward, no evidence of breeding as yet.

*   *

ROSE-BREASTED GROSBEAK
Pheucticus ludovicianus (Linnaeus)

STATUS: Banded at Austin Station.

SPRING: Very rare and irregular migrant, found both after southern storms in April and also in May.

Earliest date: April 14, 1955, at Orleans (Lund).

Average migration period: April 18–25 and again May 8–24; always single birds.

SUMMER: Wandering birds reported from June to early August, but no breeding proven.

FALL: Rare migrant.

Earliest transient date: August 25, 1963, at Monomoy (Hill, Kleber).

Average migration period: September 10–October 12; always single birds.

Latest transient date: November 6, 1938, at Sagamore (Hill, Abbott).

DISTRIBUTION: Recorded over entire Cape.

HISTORY: Satisfactory data only since 1930; no evidence of change since that date.

*   *

BLACK-HEADED GROSBEAK
Pheucticus melanocephalus (Swainson)

STATUS: Hypothetical.

Two records, both at feeders; an immature male which changed into adult plumage October 28, 1954, to April 18, 1955, at Barnstable (Lyons) and November 19, 1962, to February 24, 1963, at Orleans (Lund).

*   *

BLUE GROSBEAK

Guiraca caerulea (Linnaeus)

STATUS: Represented in BMS and Peabody Museum collections.

SPRING: Casual straggler after southern storms; earliest date April 15, 1949, banded at North Eastham (Austin Station), latest date May 19, 1940, at Chatham (Bishop).

FALL: Very rare and irregular vagrant.

Earliest transient date: August 14, 1952, at Monomoy (Griscom).

Average migration period: September 20–October 14; total of four birds collected at peak period of October 12–14 in four different years.

Latest transient date: October 27, 1959, at Chatham (Mayo).

DISTRIBUTION: Recorded from North Eastham and Brewster south to Chatham and west along the sounds to Falmouth.

HISTORY: Very irregular to 1945, more frequent since then, but by no means recorded every year.

* *

INDIGO BUNTING

Passerina cyanea (Linnaeus)

STATUS: Represented in British Museum collection.

SPRING: Arrival of residents, otherwise the most characteristic of the storm-blown stragglers in April and very rare and irregular as transient in May.

Earliest transient date: April 12, 1961, at Orleans (Fox).

Average migration period: April 17–28; usually 1–2 birds but occasionally loose flocks up to 10, often found dead or exhausted. Another small migration irregularly May 12–24.

SUMMER: Formerly recorded only as wanderer. With recent increase on mainland has become more regular; in 1961 six singing males located on Cape Cod, two of these paired and one nest with young found on June 21, 1961, at Wellfleet (Hill).

FALL: Uncommon migrant.

> Earliest transient date: August 28, 1941, banded at North Eastham (Austin Station).
>
> Average migration period: September 8–October 15; usually 1–2 birds.
>
> Latest transient date: November 12, 1941, banded at North Eastham (Austin Station).

DISTRIBUTION: Storm-blown birds in April largely on southern coast and in eastern areas. Summer residents recorded over entire Cape north to Truro. Fall migrants largely on outer Cape.

HISTORY: Data prior to 1930 incomplete except for freak dates. April birds dependent on southern storms and were especially noticeable in 1940, 1952, 1953, 1954, 1957, and 1961. Probably increasing slowly as migrant and definitely increasing recently as breeding species.

* *

PAINTED BUNTING

Passerina ciris (Linnaeus)

STATUS: Hypothetical.

Accidental straggler from the South.

Male from May 27 to June 1, 1891, at North Truro (Small) has been attributed to an escaped cage bird but might just as well be a survivor of an April storm. A male seen April 17, 1961, at Orleans (Goodspeed) and a female from January 15 to late March 1957 at feeder in Falmouth (Athearn).

* *

DICKCISSEL

Spiza americana (Gmelin)

STATUS: Represented in BMS collection.

FALL: Recently rather uncommon migrant.

> Earliest arrival date: July 22, 1953, banded at North Eastham (Austin Station).

Average migration period: August 25–October 15; see below for counts.

WINTER: Regular at feeders, average 1–2 birds recently, associating with English Sparrows and frequently surviving the season.

SPRING: Persistence of wintering birds, no evidence of migrants. Latest date May 16, 1959, at Orleans (Lund).

SUMMER: Reported in summer in 1855 (Thoreau) and presumed breeding. No other reports.

DISTRIBUTION: Recorded over entire Cape in pastures, moors, and somewhat in shore-line traps; greatest numbers from Eastham to Chatham.

HISTORY: Summary by Griscom & Snyder (1955) applies to Cape; presumed to have bred about 1850 (Thoreau), very rare straggler to 1930 and increasing steadily to about 1953 and decreasing since; e.g., 3 in 1946, 14 in 1949, 22 in 1953, 14 in 1958, and 7 in 1960.

* *

CHAFFINCH
Fringilla coelebs Linnaeus

STATUS: Photographed, on file at M.A.S.

Accidental vagrant from Old World. One bird present at feeder April 1–3, 1961, at Chatham (Reynolds, Copeland, Bailey).

* *

EVENING GROSBEAK
Hesperiphona vespertina (Cooper)

STATUS: Represented in MCZ collection.

FALL: Increasingly common and regular, arrival of wintering flocks rather than transients.

Earliest arrival date: September 2, 1957, at Provincetown (Gammell).

Average arrival period: Erratic, October to January.

WINTER: Increasingly common but largely dependent on feeding stations; see below for counts.

SPRING: Dispersal of wintering flocks, no transients.

Average departure period: Erratic, February to April.

Latest departure date: June 8, 1955, at Bourne (Crain).

DISTRIBUTION: Recorded over entire Cape with tendency to greater numbers westward, but will congregate wherever feed is made available.

HISTORY: Much later penetrating to Cape than to remainder of state. No record of occurrence on flight of 1890; first report December 5, 1903, at Wellfleet (Nichols, *Auk*, *21*, 81, 1904); in 1930 birds trapped in Sandwich had been banded in Michigan (Burbank); fairly regular from 1942 to 1950 in flocks of 10–30; increasing in numbers to 1960, maxima 125 in single flock in December 1955 at Pocasset (Crain) and 223 in several flocks on January 2, 1956, on outer Cape (C.C.).

* *

PURPLE FINCH
Carpodacus purpureus (Gmelin)

STATUS: Represented in BMS and British Museum collections.

Technically a permanent resident but tentatively separated into three populations: 1) breeding; 2) transient with some individuals wintering; and 3) erratic winter influxes.

1) BREEDING. Arrive in late April and early May, nest widely but sparsely in evergreen plantings and in native red cedar; 20 pairs at Woods Hole (Freeland), 3 pairs at Sagamore (Hill), 5 pairs in Mashpee-Cotuit area (Hill), 3–4 pairs each at Barnstable, Chatham, Orleans, Wellfleet, etc. Departure date uncertain due to merging with next population.

2) TRANSIENT.

Spring: Rare but regular migrant from late March through

April, average 1–6 birds, probably more numerous westward on Cape.

Fall: Uncommon transient, irregular in numbers.

Average migration period: September 1–30; average 2–10 birds, maximum 30 on September 9, 1951 (M.A.S.).

Winter: Uncommon to rare but probably regular; average 5–40 birds recently (C.C.).

3) ERRATIC WINTER INFLUX. Characterized by sudden appearance at variable dates, usually part of a mainland flight and usually remaining a relatively short period; e.g., 77 banded March 17–22, 1939, at Sandwich (Burbank) and 205 banded March 14–April 21, 1939, largely before April 1, at North Eastham (Austin Station), see Weaver, *Bird-Banding*, *11*, 79, 1940; also 120 on December 28, 1958 (C.C.).

DISTRIBUTION: Both breeding and migrant birds recorded over entire Cape.

HISTORY: Breeding birds probably increasing slowly with planting and growth of ornamental evergreens. No evidence of change in status of usual transient population. Winter flights on mainland in 1863 (Allen, 1864), 1883 (Brewster, 1906), and 1928 (Bagg & Eliot, 1937) were not recorded on Cape. See above for 1939 and 1958.

* *

HOUSE FINCH

Carpodacus mexicanus (Müller)

STATUS: Hypothetical.

Sight record of one at feeder January 10–20, 1963, at Cotuit (Higgins, Donald).

* *

PINE GROSBEAK
Pinicola enucleator (Linnaeus)

STATUS: Represented in MAS collection.
WINTER: Very irregular visitant.
Earliest arrival date: November 1, 1954, at Orleans (Griscom, Kleber).
Average arrival period: November 20–December 10.
Counts: Erratic; often none, average 1–10 birds in flight years, maximum 100 on January 10, 1893, at Woods Hole (Edwards).
Average departure period: February 1–20.
Latest departure date: March 30, 1958, at Orleans (Lund).
DISTRIBUTION: Recorded over entire Cape.
HISTORY: Occurs mostly in flight years and always in lower numbers than on mainland, very rarely stray birds or flocks in non-flight years. Great flight of 1892 reached from Bourne and Sandwich to Falmouth and Woods Hole (Brewster, *Auk*, *12*, 245, 1895). Minor flight of 1923 reached Centerville (Eaton). Flight of 1943 reached only to Sandwich (Burbank), that of 1951 on mainland brought only a few to the Cape, but that of 1961 brought considerable numbers scattered over entire Cape.

* *

EUROPEAN GOLDFINCH
Carduelis carduelis (Linnaeus)

STATUS: Collected, specimen now lost.
Collected at Falmouth in 1884 (Swift, *O & O*, *9*, 12, 1884) and sight record October 27 and November 7, 1962, at Barnstable (Lyon).

* *

HOARY REDPOLL
Acanthis hornemanni (Holboell)

STATUS: Hypothetical.
Three sight records in January and February of Redpoll flight years; specimens needed.

* *

COMMON REDPOLL
Acanthis flammea (Linnaeus)

STATUS: Represented in MCZ, BMS, and British Museum collections.
WINTER: Irregular visitant, absent to common.
Earliest arrival date: November 2, 1946, at Chatham (Griscom).
Average arrival period: December 20–February 1.
Counts: Variable, sometimes none, average 3–50 in flights, maximum 150 on March 28, 1953, at Orleans (Earle).
Average departure period: March 20–April 15.
Latest departure date: May 20, 1953, at Orleans (Earle).
DISTRIBUTION: Recorded over entire Cape, usually less numerous than on mainland. Seen arriving from over the ocean from northeast on February 3, 1960, at Race Point, Provincetown (Hill, Petty).
HISTORY: Frequently absent or in very small numbers; obvious flights recorded in 1890, 1944, 1947, 1953, 1958, and 1960 parallel to mainland flights. All Cape flights occur with mainland flights, but some of the latter fail to reach the Cape.
SUBSPECIES: Random collecting has shown presence of *A. f. flammea*, *A. f. holboelli*, and *A. f. rostrata*; see Griscom & Snyder, 1955.

* *

PINE SISKIN
Spinus pinus (Wilson)

STATUS: Represented in MCZ, BMS, Chicago, and British Museum collections.

FALL: Irregular migrant.

Earliest transient date: September 8, 1947, at Sagamore (Crompton).

Average migration period: October 15–December 31; probably occurs every year as transient, average 2–15 birds, maximum 150 on December 30, 1951, at Eastham (Snyder, Burnett).

WINTER: Irregular, absent to common. In flight years some remain from fall migration and numbers build up; flocks average 4–60 birds but some years in much greater numbers, maxima 355 on January 2, 1949, on outer Cape (C.C.). and about 800+ in February 1953 on entire Cape (many observers).

SPRING: Regular transient in variable numbers, also departure of winter residents.

Average departure period for wintering birds: Steady decrease through March and April.

Average transient period: May 2–31; very irregular, usually absent, maximum 25 on several occasions.

Latest transient date: May 31, 1941, at Monomoy (Cottrell).

DISTRIBUTION: Recorded over entire Cape. Migrants tend to be in pine woods, occasionally recorded along beaches, perhaps on arrival from over-water flights. Wintering birds also in pines but will collect at feeding stations.

HISTORY: Brewster's counts from 1870 to 1890 essentially same as at present, i.e., no evidence of change in status during historical period.

*   *

AMERICAN GOLDFINCH
Spinus tristis (Linnaeus)

STATUS: Represented in BMS and British Museum collections.

Technically a permanent resident but tentatively separated into three populations: 1) breeding; 2) transient which is often erratic; and 3) winter.

1) BREEDING. Probably arrive in late May, nest widely but quite sparingly in brushy areas and low deciduous woods over entire Cape, numbers variable and shift from year to year. Departure dates unknown due to merging with next population.

2) TRANSIENT.

Spring: Very erratic migrant moving through in April, often absent and never in numbers, more numerous around Canal than eastward.

Fall: Erratic migrant, usually more regular and in greater numbers than in spring.

Average migration period: September 15–November 15.

Counts: Occasionally absent as in 1944 and 1951; average 10–60 birds, maximum 250 on November 9, 1941, at Eastham and Chatham (Griscom, Hill).

3) WINTER.

Average period: November 25–February 25.

Counts variable but always present, from a few scattered individuals to 918 on January 1, 1950 (C.C.).

DISTRIBUTION: Recorded over entire Cape in wide variety of habitats.

HISTORY: No evidence of change in status.

*   *

RED CROSSBILL
Loxia curvirostra Linnaeus

STATUS: Represented in BMS, Cleveland Museum of Natural History, and British Museum collections.

Of very irregular occurrence, reported in every month of the year, the majority of records falling from November 1 to March 31. Breeding birds collected April 24–26, 1889, at North Truro (Miller, in British Museum, *Auk*, 7, 228, 1890); a few summer records of young birds may represent additional local breeding, 1936 at Brewster (Scott), 1937 at North Chatham (Tousey), 1940 at Cotuit (Shreve), and 1964 at Sagamore (Hill).

DISTRIBUTION: Occurs widely in pitch pine barrens over entire Cape; more regular and more numerous than on mainland.

HISTORY: Formerly occurred "nearly every year" (Forbush, 1929) and often in numbers, e.g., common in flocks up to 100 on November 21–22, 1886, at Great Island, Hyannis (Brewster, Cory). Decreasing steadily in last fifty years, recently averaging 3–8 birds except for 40+ in 1931 on outer Cape (Griscom), 140 on January 2, 1952, at Falmouth (Crain), and 479 on December 29, 1963, on outer Cape (C.C.).

SUBSPECIES: Most records assumed to pertain to *L. c. minor*. In addition, *L. c. pusilla* was collected November 1919 to January 1920 at Chathamport (see Bent, *Auk*, 37, 298, 1920) and banded in 1932 at North Eastham (Austin Station), both flight years; and *L. c. sitkensis* was collected December 1919 to January 1920 at Chatham (Hersey, see Godfrey, *Auk*, 62, 151, 1945); the mainland flight of this subspecies in 1941 was unreported on the Cape.

＊　＊

WHITE-WINGED CROSSBILL
Loxia leucoptera Gmelin

STATUS: Represented in BMS collection.

WINTER: Very irregular both in occurrence and in numbers.

Earliest arrival date: November 18, 1944, at East Orleans (Bradford).

Average arrival period: Late November and December.

Counts: Usually absent, stray birds occasionally accompany the more regular Red Crossbill flocks; average 1–5 birds, maximum 204 on December 29, 1963, on outer Cape (C.C.).

Average departure date: February to April.

Latest departure date: May 19, 1958, at West Harwich (McCormick).

DISTRIBUTION: Except for strays with Red Crossbills in pitch pines this species is usually found in ornamental hemlock and other evergreen plantings which are very limited and local on Cape Cod; hence species much less numerous than on mainland.

HISTORY: Straggling individuals and flocks appear with very little relationship to mainland flights; however, the general increase on the mainland is reflected on the Cape since 1944.

* *

RUFOUS-SIDED TOWHEE

Pipilo erythrophthalmus (Linnaeus)

STATUS: Represented in MCZ, BMS, American Museum (N.Y.), and British Museum collections.

SPRING: Arrival of residents; as transient common westward, less so eastward.

Earliest arrival date: Uncertain, probably about April 28.

Average arrival period: May 2–14.

SUMMER: Abundant breeding resident throughout, probably commonest land bird on Cape. Sample estimated density: 100+ pairs/100 acres at Brewster (Hill), this density prevailing through most of interior areas; 40–50 pairs/100 acres at Sagamore (Hill); 20 pairs at Woods Hole, 30 pairs at Mashpee, 40 pairs at Provincetown (Kelly), etc.

FALL: Common migrant.

Average migration period: September 6–October 20.

Peak: September 12–30; average 10–75 birds, maximum 300+ on September 17, 1944, at Brewster (Hill) after a hurricane when none could be found in coastal areas.

WINTER: Rare but increasing with mild seasons, first on Christmas Count in 1951, and missed only one year since. Rarely survives except in very mild seasons or with the help of feeding stations.

DISTRIBUTION: Breeding throughout both pine and deciduous woodlands, in brushy uplands, old pasture, margins of swamps, etc., also in isolated sand-dune thickets, but not in open moors. Spring migrants appear first near mainland, e.g., 25 at Sagamore and none on outer Cape on May 14, 1952 (Hill), and work eastward and then northward.

HISTORY: Unfortunately no data on original status when Cape was wooded or after deforestation. No evidence of change since 1930.

SUBSPECIES: An individual of one of the "spotted" western races was seen on October 12, 1957, at Monomoy (Bailey).

* *

LARK BUNTING

Calamospiza melanocorys Stejneger

STATUS: Hypothetical.
Accidental vagrant from the West.
Sight record on September 3, 1949, at Nauset (Mason); several other records less well confirmed.

* *

IPSWICH SPARROW

Passerculus princeps Maynard

STATUS: Represented in MCZ, BMS, Chicago, and British Museum collections.
FALL: Uncommon to rare migrant.
Earliest arrival date: October 10, 1948, at Nauset (Griscom).
Average migration period: October 20–December 1; average 1–3 birds only.

WINTER: Uncommon to rare resident; average 1–3 birds, maximum 10 on January 1, 1950 (C.C.); regularly survives the season.

SPRING: Uncommon to rare migrant.

Average migration period: March 15–April 12; average 1–4 birds.

Latest departure date: April 22, 1889, at North Truro (Miller, in BMS); sight records to May 11, 1930, at Sandwich (Burbank).

DISTRIBUTION: Essentially confined to the *Ammophila* beach grass on the dunes; found on the barrier beaches on the entire Cape.

HISTORY: Records are inadequate prior to 1930; there is no evidence of change since then, but the counts of this species are unsatisfactory as no careful census has ever been taken in any suitable area. Therefore, Cape Cod data neither supports nor contradicts the impression of general decrease throughout the Northeast.

* *

SAVANNAH SPARROW
Passerculus sandwichensis (Gmelin)

STATUS: Represented in MCZ, BMS, Chicago, and British Museum collections.

SPRING: Arrival of residents, very few if any transients.

Earliest arrival date: Uncertain, probably mid-March.

Average arrival period: April 1–May 1.

SUMMER: Common breeding resident along upper levels of salt marshes and lower adjacent uplands; greatest counts are 30+ pairs at Monomoy, 40–50 pairs each at Barnstable and Orleans, with smaller counts elsewhere.

FALL: Common migrant.

Average migration period: September 10–November 20.

Peak: September 20–October 20; average 15–30 birds, maximum 50 on September 28, 1953, at Brewster (Derby).

WINTER: Fairly regular in small numbers, occasionally surviving.

DISTRIBUTION: See above for breeding distribution. Nests in suitable habitat over entire Cape. Migrants more widespread and occur in all types of open country.

HISTORY: Described as "abundant" in 1876 at Monomoy (Brewster). Records since 1930 not conclusive but probably consistent with a slow moderate decline in numbers.

SUBSPECIES: *P. s. labradorius* as a migrant has been both collected and banded, may sometimes be suspected on field observation. Otherwise all specimens are *P. s. savanna.*

* *

GRASSHOPPER SPARROW
Ammodramus savannarum (Gmelin)

STATUS: Represented in British Museum collection.

SPRING: Arrival of residents, no transients.

Earliest arrival date: May 14, 1937, at Eastham (Bishop).

Average arrival period: May 20–25.

SUMMER: Rather uncommon but widespread breeding resident, occupying upland hayfields and abandoned pasture until brush grows up. Estimated 6–8 pairs each at Orleans and Eastham and scattered pairs elsewhere.

FALL: Departure of residents, possibly a few transients.

Average departure period: September 15–28.

Latest departure date: October 4, 1931, banded at North Eastham (Austin Station).

DISTRIBUTION: Recorded in suitable habitat over entire Cape out to North Truro; relatively fewer westward due to restricted habitat. More numerous than on mainland.

HISTORY: Data prior to 1930 fragmentary. Banded in considerable numbers during the summers of the 1930's, but many fewer since (Austin Station); this corroborates the decrease in counts on sight records. Decrease attributed to growth of hayfields to brush or woods and to the multiplication of houses.

* *

HENSLOW'S SPARROW

Passerherbulus henslowii (Audubon)

STATUS: Represented in BMS and Peabody Museum collections.
Exceedingly rare vagrant; collected October 20, 1951, at Mono-
moy (Griscom, in PM) and November 6, 1884, at Osterville
(Townsend, in BMS), these being *P. h. susurrans*, and also
collected November 6, 1874, at Osterville (Brewster, in BMS),
this being *P. h. henslowii*. Banded October 19, 1936, at North
Eastham (Austin Station); several unconfirmed sight records in
January and February. Forbush (1929) recorded nesting at
Brewster and Yarmouth, details now lost and records must be
questioned. No recent breeding records.

* *

SHARP-TAILED SPARROW

Ammospiza caudacuta (Gmelin)

STATUS: Represented in MCZ, BMS, and Chicago collections.
Three populations separable as subspecies and often identifiable
in the field: 1) breeding, *A. c. caudacuta*; 2) transient, *A. c.
subvirgata*; and 3) vagrant from Northwest, *A. c. nelsoni*.
1) BREEDING: *A. c. caudacuta*, Eastern Sharp-tailed Sparrow.
   SPRING: Arrival of residents, no transients.
   Earliest arrival date: May 9, 1937, at Sagamore (Hill).
   Average arrival period: May 23–June 1.
   SUMMER: Locally common to abundant breeding resident oc-
   cupying the *Spartina patens* grass of the salt marshes, generally in colonies, estimated 1000 pairs at Barnstable, 15–20
   pairs each at Nauset and Monomoy, and smaller numbers
   elsewhere.
   FALL: Withdrawal of residents, no transients.
   Average departure period: September 1–30.
   Peak: September 10–25; counts not significant.
   WINTER: Stragglers remain into early winter after mild falls,
   may very rarely survive entire season, but this is not proven.

DISTRIBUTION: Exclusively in marshes and occurs over entire Cape in suitable habitat.

HISTORY: Decreasing slowly during historical period as marshes are filled or dyked to eliminate periodic salt water flooding with resultant change in plant life. Probably some decrease at Monomoy also for no apparent reason, e.g., 20–30 pairs found there June 12, 1885 (Cahoon), vs. about 15–20 pairs at present.

2) TRANSIENT, *A. c. subvirgata,* Acadian Sharp-tailed Sparrow.

SPRING: Uncommon migrant.

Earliest transient date: May 25, 1941, at Monomoy (Griscom, Eliot).

Average migration period: May 28–June 5; average 3–5 birds, maximum 10+ on May 31, 1953, at Monomoy (Griscom, Beattie).

Latest transient date: June 15, 1940, at Monomoy (Griscom).

FALL: Uncommon migrant.

Earliest transient date: September 10, 1955, at Nauset (M.A.S.).

Average migration period: September 20–October 31.

Peak: October 1–10; average 2–6 birds, maximum 25+ on October 11, 1953, at Barnstable (Hill).

Latest transient date: November 28, 1962, at Nauset (Hill, Bryan).

DISTRIBUTION: Occurs in salt marshes with breeding race, but tends to go into the coarser *Spartina alterniflora.* Usually more numerous at Barnstable than farther eastward.

HISTORY: No evidence of change in status.

3) VAGRANT. *A. c. nelsoni,* Nelson's Sharp-tailed Sparrow, collected, one on September 23, 1884, at Chatham (Brackett, in BMS) and three on February 6–8, 1901, at Barnstable (Bigelow & Shattuck, one in MCZ). Surprisingly, there are no reports of *A. c. altera,* the James Bay Sharp-tailed Sparrow.

*   *

SEASIDE SPARROW
Ammospiza maritima (Wilson)

STATUS: Represented in MCZ and BMS collections.

Permanent resident of varying status, also probably a very few terminal and departure migrants, but no valid dates of arrival or departure.

DISTRIBUTION: Breeding stations: Barnstable, first found in 1898 (Bigelow, Shattuck) and probably continuously present though much overlooked, certainly present since 1940 (many observers) with estimated 10 pairs in 1957 (Hill); Nauset, first found in 1932 (Brown) and regular since 1950, 2–4 pairs; First Encounter marsh in Eastham, regular since 1951, 3–5 pairs; Orleans at head of Pleasant Bay, irregular since 1943; Morris Island, Chatham, irregular since 1938; and probably other locations. Wandering birds both spring and fall found more widely but little detectable migration. Wintering chiefly in breeding areas, frequently with high mortality, so effects of a severe winter may be seen for several years.

HISTORY: First known in 1890 at Monomoy (Cahoon, *Auk*, 7, 289, 1890); development of breeding stations outlined above. First winter record in 1950 and recorded every year except 1952–1953 since, maximum 20 on January 3, 1960 (C.C.).

*   *

VESPER SPARROW
Pooecetes gramineus (Gmelin)

STATUS: Represented in BMS, Chicago, and British Museum collections.

SPRING: Arrival of residents, probably no transients.

Earliest arrival date: March 21, 1938, at Chatham (Bishop).

Average arrival period: April 5–15.

SUMMER: Rather uncommon and local breeding resident, probably a few more than Grasshopper Sparrow. Scattered pairs in pastures and moors. Estimated 20 pairs in Chatham-Orleans-Eastham area and 20–25 pairs at North Truro.

FALL: Dispersal of residents, very few transients.

Average migration period: September 15–October 31; average 2–4 birds.

WINTER: Regularly lingers in mild falls until cold weather, rarely persisting into February, and never proven to have survived the entire season.

DISTRIBUTION: Breeds in brushy pastures and moorland; at present greatest density in Truro and North Wellfleet, decreasing southward to Orleans, and becoming rare and local westward.

HISTORY: Decreasing steadily throughout historical period. Described as "abundant" in 1875 (Brewster); 50 on August 4, 1889, at Falmouth (Brewster); abundant in *Hudsonia* on dunes and common over entire Cape in 1891 (Bangs), even nesting in grassy clearings in pine woods. Decrease appeared first westward, e.g., by 1904 at Forestdale (Cobb), but still 25 on September 7, 1921, at East Harwich (Cobb) and 13 on June 19, 1923, at Orleans (Earle), decreasing rapidly by 1930 and further after 1940, e.g., many fewer banded in late '40's than in the '30's (Austin Station). No evidence of change as yet north of Wellfleet. This progressive decrease parallels the eastward extension of woods replacing the grassland.

*   *

LARK SPARROW

Chondestes grammacus (Say)

STATUS: Represented in MCZ collection.

SPRING: Accidental, one May 3, 1957, banded at North Eastham (Austin Station).

FALL: Very rare migrant.

Earliest transient date: August 4, 1934, banded at North Eastham (Austin Station).

Average migration period: August 24–October 15; usually single birds, occasionally two.

Latest transient date: December 18, 1953, at Sandwich (Romaine).

WINTER: Lingered once into winter, surviving to February 3, 1960, at Eastham (Webster).

DISTRIBUTION: Recorded over most of Cape, but markedly concentrated from Eastham to Monomoy.

HISTORY: Has been reported regularly since 1930 with definite increase since 1950; this may represent increase in observation rather than a true increase in occurrence.

* *

WHITE-WINGED JUNCO
Junco aikeni Ridgway

STATUS: Hypothetical.
One sight record only.

* *

SLATE-COLORED JUNCO
Junco hyemalis (Linnaeus)

STATUS: Represented in Chicago and British Museum collections.
FALL: Common to abundant migrant.

Earliest transient date: September 7, 1958, at Sagamore (Hill).
Average migration period: September 20–November 25.

Peak: October 1–24; average 50–250 birds, maximum 600+ on October 12, 1954, in Brewster-Orleans-Chatham area (Hill, Petty).

WINTER: Regular resident, uncommon to common, always surviving the season; average 30–50 birds, maximum 200 on January 20, 1948 (Higginbotham).

SPRING: Dispersal of wintering flocks, uncommon as transient, more numerous near Canal than eastward.

Average migration period: April 1–20; small flocks only.

Average resident departure period: April 25–May 5.

Latest departure date: May 24, 1938, banded at North Eastham (Austin Station).

SUMMER: Casual breeding; one record of nest with four young on June 16, 1906, at Wellfleet (Remick, *Auk*, *24*, 102, 1907).

DISTRIBUTION: Recorded over entire Cape in great variety of habitats including sand-dune thickets. In fall flocks moving down the inner coast at Sagamore partially cross Canal and partially turn westward along the north bank; also observed October 9, 1959, at Nauset arriving from over the ocean (Bailey). Fall migrants concentrate southeastward and spring migrants near the Canal. Wintering birds more numerous eastward.

HISTORY: Data prior to 1930 unsatisfactory; no evidence of change since that date.

*   *

OREGON JUNCO
Junco oreganus (Townsend)

STATUS: Hypothetical.

A scattering of sight records including at least two adult males; specimen needed.

*   *

TREE SPARROW
Spizella arborea (Wilson)

STATUS: Represented in BMS and British Museum collections.

FALL: Common migrant, chiefly arrival of wintering birds but some transients.

Earliest arrival date: October 12, 1954, at Brewster (Hill, Petty).

Average migration period: October 28–November 30; average 5–15 birds, maximum 35 on November 26, 1938 (Griscom, Garrison).

WINTER: Common resident. Christmas Count figures average 100–200 birds, maximum 378 on January 3, 1954; always survives the season.

SPRING: Departure of wintering flocks, no transients.

Average departure period: Decreasing by mid-February, main departure April 1–10.

Latest departure date: May 17, 1931, banded at North Eastham (Austin Station).

DISTRIBUTION: Recorded over entire Cape, mostly in brushy habitats and generally open country.

HISTORY: Apparently decreasing, recorded as very abundant, "far more numerous than about Cambridge" in December 1889 at Marstons Mills (Brewster), whereas at present it is not as numerous as on the mainland.

*   *

CHIPPING SPARROW

Spizella passerina (Bechstein)

STATUS: Represented in BMS and British Museum collection.

SPRING: Arrival of residents, very few transients.

Earliest arrival date: March 25, 1960, at Orleans (Fox).

Average arrival period: April 21–May 1.

SUMMER: Common breeding resident, widespread but most numerous around villages, in orchards, and brushy edges rather than in woods, occasionally in pitch pines.

FALL: Common migrant.

Average migration period: August 15–November 20. No peak dates, average 50–150 birds, maxima 500 on August 19, 1953, at Woods Hole (Freeland) and 250 on September 25, 1944, at Eastham (Griscom).

WINTER: Regularly lingers to first cold weather and in mild seasons well into winter; collected on December 23, 1891, at Woods Hole (White, *O & O*, *17*, 82, 1892) and seen to January 19, 1954, at Sandwich (Higgins). Never known to have survived the entire season.

DISTRIBUTION: Recorded in proportionate numbers over entire Cape in breeding season, about as numerous as on mainland. Migrants usually in higher numbers nearer Canal than on outer Cape.

HISTORY: Data incomplete prior to 1930 and no evidence of change since that date.

* *

CLAY-COLORED SPARROW
Spizella pallida (Swainson)

STATUS: Represented in BMS collection.
Very rare vagrant from West.
Two adult males trapped and collected September 30, 1930, at North Eastham (Austin, in BMS, *Auk*, *48*, 126, 1931). Several additional banding records and a few sight records, September 9 to November 19. Also one singing male reported May 30 to June 17.

* *

FIELD SPARROW
Spizella pusilla (Wilson)

STATUS: Represented in British Museum collection.
SPRING: Arrival of residents, rare as transient.
    Earliest arrival date: Uncertain, probably about April 1.
    Average arrival period: April 10–20.
SUMMER: Rather uncommon and local breeding resident, probably fewer than Grasshopper Sparrow on outer Cape, but more west

of Barnstable. Breeds in brushy fields and hedgerows, rapidly driven out by growth of vegetation.

FALL: Uncommon migrant.

Average migration period: September 10–November 10; no peak period, average 2–10 birds, maximum 50 on September 28, 1953, at Orleans (Derby).

WINTER: Regular in small numbers, persisting according to severity of season with at least a few surviving most winters.

DISTRIBUTION: Recorded in suitable habitat over entire Cape to Wellfleet, but apparently either lacking or very local northward; exact location of breeding pairs shifts from year to year according to ecological change. Migrants more tolerant and often join flocks of other sparrows; usually more numerous as migrant nearer Canal than eastward.

HISTORY: Decreasing steadily throughout historical period due to regrowth of forests, e.g., "abundant" on May 8, 1876, at Chatham (Brewster) vs. estimated 5–6 pairs at present; parallel changes elsewhere. First found wintering in 1892 at Barnstable (Bangs), fairly regularly by 1930, and in increasing numbers after 1945.

* *

HARRIS' SPARROW
Zonotrichia querula (Nuttall)

STATUS: Hypothetical.

Adults seen October 20–28, 1961, at Chatham (Copeland) and October 15, 1963, at Truro (Bolton).

* *

WHITE-CROWNED SPARROW
Zonotrichia leucophrys (Forster)

STATUS: Represented in MCZ, BMS, Chicago, and British Museum collections.

SPRING: Rare but probably regular migrant.

Earliest transient date: May 2, 1949, banded at North Eastham (Austin Station); March and April dates believed to be surviving wintering birds.

Average migration period: May 8–22; usually single birds, total of 5–10 banded most years (Austin Station).

Latest transient date: May 28, 1888, at Monomoy (Cahoon, in BMS).

FALL: Uncommon migrant, occasional great flights.

Earliest transient date: September 18, 1941, banded at North Eastham (Austin Station).

Average migration period: September 28–November 1.

Peak: October 5–20; average 2–20 birds, maximum on October 13, 1958, with 250 on outer Cape (Gardler) plus 100 at Chatham (Brown).

Latest transient date: Uncertain, probably about November 16.

WINTER: Very rarely attempts to winter, usually at feeding stations. Known to have survived occasionally.

DISTRIBUTION: Records largely on outer Cape, usually found in brushy and edge habitats, but occurs in shore-line traps on migration.

HISTORY: No evidence of any change in historical period.

*   *

WHITE-THROATED SPARROW
Zonotrichia albicollis (Gmelin)

STATUS: Represented in BMS and British Museum collections.

FALL: Common migrant, occasionally abundant.

Earliest arrival date: September 4, 1955, at Monomoy (Griscom, Emery, Bailey).

Average migration period: September 15–November 15.

Peak: September 28–October 12; average 20–100 birds, maximum 200 on September 28, 1952, at Chatham and Monomoy (Griscom, Snyder, Elkins).

WINTER: Regular in small but increasing numbers, often gathering at feeding stations.

SPRING: Dispersal of wintering groups, a few transients.

Average migration period: April 25–May 20; average 3–10 birds.

Latest transient date: May 28, 1939, at Monomoy (Griscom, Alexander, Bucheister, Garrison).

DISTRIBUTION: Recorded over entire Cape. Fall migrants and wintering birds a little more numerous eastward, and spring migrants definitely more numerous westward where they average a week earlier. Less numerous than on mainland.

HISTORY: No evidence of change in status for migrants. Counts of wintering birds increasing steadily since 1930, e.g., maximum of 29 in 1930's and of 191 in 1950's (C.C.), representing some real change and some artifact due to more efficient coverage.

*   *

FOX SPARROW
Passerella iliaca (Merrem)

STATUS: Represented in British Museum collection.

FALL: Uncommon migrant, occasionally quite common.

Earliest arrival date: August 14, 1958, at Monomoy (Bailey).

Average migration period: October 15–November 25.

Peak: November 1–15; number variable from year to year, e.g., 7 banded October 17–November 8, 1930, vs. 150 banded October 13–November 25, 1931, at North Eastham (Austin Station, see Brown, *Bird-Banding*, 5, 85, 1934).

WINTER: Always a few winter, usually successfully, partially dependent on feeding stations.

SPRING: Rare migrant in very irregular numbers.

Earliest transient date: Uncertain, probably about March 10.

Average migration period: March 20–April 5; variation from 1 to 32 banded per spring migration (Austin Station, see Brown, l.c.).

Latest transient date: April 17, 1942, banded at North Eastham (Austin Station).

DISTRIBUTION: Recorded over entire Cape, less regular and less numerous than on mainland.

HISTORY: No evidence of any change in status.

* *

LINCOLN'S SPARROW
Melospiza lincolnii (Audubon)

STATUS: Represented in MCZ collection. Sight and banding records subjected to careful screening because of proven errors in identification.

SPRING: Very rare, irregular and little-known migrant. Recorded May 19, 1898, at Barnstable (Bangs, in MCZ) to May 28, 1933, banded at North Eastham (Austin Station); always single birds.

FALL: Very rare and frequently misidentified migrant.

Earliest transient date: September 9, 1951, at Chatham (Griscom).

Average migration period: September 15–October 31; usually single birds.

Latest transient date: November 3, 1936, at Harwich (Bishop).

DISTRIBUTION: Recorded largely from Wellfleet to Chatham, more sparingly west to Woods Hole, Falmouth, and the Canal.

HISTORY: Data unsatisfactory.

* *

SWAMP SPARROW
Melospiza georgiana (Latham)

STATUS: Represented in BMS, Chicago, and British Museum collections.

FALL: Rather uncommon migrant, mainly build-up of wintering population.

Earliest arrival date: September 6, 1933, banded at North Eastham (Austin Station).

Average migration period: September 15–November 30; average 2–10 birds, maximum 30 on November 9, 1952, at Monomoy (Griscom, Emery, Beattie).

WINTER: Regular in variable numbers, increasing in recent years; survives the season with moderate success.

SPRING: Wandering winter birds through April, a rare migrant otherwise.

Average migration period: April 20–May 20; average 1–3 birds, maximum 15 on May 20, 1936, at Chatham (Bishop).

Latest transient date: May 28, 1932, banded at North Eastham (Austin Station).

DISTRIBUTION: Recorded as migrant largely on outer Cape from Provincetown to Chatham, rather sparingly westward. In brush and thickets, also in shore-line traps. Wintering birds in same distributional pattern and occur largely around streams and springs which remain open all winter. Much less numerous than on mainland except in winter; unknown as breeding species.

HISTORY: No evidence of change in status of migrants. Wintering birds increased since 1950 with cycle of mild seasons.

*   *

SONG SPARROW

Melospiza melodia (Wilson)

STATUS: Represented in BMS, Chicago, and British Museum collections.

SPRING: Arrival of residents, common as migrant.

Average resident arrival period: February 26–March 25.

Average transient period: March 20–April 28; average 50–150 birds, maximum 244 on April 3–4, 1942, in Eastham-Orleans-Chatham area (Hill, Briggs).

SUMMER: Abundant breeding resident over entire Cape. Estimated 50 pairs at Provincetown, 25 pairs at Brewster, 20 pairs at Chatham, 15 pairs at Sagamore, etc.

FALL: Abundant migrant.

Average migration period: September 20–November 18.

Peak: October 1–25; average 20–75 birds, maximum "100's" on October 16, 1953, at Nauset (Mason).

WINTER: Fairly common and always survives the season with fair success.

DISTRIBUTION: Breeds in wide variety of edge, brushy, and scrub habitats, including sand-dune thickets, over entire Cape. Migrants found just as widely.

HISTORY: No evidence of any change in status.

* *

LAPLAND LONGSPUR

Calcarius lapponicus (Linnaeus)

STATUS: Represented in BMS collection.

WINTER: Rare but regular visitant.

Earliest arrival date: September 23, 1953, at Monomoy (Griscom, Maclay).

Average arrival period: October 20–November 10.

Counts: Average 2–10 birds, maximum 51 on November 11, 1940, at Monomoy (Griscom, Poor).

Average departure period: March 1–April 5.

Latest departure date: April 23, 1909, at Monomoy (Fay, in BMS).

DISTRIBUTION: Occurs in open pastures, moors, sand dunes, and beaches. Recorded in suitable habitat over entire Cape. Less common than north of Boston.

HISTORY: No evidence of any change in status.

* *

SNOW BUNTING
Plectrophenax nivalis (Linnaeus)

STATUS: Represented in MCZ, BMS, and Chicago collections.

WINTER: Fairly common resident, some transients in fall.

Earliest arrival date: September 19, 1954, at Monomoy (Griscom, Beattie, Fox).

Average arrival period: October 20–November 5.

Counts: Average 50–200 birds, maximum 400 on November 9, 1952, at Monomoy (Griscom, Emery, Barry, Bailey) in migration; average 25–150 in winter.

Average departure period: March 1–15.

Latest departure date: April 3, 1942, at Monomoy (Hill, Briggs).

DISTRIBUTION: Largely on beaches and dunes, also on moorland. Recorded over entire Cape, but largest flocks to eastward.

HISTORY: No evidence of any change in status.

Ornithological Summary
Patterns of occurrence and their development

THE SYSTEMATIC LIST has presented the summarized data on Cape Cod birds and should prove useful to field observers of all levels of interest when visiting the area. However, merely pointing to such a list, no matter how detailed or how carefully prepared, is hardly justification for its preparation and publication. More important from a broader biological viewpoint is its application to relate the avifauna of this region to that of the Northeast and indeed of the entire continent and, secondly, to trace the changes which have occurred, coincident with documented changes in the environment, over more than three centuries of civilization. An attempt at such a synthesis follows.

A. Statistical

B. Breeding

C. Wintering

D. Migration
Pre-breeding (Spring)
Post-breeding (Fall)

E. Conclusions

A. Statistical

Species represented by specimen now extant 286
   (includes: 1 extinct
                1 extirpated
                3 introduced)

Species represented by specimen handled by
ornithologist but not now extant 42
Species represented by photograph 5
Species presumed to be present on basis of
sight records only 21
    (includes: 3 extinct
           2 extirpated
           2 introduced)
Total species satisfactorily recorded 354
    (sum of above)
Species listed as hypothetical 30

Further analysis of the above statistics reveals additional useful
information about the Cape Cod avifauna. In order to avoid a
profitless discussion as to when a "vagrant" becomes a "very rare
and irregular migrant," or when a breeding species becomes "reasonably regular" rather than "casual," rounded figures are given.
As regards breeding species, just over one hundred are reasonably
regular and another fifteen nest casually or are strongly suspected
of doing so. The former figure includes nine species which have
recently become established but not sixteen species (excluding extinct and extirpated ones) which have disappeared in the historical
period.

About eighty species or populations winter reasonably regularly,
though not all in any given year. Furthermore, some of these do
not remain for the entire season but tend to range widely and may
leave the Cape altogether. This figure includes those few biologically wintering species from the Antarctic which appear in our
summer.

The statistics on migrants confirm the impression that considerably more species and populations occur as such on the Cape than
as breeding or wintering ones. They also reveal the marked dis-
proportion between spring and fall migrations. Just over *two* hundred occur in the fall and just under *one* hundred in the spring.
There are no species which occur in spring which fail to appear in

fall. Of the one hundred which appear in both migrations, the list is weighted with waterfowl and sea birds. Of the one hundred additional which appear only in fall, the list is weighted with land birds of all groups and to a lesser extent with shore birds and ducks.

The accidental vagrants have appeared on Cape Cod in considerable variety. Though they stimulate much of the popular interest in ornithology and their numbers testify to the extent, duration, and thoroughness of field work, their occurrence is of no biological importance and there is no instance known where such occurrence has here resulted in any true change in status. About seventy-five have been recorded, excluding those listed as "Hypothetical" in the Systematic List. There is no clear-cut seasonal pattern of their occurrence, though fall is a little more favored. The analysis of their origins reveals one-third from the West, one-third from the South, of which land birds outnumber sea birds two to one, about one-fifth from the North, and about one-seventh from the Old World. If those recorded as "Hypothetical" are added to these vagrants, the proportion from the West is slightly increased at the expense of those from the North and to a lesser extent of those from the South.

B. Breeding

The breeding season is biologically the most important in the annual cycle as reproductive success is the ultimate test of "fitness" and insures the continued existence of the species. The schedule of the breeding season has evolved in such a way that the maximum food requirements of the newly hatched young will coincide with the optimal development of the significant factors in the environment, cf., Horned Owls early in spring to exploit the returning migrant birds and the emerging rodents, terns to feed on schooling sand eels in early summer, insectivorous birds to coincide with swarming prey at the same time, crossbills at any season when cones are available, etc. As regards Cape Cod, the breeding season begins in mid-February and is largely terminated by mid-August, thus involving 50 per cent of the year.

There is no evidence that local weather (as opposed to climate) has any effect on the establishment of breeding populations each year. This is in contrast to the rather marked effect of weather on winter survival and on certain aspects of migration. However, extremes of temperature and precipitation may have a profound effect on individual seasons, e.g., the losses among swallows and swifts by prolonged cold rains in June 1903 and June 1959. Also, extremes of weather here or elsewhere in preceding seasons may have an effect on the potential size of breeding populations, e.g., winter losses among many species in the South in 1895, 1940, etc.

Birds are most closely bound to their environment during the breeding season. Migrants are mobile by definition, and even winter populations show some ability to move according to local conditions. In contrast, when settled for nesting, a bird must select an environment which meets the requirements of both the adults and young for a minimum of a month. Thus the habitat is the critical determinant of breeding populations. It is obvious that the number of species breeding in an area depends on the variety of habitats available and the number of pairs on the extent of the specific habitats or on even more specific factors within the habitat such as availability of suitable nesting sites. One must also remember that some species have strict ecological requirements and that others are more tolerant of borderline conditions.

There is a relative paucity of habitats on Cape Cod. As one moves east from the central highlands of Massachusetts, one ecological niche after another disappears, and only a few new ones appear. The northern spruce and hardwood forest, the hemlocks, and even the much disturbed white-pine and transition woodlands fail to approach the southeastern coast. This eliminates many species present in central Massachusetts as potential breeding birds on

Cape Cod, such as Swainson's Thrush, Barred Owl, several vireos, and many warblers. Furthermore, certain specialized habitats, notably cliffs, rocky shore line, and high altitudes, are lacking.

The original forest of Cape Cod is long since gone and there is no satisfactory description of it and its fauna. It was completely and rapidly destroyed at an early date, and the entire Cape has at one time or another been cut over. However, farm abandonment began early with consequent regrowth in many areas; even this has been repeatedly destroyed both by cutting and by forest fires which have further impoverished the loose sandy soil, which is subject to rapid drainage and hence leaching. By the time of Thoreau's visits, when he was impressed by the lack of trees and noted that pitch pines were being planted, the higher land from Sandwich east to Brewster was already wooded. East, south, and along the north shore, he found extensive rolling moors, though there were some stunted woods in the hollows of Wellfleet. Since his time much of the moorland has grown to brush, to pitch pine, and to oak. This change was due to the fact that fuels, such as kerosene, could then be imported by train so that wood lots were allowed to grow rather than subjected to repeated cutting for firewood. That the original diversified forest has not reappeared is attributed to the impoverishment of the soil. Recently there has been further rapid destruction of all habitats by the building of cottages, etc.

Thus, thanks to the profound disturbance of the land over three centuries, we are left with only four major dry-land habitats on the Cape, which, in a general way, are steps in a succession, in order: 1) grass-covered moorland; 2) old pasture association with deciduous thickets and red cedar; 3) pitch pine barrens; and 4) oak-pitch pine woods. No climax stage has yet been reached. Moorlands are found largely in Eastham and north at present, though there are a few smaller patches elsewhere. They consist of several species of grass in a dense turf, typically with a few low bushes which must be mowed periodically to prevent evolution to the next stage. The dense blueberry barrens with low oak thickets seem to be a variety of moor, and both this and the grasslands blend into the old pasture association with red cedar and deciduous thickets with its many edges. This habitat is also a stage of recovery after any disturbance and so is abundant and widespread but patchy. The forests of pure pitch pine are the next step and are very extensive throughout much of the interior of the Cape, particularly eastward. In recent decades oaks have invaded the pines and in places become dominant. Such tracts are largely westward on the Cape but are extending steadily eastward, especially along the Sandwich moraine to Brewster and beyond.

The marine-influenced habitats of Cape Cod are likewise limited in number though rather extensive in area. They have not been altered by human occupation as radically as have the land ones. These do not form a succession but rather a series of sub-climax communities where boundaries depend on a balance between moisture, exposure to salt and exposure to drying winds or wave action. The outer barrier beaches and islands have bare, hot, white sand with tide-strewn rows of dried seaweed but no living vegetation. Proceeding upward on the beach, several types of sparse vegetation appear, giving minimal cover. If the slope continues upward, the shifting dunes are covered with *Ammophila* grass but are highly subject to "blow-outs;" moist hollows among them may develop fresh-water swamps and eventually thickets which are related to the old pasture association described above. Occasionally a mature pine, oak, or beech forest develops. If the slope drops down from the beach toward a sheltered bay, mud and detritus collect and a marsh forms. In the upper levels which are never flooded with salt water, the vegetation is quite varied with grasses, weeds, and low bushes, again related to the old pasture community. As the ground drops and becomes progressively more subject to flooding, the majority of plant species disappear and we are left with almost pure *Spartina patens* grass on the level ground and *Spartina alterniflora* along the ditches and creeks.

It is unwise to be dogmatic and arbitrarily to designate birds as nesting in one or another "zone." Distribution is more a question of habitat available than of geographical location; after all, Meadowlarks are found in grassland, but it matters not whether that patch of grass is on Cape Cod, in a Vermont valley, or on an Illinois prairie! Nonetheless, the roster of breeding species on Cape Cod can be roughly divided into three groups: 1) those rather tolerant of diverse conditions and hence found widely throughout the Northeast; 2) those more characteristic of the central uplands of New England; and 3) those more characteristic of the Atlantic coastal plain.

The widespread birds of the Northeast occupy niches on Cape Cod comparable to those occupied elsewhere. Except for those species with very wide tolerance and hence found in multiple habitats, these locally happen to fall mostly into the moorland and the old pasture communities as regards major habitats. On the former occur Vesper and Grasshopper Sparrows, Meadowlarks, and formerly Bobolinks, Upland Plovers, and probably Dickcissels. These now appear widely, though none are in very great numbers. The old pasture community supports the species which are benefited by edges, such as Bobwhite, Mourning Dove, Kingbird, Catbird, Brown Thrasher, Chipping and Field Sparrows, and in the moister areas Song Sparrows and Yellowthroats; these species occur in somewhat higher densities than do the grassland birds. Other members of these groups of widespread birds are those occupying the minor habitats which are present in great variety though their aggregate area is very limited. These include fresh-water ponds and pond margins, fresh-water swamps of various types, streamside woods, groves of beech or locust, etc., bankings and cliffs, human-provided niches such as shade trees, ornamental plantings, bridges, chimneys, etc. The birds here are severely limited in number of pairs by the small areas of their habitats, but nonetheless they are the species expected in such places. Special mention should be made of selected species attracted for a short time to artificial but short-lived environments, e.g., Least Bittern, several rails,

Common Gallinule, and Ruddy Duck at Pilgrim Lake, North Truro.

On the Cape, those species more characteristic of the central uplands of Massachusetts, excluding the so-called "Canadian Zone" birds, occur largely where oak has infiltrated and become dominant over pine. They invariably occur in much lower density than on the mainland and also show a readily detectable decrease in numbers as one proceeds eastward on the Cape, parallel to the decrease in deciduous woods. These include Crested Flycatcher, Ruffed Grouse, Hairy Woodpecker, Scarlet Tanager, Black-and-white Warbler, Red-eyed Vireo, Redstart, etc. Other species of this group are rare, local, and often irregular for no known reason and fail to occupy all apparently suitable territory; these include American Bittern, Blue-winged Teal, Wood Duck (there is probably a factor of inadequate nesting sites here), several hawks, Killdeer, Phoebe, Least Flycatcher, House and Long-billed Marsh Wrens, Chestnut-sided Warbler, Indigo Bunting, and others. In the final development of this trend there is a group of species regular on the adjacent mainland which are totally lacking on the Cape, again for no apparent reason. There are no Veeries in the wet woods, no Swamp Sparrows in the swamps, no White-breasted Nuthatches, Rose-breasted Grosbeaks, or Warbling Vireos in the shade trees, no Canada Warblers in the maple or cedar swamps—and all of these occur as close as the western shores of Buzzards Bay, literally within sight of Cape Cod!

The land birds characteristic of the Atlantic coastal plain appear mostly in the pitch pine woods. There are not many species involved, but those few occur in abundance, Towhee, Pine Warbler, Wood Pewee, and locally Whip-poor-will. They are accompanied by the small local populations of Black-throated Green Warbler, Great Horned Owl, Hermit Thrush, and Red-tailed Hawk. The Prairie Warbler belongs to this group, but it occurs in greatest numbers in the low oaks of the blueberry barrens.

All of the sea birds, naturally, and some of the land birds of the marine-influenced habitats belong to the coastal group. On the most open and exposed beaches are Piping Plover and Least Terns. A few Common Terns occur here, but their greatest colonies occur higher where there is a little vegetation (which their presence rapidly increases). They are accompanied by the less abundant Roseate and the very local Arctic Terns. Recently Herring and Great Black-backed Gulls have moved in. The harsh *Ammophila* grass on the dunes seems not to support any breeding species, but in the sand-dune thickets and in the varied vegetation of the upper reaches of the salt meadows more are found—Savannah Sparrows, Meadowlarks, and locally Marsh Hawks and Short-eared Owls in the grassy areas. Yellowthroats, Catbirds, and Song Sparrows occur where there is brush. Farther out in the marsh the Sharp-tailed Sparrows occupy the *Spartina patens* and the Seaside Sparrows the *Spartina alterniflora* with a few scattered Clapper Rails, Black Ducks, and formerly Willet. The spring tide levels set the lower level of occupancy, though the still lower vegetation and the mud flats are important feeding areas.

It is of interest that the tendency for colonial nesting is much more highly developed in these ocean-influenced habitats than in the land ones. Thus selected areas have very high densities of occupancy and neighboring areas, apparently similar, are unused. The Common Terns achieve the highest density; the Least Tern colonies are less cohesive and cover relatively much more area, as do the gull nestings. The birds of the upper salt meadows are an extension of the moorland and old pasture associations of land and show less evidence of colony formation, but in the marshes themselves the Seaside Sparrow is colonial and the Sharp-tailed Sparrow markedly so, at least on Cape Cod.

The history of the breeding land birds on Cape Cod is an interesting exercise in applied ecology. We have no direct information about the original forest but can speculate concerning its contents. It seems most likely it was an extension of the hardwood forest of central New England with oak, beech, and other deciduous trees, but since it was peripheral and exposed to certain limiting factors such as poorer soil, high winds, and blown spray, it was probably less rich in species of plants and trees and less great in growth. Even so, it surely supported many species of birds now either absent or very rare and local, warblers, vireos, flycatchers, hawks, owls, and woodpeckers. Thus the birds of the upland forests were probably predominant then, a supposition which receives some support from the fact that the surviving virgin forest of neighboring Naushon Island, admittedly of small extent and even more exposed to wind and salt, still contains Veeries and White-breasted Nuthatches, also greater densities than occur on the Cape of Crested Flycatcher, Woodcock, House Wren, Black-and-White Warbler, Ovenbird, and Redstart. On the outskirts of this primeval forest areas of poorer soil undoubtedly provided additional niches supporting the appropriate birds; interestingly, it is not certain that the pitch pine, recently so prevalent, is truly indigenous. The abrupt destruction of this forest must have caused an equally abrupt change in the avifauna, but no records have come down to us.

Following deforestation, the grassland took over and persisted into the early historical period, so we have some direct knowledge of this phase. It was characterized throughout the Cape by high counts of Vesper and Grasshopper Sparrows, Meadowlarks, Upland Plover, and probably Bobolink and Dickcissel, though these last two disappeared before the moors were much diminished. All of these must have been rare and local or absent under primeval conditions. After two centuries of prosperity, they began to decrease by 1890 as the moorland grew to pasture and then to pitch pine. This clearly took place from west to east and is still progressing; details of this may be found in the sections on "History" in the Systematic List. As the grassland birds declined, those of the pitch pines began to rise in their turn and reached their highest counts in the 1920's. The recent infiltration of oaks, as with the growth of pitch pines nearly a century ago, commenced westward and is extending to the east. This evolution has resulted in a steady decline in the birds of the pitch pines. In their place there has been a steady rise in the counts of birds from the uplands, Ruffed Grouse, Crested Flycatcher, Scarlet Tanager, Red-eyed Vireo, Black-and-white Warbler, and Redstart, most marked westward, but with progressive infiltration eastward. Again, the details of this shift of populations can be traced in the sections on "History." Certain mainland birds have made their first recorded appearance as breeding species on Cape Cod since 1940, Wood Thrush, Long-billed Marsh Wren, Killdeer, Red-shouldered Hawk, Rough-winged Swallow. However, one strongly suspects that this entire group from the uplands may only be recapturing territory lost several centuries ago!

The history of the breeding birds of the marshes and beaches is one of human predation rather than of drastic environmental changes, though there has been some minor loss of marshes. These birds, in colonies, were vulnerable to mass-killing techniques and nearly all species were significantly reduced. The extreme isolation of Cape Cod and hence the necessity to rely on local game for a major part of the essential food supplies brought about a period of exploitation which continued over two hundred years. During this time we read that loons, grebes, and filleted breasts of gull were eaten! This period reduced the gulls and apparently eliminated the breeding Common Loons, Canada Geese, etc.

After easy access to the Cape was achieved about 1870 the picture changed drastically. Food of a more varied nature, especially red meat, could be imported, and local game became less important. At this point birds, or at least selected species, became items in the luxury trade. This reached its epitome in the plume traffic. Locally the tern colonies were the chief victims and all species were reduced, but probably only the Roseate was completely though temporarily eliminated. Market gunning rose to great heights at the same time, and we read of barrels of shore birds being shipped to the city markets. Though the chief victims here were the migrants, this activity spelled the end of the breeding Willet and Upland Plover and seriously reduced the Meadowlark which was called "Marsh Quail" and assiduously hunted. During this period the hawks and owls were steadily shot as "vermin" and all the larger birds were destroyed simply because they were good targets. These abuses were corrected by legislative action in the early decades of this century, though strict enforcement had to wait until the older generation of gunners was incapacitated by age, illness, and death. With the release of the pressure of market gunning and of the so-called "sportsmen," the sea-bird populations began to stabilize and then increase, slowly at first and then at a rapid rate, apparently following an exponential curve until the habitat reached saturation. This appeared first with the terns, whose colonies are now great spectacles, and is at present occurring with the gulls, whose increase is again threatening the terns. The gulls, like certain land birds mentioned above, are probably only recapturing long-lost territory. Some lost species such as Willet have not yet returned.

Apart from changes in the avifauna from obvious causes noted above, there are changes apparently due to the long-term warming trend of the climate. This involves birds formerly breeding and those recently established or increasing. Those reported formerly include Olive-sided Flycatcher, Junco, Red Crossbill, Golden-crowned Kinglet, Brown Creeper, and Red-breasted Nuthatch, and those recently appearing or markedly increasing include Clapper Rail, Snowy Egret, Black Skimmer (actually only a return), Barn Owl, Fish Crow, Seaside Sparrow and Rough-winged Swallow. The Cardinal and Tufted Titmouse which have recently established breeding on the adjacent mainland have not yet done so on Cape Cod but should be expected at any time. Though many of these have been erratic or casual at best and breeding often suspected rather than proven, the pattern suggests a withdrawal of northern forms and an invasion of southern ones.

Finally, there is a very small group of birds for which no cause can be assigned for their disappearance except to note that the same thing has occurred elsewhere in the Northeast. Nighthawk, Red-headed Woodpecker, Dickcissel, and Cliff Swallow are examples. Other special instances of either increase or decrease which fail to fit into a specific pattern may be found in the Systematic List.

C. Wintering

The wintering season for birds may be defined as a season with non-breeding but fairly stable populations, occurring locally at a time of generally unfavorable and extreme weather conditions. The stability of the populations is not as great as when settled for breeding but is obviously much greater than during migration. Though suitable habitats must provide sufficient food and cover, it is clear that the weather is the decisive factor in determining survival and indeed makes this season a critical one in the annual cycle.

Due to the surrounding ocean, winter weather on Cape Cod averages milder than on the mainland. The average winter temperature rises steadily as one approaches the coast from central Massachusetts, and this rise is even sharper as one proceeds eastward on the Cape. This means that ponds freeze later, that many storms leave rain instead of snow, and that ponds open and snows melt earlier. However, the variability of winter weather is remarkable, far greater than the differences within other seasons. For example, contrast the winter of 1952–1953, which was warm and wet with no permanent snow and ponds never frozen, with that of 1960–1961, which had a series of blizzards and was well below freezing for over two weeks so even the salt-water bays and estuaries were frozen and chunks of sea ice closed the Canal to shipping and heaped up on the beaches and flats.

In keeping with the variability of the weather, the winter bird populations are also more variable than those of any other season, both in content of the species list and in survival. Heavy snows which bury food supplies diminish the land birds, and heavy ice conditions secondary to low temperatures diminish the water birds. Furthermore, heavy snow and severe cold do not necessarily accompany each other, so these groups may vary independently.

As with the breeding birds, the composition of the species list in winter includes three groups: 1) the common and widespread birds shared in general with the mainland; 2) a group with southern affinities; and 3) a group with northern affinities.

The common and widespread species may be further subdivided. First, there are a small number of permanent residents, such as Red-tailed Hawk, Ruffed Grouse, Bobwhite, several owls, several woodpeckers, and part of the Chickadee and Crow populations in which the same individuals are apparently present throughout the year. Second, with many other species, e.g., Herring Gull, several hawks, Blue Jay, Starling, Black Duck, Purple Finch, and Goldfinch, the individuals are replaced from one season to the next though the species is continuously present. Finally, there is a larger list of species for which the Cape is well within the normal wintering range but which nest northward; this group contains Common Loon, Horned Grebe, Great Cormorant, many sea ducks, Rough-legged Hawk, Great Black-backed Gull, Junco, Tree Sparrow, and Snow Bunting. The members of all three of these groups are hardy species and are always reasonably successful in surviving, even in severe seasons.

The southern element in the winter list is much more evident on Cape Cod than on the mainland and also falls into several categories. First are those species for which Cape Cod is at or near the northern periphery of the normal wintering range which is usually on the southern coastal plain, e.g., Brant, Canada Goose, Red-throated Loon, Great Blue Heron, Black-crowned Night Heron, several river ducks, Sanderling, Dunlin, Mourning Dove, Kingfisher, Robin, Bluebird, Myrtle Warbler, and several sparrows. Second are the more irregular species for which Cape Cod lies well to the north of the main wintering range, e.g., Pied-billed Grebe, American Bittern, several more river and pond ducks, Virginia Rail, Snipe, Knot, Catbird, Long-billed Marsh Wren, Hermit Thrush, Pine and Palm Warblers, and several other sparrows. Finally, there is a long list of casual southern stragglers which are present for a variable period at the beginning of the season, being sometimes recorded on Christmas Counts and occasionally later, e.g., several other rails, several warblers, several Icterids, Tree Swallow, Barn Owl, Laughing Gull, Common Tern, Woodcock, both Yellowlegs, Turnstone, Chipping and Sharp-tailed Sparrows, and many others. These three groups contribute much to the variability of winter bird life. They show a progressive decrease in probability of survival, the first doing well only in mild years, the second being markedly diminished even in mild years, and the last being always eliminated by the first cold weather except for a few individuals surviving at feeding stations. The marked increase in feeding stations since about 1945 has permitted the occasional survival of individuals of all these southern groups and has artificially changed the picture; this is a historical fact worth recording, as withdrawal of this support would cause immediate reversion to the original status.

Historically speaking, there is little evidence of significant changes in the land birds of the widespread wintering groups, other than among the permanent residents which were discussed in the section on breeding. Among the waterfowl the picture is mixed in that the flocks wintering on the outer shoals were protected by their inaccessibility whereas the flocks in the bays and sounds were considerably diminished by gunning. These latter are now showing progressive recovery in numbers. The southern element in the winter birds has been increasing steadily throughout the historical period, both in isolated records and in success at survival. First winter records were made for Knot in 1879, Field Sparrow in 1892, Black-crowned Night Heron in 1894, Sanderling in 1895, Scaup in 1898, Dunlin in 1903, etc., and these have steadily increased since. Pied-billed Grebe and Swamp Sparrow first survived the entire season in 1949 and American Bittern in 1954. Concurrently many species have shown progressively more success at survival, e.g., Red-throated Loon, Gannet, Canada Goose, Baldpate, Black-bellied Plover, Ring-billed Gull, Mourning Dove, Fox and Song Sparrows. This trend has been continuous for nearly a century, though there have been some short-term interruptions.

Those species which normally winter to the north are always irregular on Cape Cod, often little more than vagrants, and thus also contribute to the variability of the bird life. These include Goshawk, Bald (northern race) and Golden Eagles, several Alcids, Iceland and Glaucous Gulls, Snowy Owl, Pine Grosbeak, White-winged Crossbill, Redpoll, Lapland Longspur, Three-toed Woodpecker, Brown-capped Chickadee, Harlequin Duck, and Barrow's Golden-eye. To a considerable extent, the irregularity of occurrence of these groups is due to lack of a specific habitat as some of these prefer rocky coasts or deep coniferous woods. These species usually occur as part of a mainland flight and are present on Cape Cod only because of food failure elsewhere, not because the Cape has any intrinsic attraction for them. Furthermore, at the present time Cape Cod often cannot support them for a full season and they are present for only a fraction of the winter. The history of the group is obscure due to lack of really early data, but there is some suggestion, particularly in Brewster's records, that they were once more numerous and that they have decreased to an irregular status parallel to but more marked than elsewhere in New England.

The distribution of birds in winter is not uniform over the entire Cape and is partially correlated with the climate. The greatest numbers of winter residents, both land birds and water birds, are found toward the southeast, from Chatham west to Harwich and Brewster and north to Eastham. North of Wellfleet, habitats are more limited both in variety and in extent and hence fail to support as many individuals. Westward there are some numbers found along the sound shores but fewer along the bay and many fewer inland. This distribution is also correlated to some extent with the fall migration which is maximal from the northwest so the birds collect to the southeast, i.e., the "land's end" effect, but, more important, this area averages warmer than elsewhere, being most distant from the colder mainland and in closest proximity to the relatively warmer waters southward. In addition, the species which have used a specific migration route in the fall tend to be found in the corresponding areas in the winter, e.g., Horned Grebe in Buzzards Bay vs. Eider eastward.

This discussion of distribution highlights the one great deficiency in our ornithological information, the pelagic birds in winter. Fulmars, some Alcids, and perhaps Skuas and Leach's Petrels are reported, but the inaccessibility of their area presents great difficulties in study and little is really known. Winter sea trips call for seaworthy boats and extremely rugged ornithologists with strong stomachs!

Finally and paradoxically, there are some biologically wintering birds which occur in our warm season. These are the Greater and Sooty Shearwaters and the Wilson's Petrel which nest south of the Equator. They migrate north along the Gulf Stream in the western North Atlantic, and most individuals spread eastward to European coasts, returning southward off West Africa. A small group, however, spends the season in the Gulf of Maine, and it is these which are recorded off Cape Cod (see Wynne-Edwards, 1935). Their presence is exceedingly erratic, going through unexplained long-term cycles as well as short-term fluctuations related to the plankton in the water. In general, high numbers of plankton attract bait fish, so the mackerel and tuna fishing is good and the shearwaters, petrels, terns, and jaegers are present. High counts of these birds were described in the 1880's, at which time the local fishermen shot them in great numbers for bait. Following this, there was a long period of low counts as well as much time during which no observations were reported. In the late 1940's and throughout the 1950's they were again numerous, but as of this writing (1963) they have once more become scarce for no known reason.

D. Migration

The simplest definition of bird migration, and one which is applicable to Cape Cod, is a regular movement of populations of birds to and from different seasonal ranges, this movement providing some adaptive advantage to the species. The initiating stimuli are often obscure and the distances covered extremely variable, but this movement brings about the appearance of the species involved in any given area on a predictable schedule.

As was indicated in the foregoing section on statistics, Cape Cod intercepts a large flow of migrating birds. The concept of flyways is applicable to the description of this flow but may be misleading if it is taken to imply their exclusive use. After all, birds migrate over a broad front and thus pass over every point on the map, concentrating, however, in several lanes or flyways. The first of these is along the inner coast, including both the adjacent land and the adjacent water; this passes along the western edge of Cape Cod Bay, crosses the Cape at the Canal, and includes the whole of Buzzards Bay. The outer coast route covers the whole of the outer Cape from Provincetown south to Monomoy and about as far west as Brewster and Harwich; it carries somewhat less volume than the inner route though the concentration is greater. A secondary and rather small route crosses the Cape in the region of Barnstable and Hyannis and receives birds from both the inner and outer routes. The final route is pelagic and passes in a north-south or northeast-southwest direction to the east of the Cape, approaching closest to the outer beaches from Eastham to Monomoy. The details of the usage of these routes and the schedule of migratory activity follow. The reader is reminded that there are twice as many species and vastly more individuals passing through in the fall than in the spring. In addition, events occurring elsewhere may have an effect on the size of the migrating populations, e.g., varying success of breeding seasons or unusual losses in the wintering range.

Pre-breeding Migration (Spring)

Spring weather on Cape Cod is characterized by the disappearance of snow and ice earlier than on the mainland, followed by a prolonged period of cloudy, foggy, and rainy weather, much cooler than inland, again the result of the surrounding ocean water. The development of the vegetation gradually falls behind that on the mainland until it lags by two or three weeks, the foliage often not reaching its full development until well into early June. The stable pattern of pleasant weather is often not established until late in June.

The pattern of spring migration in Massachusetts and indeed the entire Northeast is one of a gradient of decreasing numbers of migrants of all groups, both in numbers of species and numbers of individuals, as one progresses north and east. This is brought about by: 1) a tendency of waterfowl and some shore birds which nest in the Northwest to leave the Atlantic coast south of New England; and 2) a tendency of many land birds to migrate along the highlands and interior river valleys and to avoid the coastal plain. Many previous publications have described the steady decrease in migrants eastward (Griscom, 1933; Bagg & Eliot, 1937; Griscom & Snyder, 1955; Griscom, Bird-Lore, 42, 161 & 259, 1940; Townsend, 1905 & 1920; etc.) and Cape Cod has a predictably unimpressive spring migration. The exceptions are: 1) those species or populations using a northeasterly route; 2) those which require open ocean or outer beaches and hence restrict themselves to a pelagic or an outer coast route; and 3) special weather conditions which a) drift mainland migrants eastward, or b) bring in premature migrants from the South.

The first evidence of spring migration on the Cape is the disappearance of some of the wintering waterfowl and then the appearance of transients moving along the coastal flyways to the northeast. The waterfowl which have wintered begin to leave with the first warm days in February and continue to drift away without marked gatherings even into May. Transients are passing by from March through May with greatest numbers in April. There are a number of species, Black Duck, Canada Goose, Brant, Goldeneye, the scoters, Oldsquaw, Eider, which occur in considerable numbers, but there is a large list of species, usually common in the fall, which are much less numerous in the spring, some even being absent as their principal route lies well to the west—Pied-billed Grebe, American Bittern, Mallard and other river ducks, Ring-necked Duck, Ruddy Duck, Hooded Merganser, Coot and the other rails, Bonaparte's Gull, etc. In general, the few spring records of these species are attributed to surviving wintering birds or to arriving breeding residents rather than transients.

The inner coastal route is of greater relative importance in the spring than in the fall as might be predicted from an inspection of the trend of the coast line of the entire Atlantic coast. Gannet, Brant, and Eider are most conspicuous on the outer route. Red-necked and Horned Grebes, Double-crested Cormorant, the transient population of Canada Goose, Surf Scoter, Scaup, etc., occur predominantly on the inner route as well as considerable numbers of Goldeneye, Red-breasted Mergansers, White-winged Scoters, and Oldsquaws which also occur eastward. Western Cape Cod Bay often holds rafts of several thousand waterfowl in late April. The waterfowl migration is largely completed by mid-May, with straggling flocks and individuals being recorded to early June.

The previously described situation of decreasing numbers of migrants across New England applies to all land birds but is most striking with those which have wintered in Central and South America. Whether they have migrated across the Caribbean Sea or across the Gulf of Mexico matters not; they are progressively less common eastward, and on Cape Cod many species such as Olive-sided Flycatcher, Gray-cheeked Thrush, Veery, many warblers, several vireos, Rose-breasted Grosbeak, Lincoln's Sparrow, etc., all regular migrants inland, are either unrecorded or very rare in spring. To some extent this gradient can be traced even within the Cape as Nighthawk, Sapsucker, several hawks, Junco, Barn and Bank Swallows, White-breasted Nuthatch, Chipping Sparrow, and certain warblers are present in greater numbers nearer the Canal than eastward, though still much less numerous than inland. There would appear to be three reasons for this lack of spring migrants on the Cape: 1) the previously mentioned "aversion" of these species for the coastal plain; 2) the extreme tardiness of the development of the vegetation which restricts food supply and cover; and 3) the geographical fact that the southwest wind on which waves of migrants depend reaches the Cape over water so that a) it is cold and often so damp it produces fog, and b) it has not passed over any staging areas for migratory flights. The few individuals of all these land birds which do reach the outer Cape occur during major mainland waves which are moving on such a broad front that some marginal birds reach far eastward. This is more likely to occur if the wave is terminated by a shift of the wind to the west or northwest, causing an obvious easterly drift. Under such conditions it is occasionally possible to see one to five individuals of one to eight transient warblers on outer Cape Cod; note the contrast with the Boston area or the Connecticut valley! The late-May and early-June flights are more likely to penetrate to the Cape than are the early or mid-May ones. Even the resident birds are much later arriving than on the mainland, possibly due to the tardiness of the vegetation, and they progress east and then north quite slowly, e.g., Towhee, Baltimore Oriole, and Red-eyed Vireo, so that some residents are still arriving into June, thus delaying the nesting season by three or more weeks.

The earlier land-bird flights which involve species which have wintered in southern United States, particularly on the coastal plain, have a different pattern. These birds move north along the coast as soon as ice and snow are gone, anywhere from late February to early April, and hence arrive on the Cape earlier than inland. More individuals arrive than remain to nest, so the excess numbers presumably move inland or north as the countryside opens up. With this group, which includes Robin, Grackle, Cowbird, Redwinged Blackbird, Flicker, Mourning Dove, etc., the greatest counts are recorded eastward rather than near the Canal, which suggests an over-water migration route. The excess individuals disappear by mid-April, route not known, but some evidence suggests they cross Cape Cod Bay and Massachusetts Bay to the northwest.

The most spectacular of the "freak" weather-borne migrations have been described by Bagg (*Bull. Mass. Audubon Soc.*, *39*, 106 & 159, 1955). The development of a characteristic weather pattern is critical; it requires a strong air flow from the south, originating in the region of the central part of the Gulf of Mexico, crossing the Florida peninsula, and continuing north over the Atlantic Ocean. Under such conditions there may appear individuals and small flocks of migrants from the Central American flyway, never from the West Indian. It is believed that these have been carried non-stop from Yucatan and they make their landfall where the coast turns eastward from Long Island to Nova Scotia and even Newfoundland. The prominent geography of Cape Cod intercepts many of these migrants and they are found largely on the southern and eastern shores. They are usually exhausted and many fail to survive. The Indigo Bunting is the species involved in this phenomenon *par excellence*, but many others are recorded: Scarlet and Summer Tanagers, Painted Bunting, Blue and Rose-breasted Grosbeaks, the orioles, Catbird, Snowy Egret, certain warblers, Glossy Ibis, Purple Gallinule, Lesser Yellowlegs, etc. These flights occur most often in mid-April when maximum numbers of birds are aloft over the Gulf of Mexico but have been recorded in late March; by late April and May recognition of such flights is difficult due to early stragglers arriving by more normal routes.

The passage of the shore birds, both spring and fall, affords one of the great ornithological spectacles of Cape Cod. In spring they and the terns are the chief occupants of the outer coastal route; the inner route is essentially unused by them at this season. These birds begin to appear in April and early May and, for the shore birds, culminate in a great burst of migration in late May and the first few days of June when the beaches become a staging area for flights to the Arctic. Because of the compression of the timetable, spectacular numbers are present, though of relatively few species, particularly Sanderling, Semipalmated Sandpiper, Knot, Black-bellied Plover, and Turnstone. The regularity of the flight regardless of the weather is remarkable. It is of considerable interest also that all these species are those of the sand beaches rather than of the marshes; this is probably correlated as with the land birds with the late seasonal development of the vegetation. Some species which winter on or migrate along the southern Atlantic coast, Whimbrel, Dunlin, and Short-billed Dowitcher, appear in irregular numbers from year to year, presumably because of variation in their point of departure from the coast to the Northwest. In addition, as might be expected, the "western" contingent which normally migrate up the Mississippi Valley or the Plains is accidental in spring—Stilt Sandpiper, Hudsonian and Marbled Godwits, Pectoral Sandpiper, Lesser Yellowlegs, Upland Plover, Golden Plover, and formerly Eskimo Curlew.

Finally, those species using the pelagic route are less well known due to obvious difficulties involved. They appear to have the following pattern: Red Phalarope and Greater Shearwater in late April and May, Northern Phalarope and the jaegers throughout May, and Sooty Shearwater and Wilson's Petrel in late May and June.

Historically, there is no evidence of significant long-term changes in any migrant land birds. However, the waterfowl migrants were reduced and apparently some populations practically eliminated during the period of unrestricted shooting. Partial recovery of numbers has occurred but, generally speaking, these changes were not due primarily to shooting on Cape Cod but to such activity on the breeding ranges, in the wintering grounds, or elsewhere on migration. Disturbance of breeding areas by agriculture has also been a factor. As regards shore birds, the only known qualitative difference in the past was the more frequent appearance of the western group in spring, but quantitatively there was a precipitous and very marked decrease in migrants after 1860 which was not reversed until effective legislation and its enforcement curtailed spring shooting in particular and market gunning in general. Details of the recovery of particular species is discussed in the section on fall migration.

Post-breeding Migration (Fall)

Fall weather on Cape Cod, in marked contrast to spring, is warmer and the season more prolonged than on the mainland, again the result of the surrounding ocean. Consequently frost and snow are delayed, so food and cover persist longer. From the human point of view, fall is the most delightful season on the Cape!

The geographical location of the Cape is as conducive to a large fall migration as it is inhibitive of a spring one. It lies obviously in the path of the coastal flyways from the northeast and north. In addition, an easterly drift from the winds often develops on flight lines inland in New England. These migrants then continue toward the southeast to the outer Cape where they are precipitated in the "shore-line traps," i.e., the thickets nearest the outer beaches and among the dunes. This concentration has been termed a "land's end effect" on the assumption that the migrants fly on as long as land lies ahead, and it reaches its maximum development with the waves riding a northwest cold front. Finally, there is evidence that some species actually approach New England from the west or even southwest, e.g., the post-breeding southern herons, King Eider, Redhead, and Chat. Thus, with flights coming from 180°

of the compass, the stage is set for a large migrational flow through the area. Furthermore, the number of birds migrating is substantially greater than in the spring due to the production of young and the as yet inadequate time for significant mortality.

Straggling shore birds, presumably those individuals unsuccessful at nesting, are the first migrants of fall, always appearing by early July and occasionally in the last few days of June. The shore bird movement is a long, leisurely, protracted one, so that the daily counts are lower than the spring peaks, though the total number of individuals passing through is considerably greater. Characteristically, and almost regardless of weather conditions, the counts build up to a marked peak of adult birds, many still in breeding plumage, in the final one-third of July or early August, this peak being most apparent on the outer coast. This is followed by a decrease in numbers and then another rise in late August and September when the young of the year arrive; the second peak is not as sharply marked as the first but is apparent on both the outer and inner coasts. Though either peak may fail for any species, the general pattern is as follows: 1) both peaks usually well marked for Semipalmated Plover, Knot, Whimbrel, also Lesser Yellowlegs on the inner coast, and some three weeks later for Black-bellied Plover; 2) predominant numbers in the first peak for Turnstone, Least Sandpiper, Short-billed Dowitcher, Semipalmated Sandpiper, and Sanderling; and 3) predominant numbers in the late peak for Greater Yellowlegs, Pectoral Sandpiper, and Dunlin. Some species are so variable that the timing of their maximum counts shifts from year to year or otherwise shows no consistent pattern. It is only in fall that the "western" contingent is regularly present— Wilson's Phalarope, Marbled Godwit, Baird's, Stilt, Pectoral, Western Sandpipers, etc. The offshore route of the adult Golden Plover, Hudsonian Godwit, formerly Eskimo Curlew, and perhaps Snipe and Eastern Willet has long been known. They and the Knot and Sanderling which concentrate on the outer coastal route are most numerous on the outer Cape. Lesser Yellowlegs are largely found on the inner coast, and the entire Cape is well east of the main flight of Solitary Sandpiper and Upland Plover. Most other species are more widely distributed and apparently migrate on a wider front, congregating where there is adequate feed. The importance of feed in attracting high counts must not be underestimated as demonstrated by the shift in the counts according to local conditions from year to year. At the end of migration the numbers slowly diminish, but many stragglers linger late into the fall or even early winter.

This over-all pattern of shore-bird migration has been described throughout the historical period, and there is no reason to believe it was different at earlier dates, though specific data are lacking. As in spring, the chief historical changes are quantitative, the marked and precipitous drop caused by overshooting and then the recovery with establishment of protection. As mentioned under "Breeding" in regard to the terns, the sequence of events in recovery appears to be, first, a stabilization of numbers, then an accelerating rate of increase, and finally stabilization at a higher level which is assumed to represent saturation of the available habitat. If this is so, and judging from the sequence of counts as given under "History" of the appropriate species in the Systematic List, complete recovery has apparently taken place with Semipalmated and Black-bellied Plover, Turnstone, Whimbrel, Greater Yellowlegs, and Semipalmated Sandpipers, whereas Knot, Short-billed Dowitcher, and Hudsonian Godwit are still in the stage of accelerating increase. Sanderling and Dunlin appear to be stabilizing now. A few whose breeding grounds are more southern and hence more subject to disturbance are still decreasing, e.g., Spotted Sandpiper, Snipe, Woodcock, and Upland Plover. A changed local environment is probably a factor in lower numbers of Lesser Yellowlegs, Pectoral Sandpiper, and Stilt Sandpiper.

The migration of the terns and the Ring-billed Gull follows the pattern of the shore birds and exhibits two periods of peak counts at approximately the same dates. The gatherings of the terns re-

quire a successful breeding season followed by persistence of adequate feed in inshore waters. Otherwise they drift away steadily
from midsummer on. The jaeger counts are dependent on the presence of terns in numbers; in their absence these predators move
through very rapidly and are recorded only individually.

The land-bird movements show two contrasting patterns: 1)
"normal" migration on the "normal" prevailing southwest winds;
and 2) explosive waves on northwest winds. Note that as in spring
we again see the pattern of dependence of the land birds on
weather conditions in contrast to the shore birds. The first type of
migration occurs mostly inland in New England, though there is a
steady trickle of migrants along the inner coast and near the Canal.
Most of these turn west at the Canal and remain on the mainland,
though a few cross and move down to the Woods Hole area. This
movement is leisurely and progresses in short flights in the daytime
with feeding en route. Except for stray Northern Waterthrushes
and Yellow Warblers, the outer Cape is devoid of migrants under
these conditions, though there are wandering mixed flocks of
breeding species.

The second type of migration affords another of the great ornithological spectacles of the Cape. The periodic invasion of dry,
cool Arctic air is characteristic of late summer and fall in New
England, sometimes beginning in August and occurring regularly
by September. The sudden cooling produces a burst of migrational
activity with long night flights, and the northwest winds displace
many migrants to and beyond the shore line, so the southeastern
Cape is deluged with birds. Under such conditions it is often possible to record most of the warblers, vireos, flycatchers, thrushes,
etc., of eastern North America at Monomoy alone. The greatest
flights appear with a northwest wind of less than gale force and
with clear air. North or west winds bring fewer migrants, and
clouds, fog or gales reduce the flight even on a northwester. The
birds apparently come from all along the New England coast north
of the Cape and they leave, also over water, to the southwest,

south, or even southeast. There is usually a complete turnover each night that the "norther" persists, and local birds often take advantage of these conditions to depart. A high count of any migrant on the Cape demands only that such a cold front pass through New England at the peak of migrational activity of that species. Thus the flights of *Empidonax* flycatchers and the early warblers appear in the latter half of August, of the other flycatchers and the maximum of warblers in the first half of September, of the sparrows, thrushes, and some finches in the latter half of September and October, and of winter residents in November and December. This pattern has been described throughout the historical period, having been noted by both Cahoon and Miller in the 1880's, and there is no indication of any change in numbers of individuals involved.

Almost all species of land birds are more numerous, some markedly so, in fall than in spring, and a few are as yet unrecorded except in fall. The only exceptions to the rule of greater numbers in fall are the Redwinged Blackbird generally and the Grackle as regards the outer Cape. Some species are regularly recorded on both inner and outer routes but in greater numbers on the former; these include Tree and Bank Swallows, Cowbird, Nighthawk, White-breasted Nuthatch, Chimney Swift, several Buteos, Phoebe, Field Sparrow, and House Wren. There are no land birds which concentrate on the outer coast route; they occur there only under the special weather conditions described above. The strong representation of western birds is also characteristic of fall. Western Kingbird, Dickcissel, Orange-crowned Warbler, Western Palm Warbler, Connecticut Warbler, Lark Sparrow, etc., are to be expected; many others have been recorded less regularly, as may be noted in the Systematic List. This season and this tendency account for about one-third of the species considered accidental vagrants.

The terminal migrants which will remain on the Cape for the winter season arrive on both types of flights. From mid-October on each flight contains a higher percentage of individuals which will remain. This can be detected in the increasing numbers of inner-coast migrants which cross the Canal and turn east and in the flights arriving over the ocean from the north and northeast.

The waterfowl migrations start slowly with gatherings of locally raised Black Ducks in August, followed in September and October by the flights of river ducks which are never as numerous as on the mainland. The great flights of Eiders, scoters, and Oldsquaws begin in late August and September with peaks of movement in October. These arrive from the northeast, north, and overland from the northwest and accumulate in great gatherings on the shoals, darkening the ocean for miles and affording an impressive sight for those hardy enough to venture offshore with local fishermen in November and December. It must be noted, however, that only the Eiders remain in full numbers all winter, as the scoters and probably Oldsquaws move out with colder weather; whether this is due to the cold or to exhaustion of their food supply is not known. Some species of waterfowl do not arrive in full numbers until really cold weather, occasionally as late as early January, e.g., Goldeneyes, American Mergansers, the wintering population of Canada Geese, and others. There is evidence that a considerable flight of Alcids passes by during the latter half of November, usually well offshore, though how long these remain on the Cape shoals is not known. Leach's Petrels and perhaps Skuas and Fulmars are also present. The history of the fall waterfowl migrants is no different from spring, i.e., moderate though somewhat spotty diminution and now partial recovery.

As in spring, there is considerable segregation into those species using predominantly the inner or the outer coastal routes. However, the outer route is of greater relative importance in the fall. The inner coast group includes Horned Grebe, Double-crested Cormorant, Surf Scoter, Caspian Tern, Bonaparte's Gull, and the transient population of Canada Goose. The outer group includes Gannet, Brant, Eider, and the wintering populations of Canada Goose and Black Duck.

The post-breeding wandering of certain species is a phenomenon of the fall migration, though it lacks the purposeful direction of most movements. The majority of Cape records of Common Egret, Little Blue Heron, Snowy Egret, the southern race of the Bald Eagle, Black Skimmer, and some southern terns (exclusive of hurricane vagrants) are due to this wandering, and probably the appearance of the Cory's Shearwater should be included here. This type of movement is not all toward the Cape, however, as the Cape Cod Black-crowned Night Heron colonies scatter after breeding north to Quebec and west to Michigan and Louisiana (Forbush, 1925). These movements are characteristically erratic, occurring in some seasons and not in others for no very apparent reason. Historically, as regards the herons, there is reason in the colonial records for the supposition that this wandering occurred then. With the decimation of the southern colonies by the plume hunters, the flights disappeared in the North but returned as soon as protection allowed the populations to recover in the South. They have never penetrated to Cape Cod in as great numbers as on the mainland of Massachusetts, even in the great flight of 1948. As regards the Bald Eagle, counts have steadily decreased throughout the historical period with a sharp drop since 1950.

Finally, hurricanes are a regular feature of the western North Atlantic Ocean in fall. These usually pass offshore, giving the Cape only a northeast gale, but on some memorable occasions the centers have struck Cape Cod or the nearby mainland, notably in 1938, 1944, and 1954. These storms have brought long lists of vagrants such as Sooty, Bridled, Gull-billed, Cabot's, and Royal Terns, Black Skimmers, Boobies, etc. They have also provided the weather necessary to drive in flights of Golden Plover, Hudsonian Godwit, and formerly Eskimo Curlew from their pelagic migration route. Also, land-bird stragglers from the South may appear, having apparently been picked up while migrating. These include species which have already departed from New England and species which nest only in the South. Detection of the former may be difficult among remaining stragglers, but an influx after most individuals have departed speaks for itself. There is obviously no difficulty in detecting the latter group. The series of hurricanes in 1954, nick-named "Carol," "Edna," and "Hazel," particularly the second, was outstanding for the deposition of land birds on Cape Cod. Hurricane vagrants have received much attention in the appropriate Season Reports in *Audubon Field Notes*, and additional details may be found there.

E. Conclusions

1. The breeding habitats for birds on Cape Cod are severely limited, first by lack of many which occur on the mainland, and secondly by marked disturbance of the land over three centuries of civilization. The several shore line habitats have been less disturbed, but the bird populations have been modified by human predation. In general, the nesting birds of the pitch pine forests and those of the marine-influenced habitats are associated with the Atlantic coastal plain; those of the grasslands, of the old pasture association, and of many minor habitats are found widely throughout the Northeast; and those of the oak woods are associated with the central uplands of the state. There is historical evidence of changes in the relative proportions of these groups secondary to known ecological changes in the environments. Approximately one hundred species breed regularly at the present time.

2. Because of the milder oceanic climate, Cape Cod generally escapes the bleakness and birdlessness of inland winters and is, in fact, an important wintering area for many species of both land and sea birds, in many instances their northernmost regular station. Apart from a nucleus of permanent residents and of widespread wintering species, the affinities of Cape Cod winter birds are with the coastal plain areas south of New England, though survival of some of these birds may be low in

severe seasons. Northern birds are conspicuous by their irregularity and by their low numbers. Historically, a long-term trend toward milder winters and short-term warm cycles have steadily strengthened the southern element.

3. Spring and fall migrations on Cape Cod involve about one hundred and two hundred species respectively, with vastly greater numbers of individuals in the latter. In the spring the area is far to the east of the major flyways of the continent and, in general, receives only those populations using the northeast coastal and the pelagic routes. The exceptions are due to abnormal weather conditions which may bring in casual or accidental vagrants or abnormally early migrants. In the fall a convergence of flyways along the coast with migrants approaching from 180° of the compass produces a voluminous migration, one characteristic of which is the large number of western species. In addition, hurricanes are responsible for many southern vagrants, both land and sea birds. Historically, there is no evidence of significant change in numbers among the migrant land birds, but the waterfowl and particularly the shore birds have experienced profound changes in numbers secondary to human predation or protection therefrom.

Bibliography

PERIODICALS:

The Auk (1884–present), American Ornithologists Union.

Audubon Field Notes (1947–present), National Audubon Society, New York, N.Y.

Audubon Magazine (1941–present), National Audubon Society, New York, N.Y.

Bird-Banding (1930–present), The Northeastern, Eastern and Inland Bird-Banding Associations.

Bird Lore (1899–1940), National Audubon Society, New York, N.Y.

Bulletin of the Massachusetts Audubon Society (1917–present), Boston, Mass.

Bulletin of the New England Bird-Banding Association (1925–1929), Boston, Mass.

Bulletin of New England Bird-Life (1937–1944), New England Museum of Natural History, Boston, Mass.

Bulletin of the Nuttall Ornithological Club (1876–1883), Cambridge, Mass.

The Ibis (1859–present), British Ornithologists Union, London, England.

Ornithologist and Oologist (1875–1893), privately printed, Boston, Mass.

Records of New England Birds (1945–1955 and 1958–1959), Massachusetts Audubon Society, Boston, Mass.

The Wilson Bulletin (New series, 1894–present), Wilson Ornithological Club.

345

BOOKS:

Allen, F. H., Ed., *Notes on New England Birds by Henry D. Thoreau.* Boston and New York, Houghton Mifflin, 1910.

Bagg, A. C., and Eliot, S. A., Jr., *Birds of the Connecticut Valley in Massachusetts.* Northampton, Mass., Hampshire Bookshop, 1937.

Bailey, W., *Birds in Massachusetts and Where To Find Them.* So. Lancaster, Mass., privately printed, 1955.

Baird, S. F., Brewer, T. M., and Ridgway, R., *Water Birds of North America,* Memoirs Museum of Comp. Zoology, Vol. 12, Cambridge, Mass., 1884.

Bent, A. C. (1919–present), *Life Histories of North American Birds,* Bull. U. S. Nat. Museum, Washington, D.C.

Beston, H., *The Outermost House.* Garden City, N.Y., Doubleday Doran, 1928.

Brewster, W., *The Birds of the Cambridge Region of Massachusetts,* Memoirs Nuttall Ornith. Club, No. IV. Cambridge, Mass., 1906.

Cory, C. B., Hellmayr, C. E., and Conover, B. (1918–1942), *A Catalogue of Birds of the Americas,* Field Museum of Natural History, Chicago, Ill.

Emmons, E., in Edward Hitchcock's *Report on the Geology, Mineralogy, Botany and Zoology of Massachusetts.* Amherst, Mass., 1833.

Fernald, M. L., *Gray's Manual of Botany,* 8th edition. American Book Co., 1950.

Forbush, E. H., *A History of the Game Birds, Wild-fowl and Shore Birds of Massachusetts and Adjacent States.* Boston, Mass., Mass. State Board of Agriculture, 1912.

Forbush, E. H., *Birds of Massachusetts and Other New England States.* Boston, Mass., Mass. Dept. Agriculture, 1925, 1927, and 1929.

Griscom, L., *The Birds of Dutchess County, New York,* Trans. Linnaean Soc., Vol. III, New York, N.Y., 1933.

Griscom, L., and Folger, E., *The Birds of Nantucket.* Cambridge, Mass., Harvard University Press, 1948.

Griscom, L., *The Birds of Concord.* Cambridge, Mass., Harvard University Press, 1949.

Griscom, L., and Snyder, D. E., *The Birds of Massachusetts.* Salem, Mass., Peabody Museum, 1955.

Griscom, L., and Emerson, G., *Birds of Martha's Vineyard.* Martha's Vineyard, Mass., privately printed, 1959.

Howe, R. H., and Allen, G. M., *The Birds of Massachusetts*, Cambridge, Mass., 1901.

Kittredge, H. C., *Cape Cod, Its People and Their History*. Cambridge, Mass., Riverside Press, 1930.

Mendall, H. L., *The Ring-necked Duck in the Northeast*. Orono, Me., University Press, 1958.

Nuttall, T., *A Manual of the Ornithology of the United States and of Canada*, Boston, Mass., 1832 and 1834.

Palmer, R. S., Birds of Maine, Bull. Mus. Comp. Zoology, Vol. 102, Cambridge, Mass., 1949.

Peabody, W. B. O., *A Report on the Birds of Massachusetts Made to the Legislature in the Session of 1838–9*. Boston, Mass., Boston Soc. Nat. History, 1840.

Phillips, J. C., *Shooting Stands of Eastern Massachusetts*. Cambridge, Mass., privately printed, 1929.

Randall, W. E., and Vinal, W. G., *Report of a Biological Investigation on a Portion of Cape Cod, Massachusetts*, in "Cape Cod," U. S. Dept. of the Interior, National Park Service, 1958.

Richardson, W., *The House on Nauset Marsh*, New York, N.Y., Norton, 1955.

Robbins, C. S., and Stewart, R. E., *Birds of Maryland and the District of Columbia*. Washington, D.C., U. S. Dept. of the Interior, Fish and Wildlife Service, 1958.

Stone, W., *Bird Studies at Old Cape May*. Philadelphia, Pa., Acad. Nat. Sciences, 1937.

Thoreau, H. D., *Cape Cod*. New York, N.Y., Norton, 1951.

Townsend, C. W., *The Birds of Essex County, Massachusetts*, Memoirs Nuttall Ornith. Club, No. III, Cambridge, Mass., 1905.

Townsend, C. W., *Supplement to the Birds of Essex County, Massachusetts*, Memoirs Nuttall Ornith. Club, No. V, Cambridge, Mass., 1920.

Wynne-Edwards, V. C., *On the Habits and Distribution of Birds on the North Atlantic*. Proc. Boston Soc. Nat. Hist., 40, 233, Boston, Mass., 1935.

Index

Index

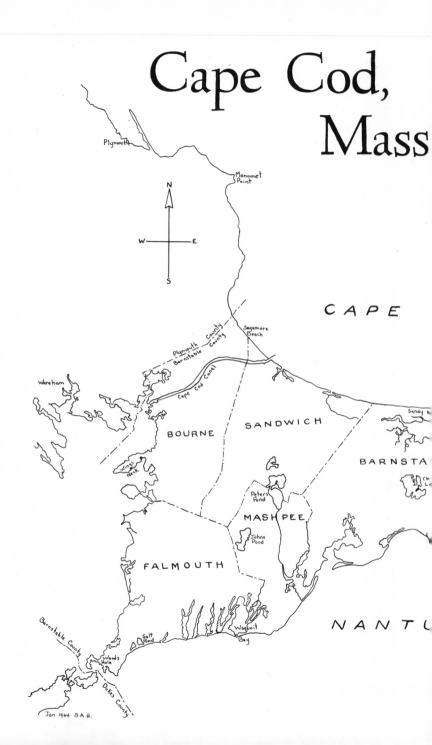

Cape Cod,
Mass

Plymouth

Manomet
Point

N
W — E
S

C A P E

Sagamore
Beach

Plymouth County
Barnstable County

Wareham

Cape Cod Canal

Sandy N

BOURNE

SANDWICH

BARNSTA

Wings
Neck

Peters
Pond

MASHPEE

Johns
Pond

FALMOUTH

Barnstable County

Salt
Pond

Waquoit
Bay

N A N T U

Woods
Hole

Dukes County

Jan 1964 B.A.H.